3/96

D0060271

Engineering Wonders
of the World

Engineering Wonders of the World

RENÉ POIRIER

Translated by

MARGARET CROSLAND

BARNES
&NOBLE
BOOKS
NEW YORK

This book was originally published in French under the title
L'Epopée des Grandes Travaux; the English translation was
originally published as *The Fifteen Wonders of the World*.

This edition published by Barnes & Noble, Inc.,
by arrangement with Random House, Inc.

1993 Barnes & Noble Books

ISBN 1-56619-322-2

Printed and bound in the United States of America

M   9   8   7   6   5   4   3   2   1

TO MY WIFE

ACKNOWLEDGEMENTS

MOST OF THE studies in this book are based on literature made available to me by libraries or information services. I have also enjoyed the privilege of going over some of these important structures in their finished or unfinished state, and this has provided me with valuable information. In particular therefore I should like to thank:

Monsieur A. Parrot, chief curator of the French national museums, and the historian of the Tower of Babel.

Mademoiselle Agnès Joly, assistant curator of the municipal library of Versailles, and Monsieur Racinais, chief architect for the Palace of Versailles and the Trianon.

The Library and Information Service of the American Embassy in Paris.

The Publicity Department of the London Transport Executive, and Messrs. Baddeley and Page.

Madame Granet, grand-daughter of Gustave Eiffel, who was kind enough to show me extremely helpful papers, and Monsieur Vannesson, commercial director of the Eiffel Tower.

The Swiss Federal Railways, and Monsieur Blaser of the Paris office; Messieurs Marguerat and Nointelet, of the Lausanne office, Messieurs Caspar and Wenzer, of the Central Office in Berne; and Monsieur Capponi and his staff at Brig station at the entrance to the Simplon Tunnel.

Monsieur Sadi de Gorter, Press attaché at the Netherlands Embassy in Paris, and the technicians of the Waterstaat at The Hague.

And lastly all my friends among booksellers and book-collectors, who allowed me to browse over their shelves, and the technicians and experts who gave me such sound, helpful advice.

R. P.

CONTENTS

I

THE TOWER OF BABEL

I

CONFUSION OF TONGUES

Men have spent a great part of the last fifty years in destruction, but fortunately the faster they destroy the more rapidly they build again and discover new solutions to their newly created problems. National feeling runs high, co-operation within or between countries is problematic. But these intangible forces release immense energy in the fields of science and technology, and as the twentieth century progresses collective effort leads to a succession of splendid achievements.

The ancestors of these great enterprises had a different motivation. They were symbols of union or disunion between Man and the Divine, as we can see clearly from the Tower of Babel and the Pyramids. The story of the flood occurs in nearly all mythologies but the story of Babel is much less widespread and is hardly ever linked with it except in the Book of Genesis.

This episode of the Tower of Babel (sometimes called the Town instead, depending on which text is used) is described in the first nine verses of the Eleventh Chapter, between the "families of the sons of Noah after their generations" and the story of Abraham, the "father of many nations" and ancestor of the Hebrews.

The Great Flood destroyed all animals; and humanity was reduced to the small group of Noah, his wife, their sons and their wives. Life had to begin all over again. After leaving the Ark Noah planted a vineyard and drank too much wine, which is understandable, after seeing so much water for forty days. Presumably his descendants abandoned their nomadic pastoral life and gradually became farmers.

In their new peasant life the pioneers had to observe the discipline of sowing and reaping, which was a fresh experience for them. They developed tools which, however primitive, gave rise to a second category of workers, the artisans, who led a settled life like the peasants.

In this way villages and cities came into being and finally the cities and their surrounding villages were to form a characteristic autochthonous group which became the nation, covering a more or less fixed area that people regarded as their country. The successive generations of Noah's three sons, Shem, Ham and Japhet, came to constitute, according to the Bible, the great races of humanity who conquered the earth.

However, the great-grandsons of Noah do not seem to have spread beyond a fairly restricted area covering what we now call Asia Minor. The descendants of Ham for instance seem to have settled in the Mesopotamian valley of Chaldea, because it lies between the Tigris and the Euphrates. Its capital city may well have been Babylon, although at this stage it was far from possessing the importance and splendour that it achieved under Queen Semiramis or Nebuchadnezzar. Then Genesis takes up the story:

"And they said, Go to, let us build us a city, and a tower whose top may reach unto heaven; and let us make us a name, lest we be scattered abroad upon the face of the whole earth."

The story goes on:

"And the whole earth was of one language, and of one speech.

"And it came to pass, as they journeyed from the east, that they found a plain in the land of Shinar; and they dwelt there.

"And they said one to another, Go to, let us make brick, and burn them thoroughly. And they had brick for stone, and slime had they for mortar. . . .

"And the Lord came down to see the city and the tower, which the children of men builded.

"And the Lord said, Behold, the people is one, and they have all one language; and this they begin to do: and now nothing will be restrained from them, which they will have imagined to do.

"Go to, let us go down, and there confound their language, that they may not understand one another's speech.

"So the Lord scattered them abroad from thence upon the face of all the earth: and they left off to build the city.

"Therefore is the name of it called Babel; because the Lord did there confound the language of all the earth and from thence did the Lord scatter them abroad upon the face of all the earth."

It is interesting to compare with the Biblical text the account by the Jewish historian Flavius Josephus, who in spite of the Bible's silence on the point, states that Nimrod was in charge of the "enterprise," a description which brings it within the scope of this book:

"Nimrod, one of the grandsons of Ham, who was the son of Noah, had gradually attained supremacy and aspired to tyrannical power; he tried to persuade the multitude to put themselves under his protection, assuring them that this was the only means of escaping from the fear of God, against whom he promised to defend them if he should ever wish to submerge the earth beneath a second flood. He said that he wanted to build a tower which would be so high that the water could never rise above it, and in this way they could finally avenge the death of their forefathers.

"The multitude, believing that obedience to God was weakness, hastened to believe Nimrod's rash promises. The people built this tower with incredible energy and due to the great number of workers the building was finished more quickly than had been hoped. The circumference was so great that the height appeared to be less than it was. Instead of stone they used bricks and bound them together with pitch, for fear the rain should cause the entire building to collapse. When God saw their rash enterprise, seeing also that the punishment of their fathers had not caused them to repent, he decided not to destroy them utterly but merely caused division among them, by making them speak different languages so that they would not understand each other at all."

Apart from his purely ideological reasons for deviating from the authority of the Creator and even entering into hostilities with him, the proud Nimrod's plan was concerned with defence against the possibility of a new flood, or even against the annual flooding of the Tigris and Euphrates rivers. In any such disaster the gigantic Tower of Babel would form a communal shelter for the entire population of the towns and villages of Mesopotamia. Its role would be similar to that of the feudal castle during the Middle Ages, where the serfs and villagers would assemble rapidly and act as defenders as soon as any warning of attack was given, while the animals and food available in the village would provide ample supplies in case of siege.

The Tower of Babel was the work of a megalomaniac but it was also a collective enterprise, a technical operation which certainly formed one of the first great undertakings of early humanity.

The distinguished but conservative French critic, Father Gillet, like his nineteenth-century contemporaries, was unaware of the economic geography of this distant Middle Eastern country. "If Nimrod's motive," he wrote somewhat naïvely in his commentary on Josephus' text, "was to build a tower as protection from another flood, why did he not build it on top of a high mountain? Nobody builds a town on a plain if they wish to escape floods."

How could Nimrod have acted differently? There are no hills in the district and there was no reason why he should perch a town on a bare mountainside when he had the rich Chaldea fertilised with the water from the rivers in flood, just as Egypt is fertilised by the Nile.

"If Egypt," wrote Daniel-Rops in his *Histoire Sainte*, "is a 'gift of the Nile,' Mesopotamia is the gift of the Tigris and the Euphrates, but it is a returnable gift that has often been contested. Many parts of the ground lie beyond the level of the waters when they rise, and before water could be there all the time there would have to be a vast system of canals and dams, the kind of irrigation system that the men of four thousand years ago operated in a masterly way; when it was abandoned the country fell into the state of poverty in which it lay at about the turn of the century.

"Mesopotamia certainly looks like a garden; it is certainly the country where barley and wheat originated and if the rainfall is sufficient there can be three crops a year. The date-palm has a regal air about it; it produces sweetmeats, honey, wine and a hundred different kinds of fabric."

There was no freestone and the making of mortar was unknown, but the descendants of Ham had first-class materials at their disposal— baked or unbaked brick, and pitch in quantity, from which oil is now extracted. Mesopotamia is a strange and magnificent country, first the garden of Eden, then a desert, now Iraq, a nation which has become rich and powerful through its oil deposits.

The historian Flavius Josephus had the support of the Rabbinical tradition and the Judaic expounders of the Old Testament when he decided between various alternatives that the Tower of Babel was a work of defence:

"When men built this Tower their first consideration was defence. Water could not submerge it, fire could not take hold of it. The different tiers of the building could be isolated in order to kill any approaching enemies who were preparing to attack. They intended to erect a statue in the tower, which would foretell the future and issue orders. This was to be a winged statue which would protect the whole town, eternally warding off any rain of fire or rising waters. It would also withstand any harbinger of destruction. The one reason for all this was the fear of a second flood."

This is a practical interpretation but it does not take into account everything that the Bible has to say. The men who built the Tower of Babel wanted most of all to mount up to heaven and enter into contact with God. Naturally the miraculous is not lacking in this story:

"The building of the tower proceeded and it grew so high that it took a whole year to take the bricks and mortar from the foot of it to the masons who were working at the top. While the building went on the workers fired arrows up into the sky. They fell down upon them covered with blood. When they saw this the men thought they had killed everything that was on high. But this was only a stratagem on the part of the Lord to destroy them and remove them from the face of the earth.

"The demolition of the tower—which incidentally is not mentioned in the Biblical tradition—was also a miraculous event. The earth opened and swallowed up one-third of the building. Fire came down from heaven and consumed the rest. What remains is still imposing, for it casts a shadow over a distance equal to three days' march. Anyone who climbs to the top finds that the trees of the forest look as small as locusts."[1]

The story of the Tower of Babel is not, as previously mentioned, restricted to the Old Testament; it is not surprising that we find it in the Babylonian-Assyrian religion, but in this context everything appears miraculous:

"It is said that the first men, swollen with their own power and greatness, despised the gods and believed themselves superior to them; they therefore built a very high tower at the place where Babylon now stands. It was already approaching heaven when the winds rushed to the assistance of the gods and blew the building down on top of the workers. The ruins are called Babel. Until that time all men had spoken one language, but from that time onwards the gods forced them to speak different tongues."[2]

There is also a remote parallel to the Tower of Babel story in Greek mythology. When the Giants revolted against Zeus they piled up mountains on top of each other to reach Olympus. Claudian, a Roman poet of the fourth century A.D., described the incident thus: "One giant, with his strong arm, shook Oeta in Thessaly; another seized hold of the summits of Pangaeus in his mighty hand; a third took the snows of Mount Athos for his weapons, yet another laid his hands on Rhodope. From all sides rang out a fearful din. . . ." One can well believe it!

An English missionary who had converted the Gold Coast to Christianity during the mid-nineteenth century brought home another Tower of Babel story told by the Ashanti negroes.

"One day after the separation of the earth and the sky, men resolved to reach it. In order to do so they piled up all their grain mortars on top of each other. Only one extra was needed in order to reach the

[1] André Parrot, *Ziggurats et Tour de Babel*. Paris, 1949.
[2] Berossus, Chaldean historian and astronomer of the fourth century B.C., quoted by Maspero in *Histoire Ancienne des peuples de l'Orient*. Paris, 1886.

sky, but they possessed no more. They thought of taking the one at the bottom, on which all the others stood, and putting it on the top. But when they took it the whole column collapsed and would have killed them to the last man, if they had not fled at once. In their sudden terror they began to speak new tongues and this is why there are so many languages under the sun; before that there was only one in all the world."

When Monsieur André Parrot, the French scholar, was told of this story he wisely pointed out that it could embody native recollections of the Tower of Babel story which the Ashanti had heard from European travellers. There is all the more reason for accepting the learned archeologist's opinion in as much as white "penetration" into this part of Africa was particularly active during the eighteenth century and the first half of the nineteenth century, because of the slave trade.

The Tower of Babel may have made a vivid impression on the natives of the Gold Coast but it was by no means forgotten by the civilised world, and for more than two thousand years they have been trying to establish the truth of the story and discover the ruins.

II

REALITY AND IMAGINATION

Scholars, travellers of ancient times and archeologists of the modern world agree unanimously that the Tower of Babel must have been very near to Babylon, but they disagree utterly about the origins and meaning of the names for Nimrod's town and Nebuchadnezzar's capital. Although the two names seem practically identical some scholars say that "Babel" comes from the Hebrew root *babal*, to confuse, and others that it derives from the Chaldean root *bab-ilu*, meaning the gate of God, which is more applicable to Babylon.

This town was founded during the third millennium and grew to a colossal size. It occupied an area of thirteen square miles, almost as big as London. It was said that caravans took more than one complete day to travel from the North to the South gate. The town was surrounded by a wall seventy-five feet high, and may have been visited by Herodotus five centuries before Christ, and later by Diodorus Siculus and Strabo. After it had been pillaged during the sixth century B.C. by Cyrus II, King of the Persians, Babylon was chosen by Alexander the Great during the fourth century B.C. as the capital of his empire in Asia.

Even during the first century A.D. the ruined capital had still not been forgotten by mankind.

During the twelfth century the Spanish Rabbi Benjamin of Tudela visited Babylon but he was unable to establish the exact site of the Tower of Babel.

"In the centre of a huge plain," he writes, "about half a mile from the Euphrates, stands a massive building constructed entirely in one piece and looking like a mountain. It is square in shape and terminates in a tower or pyramid. Its size, position and shape all correspond exactly with the pyramid that Strabo calls the tomb of Belus and which

1. Nimrod's ziggurat (from *The Five Great Monarchies* (I) by G. Rawlinson)

must be the building described as the Tower of Nimrod, at Babylon or Babel, as the inhabitants of the country still call it today. Like all ruins it has no shape and the ground round about is very uneven, for in some places it is steep and in others it slopes gently and can be easily climbed, while rain has hollowed out channels through it.

"There is no trace of any stairways or doors, which bears out the opinion that it was entered by ramps encircling the outside walls, but no trace of them remains. . . . The material of which it is constructed is the strangest thing in the world, and in order to study it more carefully we broke open the surface with picks in various places.

"This material consists of large wide bricks, dried in the sun and cemented together not only with good lime but with a kind of clay, while those which formed supports have been baked in the fire. . . .

I asked my artist to draw for me the two most distinct views of these ruins.

"I have no doubt that this is the ancient Tower of Babel built by Nimrod, for not only does the site afford obvious proof of this but in addition the inhabitants of the district are convinced of the fact and still call it Babel in Arabic, pronouncing it Babyl as is their custom."

Modern archeologists visited Babylon on many occasions, but detailed descriptions were made at an earlier date by Robert Ker Porter, British Consul in Baghdad in 1820, who was also a painter and writer. He believed that the ruin had previously been a temple of Baal and that as it stood it revealed three periods of architecture—the actual edifice built by Nimrod and two sections which had been restored by Queen Semiramis and Nebuchadnezzar.

When Porter saw the ruins of Babel for the first time they were occupied by lions basking in the sunshine. The shouts of the Arab guides barely disturbed them at all and they came down slowly and with seeming regret.

Archeological research, backed up by careful excavations which have been carried out for a century by experts such as Monsieur André Parrot, has led to the conclusion that the Tower of Babel was a *ziggurat*, a kind of "step" pyramid consisting of platforms of diminishing size. There are thirty-three of these ziggurats to be found on twenty-seven different sites in Chaldea, and Monsieur Parrot states that there must certainly be more.

We are not entirely clear as to the purpose of these monuments. The men who built them probably intended them merely as individual temples into which the divinity might descend, or else means of access to a temple which was to be placed at the highest possible point, as close to heaven as could be.

"In period 12 (VI) at Erech (the intermediate period between the stone age and the bronze age) the citizens combined to rear an artificial mountain upon which god Anu or his more vaguely conceived precursor might descend. This mountain, the prototype of the ziggurat that was attached to the chief sanctuaries of Babylonia and even Assyria throughout historical times, was already twelve metres high. It was composed of mere lumps of clay piled up in layers with strata of bitumen interlarded between them. . . . Less than half the platform on the top of the ziggurat was occupied by the White Temple, a little sanctuary 22·3 × 17·5 metres, built of big square mud bricks covered with whitewash."[1]

[1] V. Gordon Childe, *New Light on the Most Ancient East.* 1934.

There were three types of ziggurat in Mesopotamia; some were rectangular, entered by stairways, some were square, entered by ramps, and some were a combination of both shapes entered by both stairways and ramps.

They were built of bricks, some of which bear cuneiform inscriptions, giving the impression that the ziggurats were indeed sanctuaries, temples made up of different storeys each painted a different colour and possibly consecrated to a different divinity.

Although archeologists have made imaginary calculations about the shapes of the ziggurats, based on their ruins, and given their precise measurements, they cannot tell us anything about the techniques used for building them, for the cuneiform inscriptions which have been deciphered from the bricks are usually only concerned with listing the riches of the temple.

"In the Red Temple," wrote V. Gordon Childe in *New Light on the Most Ancient East*, "the Germans found several tablets, evidently the accounts of those temple revenues which formed the economic reserves of a Sumerian city. For their preservation and transmission the priests have devised a pictographic script simplifying by abstraction the representations of objects to bare symbols."[1]

There can be no proof that the Tower of Babel was the archetype of the ziggurats, but learned archeologists, who have already performed miracles, are convinced that they will discover the answer and reconstruct for us one day the real "Tower of Confusion."

The artists of the Christian era have had no scruples of this kind and have created Towers of Babel out of their own imagination. Interpreting the Biblical story with varying degrees of fantasy they have shown the Tower as round, square, in the course of construction, in ruins or as stricken by divine wrath. The story is to be found everywhere, in ivory carvings or mosaics, frescoes or paintings, of which we can only mention a few. In his book on the Tower of Babel and the ziggurats Monsieur André Parrot has given an interesting list of the principal representations of the legendary building.

Disregarding all artistic merit, the most valuable, from the documentary point of view, are those which show us some aspect of the actual building work. The artists obviously took their ideas from the means of transport and the building tools they could see round about

---

[1] "This reconstruction (by Businck)," says Monsieur André Parrot, "seems to correspond with the facts as given by Herodotus. This was how the Tower of Babel rose above the plain of Shinar, with simple lines and proportions which were not lacking in harmony and balance."

them. They included carts, but we do not know if the builders of this period had discovered the wheel. The bricks were piled in baskets and usually transported on the men's backs; there were probably also primitive "derricks" which no doubt worked without pulleys.

There was no shortage of labour, for prisoners of war were always available, and their lives were spared for the sole purpose of obtaining additional workers. In particular they were detailed to transport the bricks. Architects and specialised masons could be found easily in Mesopotamia where the famous "Hanging Gardens of Babylon" were built.

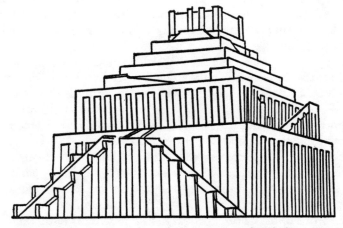

2. Busink's reconstruction of the Tower of Babel ziggurat

But these paintings are merely the embodiment of conjecture and artistic vision. The Tower of Babel shown in the frescoes of the Church of Saint-Savin is a Romanesque belfry tower of the twelfth century. God is shown speaking to the men, no doubt telling them of the vanity of their enterprise. The miniature by Herzog of Bedford (fifteenth century) is a delightful building in the Italian style with an outside staircase. The paintings by Brueghel the Elder, the wonderful sixteenth-century Flemish painter, are masterpieces of grace, colour and architecture, and the powerful fortresses he drew, with their side buttresses, were no doubt inspired by the Colosseum in Rome. He painted at least two Towers of Babel, one now in the Vienna Museum and the other in the Van Beuningen collection in Rotterdam; one is built in storeys, the other is entered by ramps. Gustave Doré drew a romantic Tower of Babel for his illustrated Bible but in spite of the accuracy of the costumes it shows a complete disregard for the account given in Genesis.

But all this is immaterial. The Tower of Babel, whether it is a sanctuary, a masterpiece of town planning, the centrepiece of a museum or merely a Biblical story condemning human pride, embodies the collective spirit of what was probably the first great enterprise ever carried out on earth.

II

THE PYRAMIDS

Someone appeared to me from the distant past,
A young workman from the lofty pyramids,
Lost in the host of frightened men
Who were crushed by Cheops' granite tomb . . .

Up and down he went, seeking justice from the gods,
While for three thousand years the glorious Cheops
Has slept unchanging in his massive vault.

Sully-Prudhomme

IN THE SHADOW OF THE PYRAMIDS

O F THE SEVEN wonders of the world[1] which can be recited at will the Great Pyramid of Giza is the only one we can still admire today. In fact it was only rediscovered just over a century and a half ago, when, on July 21st, 1798, Bonaparte solemnly showed it to his troops, who had just overthrown in France a thousand-year-old régime which from certain points of view was comparable to that of the Pharaohs.[2]

At the end of the eighteenth century, when the excavation work began at Pompeii,[3] after that city had lain buried under ash for seven hundred years, ancient Egypt had almost faded from the memory of mankind. First of all, in the fourth century A.D., Theodosius the Great, in the name of Christianity, caused the temples to be destroyed; the statues and carvings were broken up and the few priests who had been initiated into their mysteries were put to death, taking the secret of the hieroglyphics into the tomb with them.

The Islamic religion dealt the second blow, for as its converts spread through the Nile valley many of the buildings were used as quarries for the building of new temples, just as the men of Mediaeval Rome used the pagan temples to build their churches.

The only remaining trace of the civilisation of the Pharaohs therefore was in the writings of Herodotus (480–425 B.C.), Strabo (first century B.C.) and Diodorus Siculus (58 B.C.). Since their memorable journeys or the accounts they wrote of them, the buildings of ancient Egypt, especially the pyramids, appealed only to the greed of the Arabs, especially of the Caliph Ma'mun who, in the year A.D. 820, opened the Great Pyramid but decided at once that the few treasures he would get out of it would not equal the expenses of the undertaking.

---

[1] A list drawn up during the tenth century by the Greek philosopher Philo of Byzantium differs noticeably from the classic list we know today: the Capitol of Rome, the statue of Bellerophon at Smyrna, the theatre of Heraclitus, the baths of Apollonius of Tyana, etc.

[2] The famous speech, "Soldiers, reflect that from the summit of these pyramids forty centuries look down upon you," does not seem to have been actually delivered by Bonaparte, but only mentioned in 1803 in an anonymous document, and later sanctioned by Napoleon at St. Helena in the Memoirs he dictated to General Bertrand.

[3] See Count Corti's book *La Résurrection d'Herculanum et de Pompéi.*

The pilgrims who crossed Egypt during the Middle Ages saw the country only in the light of the Bible and merely imagined that the pyramids were the vast storehouses in which Joseph, after his famous dream, stored the grain from the "seven years of plenty"; as a result they were called "Joseph-Barns," or "Pharaoh-Barns."

In 1554 the shoemaker André Thevet, almoner to Catherine de Medici, wrote in his *Cosmographie du Levant*:

"These pyramids are built in a pointed diamond-like shape, as tall as towers . . . the geometers call them 'pyramids' from the Greek word for fire, πῦρ."[1] Pierre Belon, a fourteenth-century traveller from Le Mans, supposed like Herodotus that they contained royal tombs. "For I have seen," he wrote, "great marble stones carved in the shape of coffins."[2]

During the following centuries the Nile valley was visited by many scholars or explorers, German, British or French, to whom the pyramids were enigmas which they attempted to solve with a certain degree of shrewdness, an attitude which is very understandable since Egyptology had not yet come into being as a science.

Faced on all sides by the hostility of the natives, they explored the surroundings of the pyramids, worked out some measurements and described the bond used, hoping along with Volney,[3] "If only Egypt were to pass into other hands than those of the Mamelukes, and that the whole of the Nile region and the sands of Libya could be excavated. . . . It is to this period, not so far-distant perhaps as we think, that we must look for the fulfilment of our hopes and wishes."

Thirteen years later Bonaparte appeared with his troops and created the Institut d'Egypte. His troops ousted the Mamelukes, and the valley of the Nile, now liberated, invited scholars to unlock its secrets.

From the sand at the foot of the pyramids there emerged a sphinx which had nothing in common with that of Greek mythology except its name; it was in fact the Egyptian god Harmakis, symbol of the life-giving sun, and this sphinx asked no questions. It had been silent for five thousand years and for scholars it personified the secret of the hieroglyphics, the indecipherable signs that could be seen carved more

---

[1] In the absence of any satisfactory Egyptian etymology, modern archeologists think that the word pyramid is of Greek origin, unconnected with any Egyptian noun. It has been suggested that the Greeks, as soon as they saw the pyramids, compared them, humorously enough, to the cakes that they used as a funeral offering. The same was adopted in the case of the obelisk, which they compared to the shape of a little sword (οξελισχοζ).

[2] See J. P. Lauer, *Le Problème des pyramides d'Egypte*. Paris, 1952. I have quoted often from this well-documented work which is based on first-hand knowledge.

[3] *Voyage en Syrie et en Egypte pendant les années 1783, 1784 et 1785.*

or less everywhere on countless monuments or stone ruins in the Nile valley.

Where was the new Oedipus who could cause the Sphinx to speak? He was called Jean-François Champollion, and came from Languedoc in France. He was to decipher the written, if not the spoken, language of another Mediterranean province, the Egypt of the Pharaohs.

When Bonaparte discovered the pyramids Champollion was only a boy, but when, twenty-three years later, he explained to the world the enigma of the Rosetta stone the pyramids began to yield up their secrets. A hundred years have passed, and they have not yet disclosed everything. But this is what we know so far.

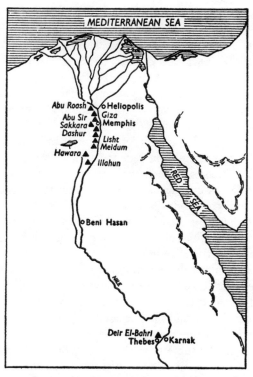

3. Map showing the sites of the pyramids of Egypt

II

THE KING IS GOD

There is no doubt today that the pyramids are royal mausoleums, but the reasons which led to such immense structures built in such an astonishing way are still not clear. Egyptologists have come to establish however that the pyramids constituted both a resting place for the royal remains, which were mummified with unbelievable care, and a dwelling, a temple in which the monarch could pursue a mythical existence after death.

The Egyptians believed that man consisted of two elements, a visible body and an invisible double named "ka." Gaston Maspero, the French Egyptologist, describes this double as "an exact reproduction of the body in matter that was less dense, a coloured but airy projection of the individual, reproducing him line by line, a child in the case of a child, a woman in the case of a woman, a man in the case of a man." This double was in some way a twin of the body, made of the same substance and coeval with it.

Adolf Erman, the German Egyptologist, regarded it as the embodiment of the life principle, in fact the soul as we imagine it in its immortality. J. H. Breasted believes that the "ka" is more of a protective genius, a sort of guardian angel comparable to the one with which the Christian religion endows us.

Kees, another German scholar, believes that the "ka" is the personification of distinct qualities like power, or honours received, which were to be continued in the after-life.

We have reason to believe that in the religion of the third Dynasty, this "double" was linked with the preservation of the physical body. When the body decayed and eventually turned into dust, the "ka" itself no longer existed and the human being died for the second time, disappearing finally into the void.

For this reason the subjects or the parents of the dead took infinite precautions to arrange for the material form to be preserved for ever in its most complete state.

The preservation of corpses by means of mummification is in any case not restricted to Egypt. The Incas carried out the same rites, so did the Jivaro Indians, who preserve shrunken heads, while many other races carry out the same practice in very different ways. The embalmed bodies of Lenin and Stalin which are displayed to worshipping crowds in Moscow are a contemporary form of mummy-worship, somewhat unexpected in the atomic age of today.

The Egyptian king was the incarnation of Ra, the Sun God, without whom life on earth could not exist, and his subjects took care that his "double" should not disappear, for this would have led to the extinction of the sun and the end of the world.

The worship of the "ka" and the eternity of the king's body formed one single religion. The body became a mummy and the tomb was an edifice rising towards the sun in the form of a pyramid, and its pyramidic form with its different faces, its angles and crowning pyramidion symbolised the sun's rays as they shone down over the land of the Pharaohs. The pyramidion moreover was the exact representation of the *benben*, the sacred stone placed in the interior courtyard of the temples dedicated to Ra, the stone before which the priests of Heliopolis, the city of the sun, made their sacrifices to the star of light.

"It appears," wrote Arthur Weigall, "that King Seneferu, founder of the third dynasty, was the first to want his tomb built in this shape, for he desired that his body should repose eternally within a vast *benben*, that is at the heart of the symbol of the Sun God Ra, just as more than one Christian monarch expressed the wish that his tomb should assume the shape of a cross."

This is one explanation of the building and shape of the monuments put forward by certain Egyptologists.

However, there was hardly any sign of the pyramid-tomb before the fourth dynasty. A series of changes had taken place by that time.

The kings of the earliest dynasties had been content with mediocre palaces built of dried brick, but their tombs or mastabas[1] were more solid structures of stone. A mastaba was a square edifice with slightly sloping walls of very varying dimensions; it has in fact been assumed that the king's tomb was in proportion to the length of his life. It was begun and continued during his life time and then finished rapidly after his death.

The four sides of the mastaba faced the cardinal points of the compass, and the main axis ran from north to south. There were two doors, usually set on the east side, facing the rising sun. One was the entrance for the dead man, or men, for sometimes several tombs were included in the same building, and the other was for the living who came and

---

[1] This name was given to these tombs by the first Arabs in Egypt because their shape was not dissimilar to the stone bench of the same name which stood in front of their houses.

went with their offerings, especially food, which was set on an altar
built in a kind of chapel placed above the funeral chamber.

The donors thought that the food would retain its nutritional value
if they wrote out a description of it on the chapel walls, which in this
way, as Maspero mischievously remarks, set out "the dead man's
dinner." Apart from these gastronomic details the mastaba bore some
resemblance to the rich chapels in the Montmartre or Père Lachaise
cemeteries which are built over vaults.

But as the years passed this devout contract was no longer carried
out by the living, and in the hope of terminating it without incurring
any harm to themselves they hit on a strategy which had its own grim
humour; they placed a carved tablet in the chapel which simply stated
that the dead man had received the ritual offerings with abundance and
regularity. And over this inscription the dead man was even represented seated at his table before appetising quantities of food, as
abundant as it was deceptive.

The tomb itself was placed in a vault reached by a perpendicular
shaft, descending to a depth of anything from nine to sixty feet. The
mummy was placed there in accordance with the prescribed ceremonies,
after which it was immured for ever, together with a great number of
vases, pieces of furniture or everyday objects placed either close by
or in the numerous adjacent chambers with a bounty more or less in
accordance with the rank of the dead man and the generosity of his
family.

Later, about the period of the third dynasty, the interior of the
mastaba was adorned with a statue or merely a bust of the dead man,
but so that his spirit could recognise its material embodiment, the

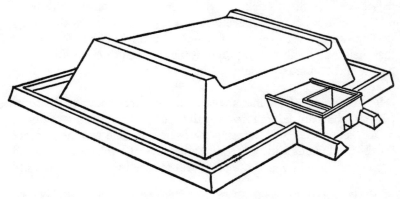

4. Jéquier's reconstruction of the Fara'oun mastaba

5. The architect of the pyramid has an audience of the Pharaoh

names, titles and ranks of the dead man were usually inscribed in hieroglyphics. And in the same way the most outstanding incidents of his life were carved in relief, along with representations of the relations, friends or servants who had taken part in them.

This was the general structure of the mastaba, which was to undergo continued development until the fourth dynasty, when the pyramids of Giza and their "complexes" first appeared.

The "step" pyramid was the first type of building to follow the rectangular mastaba, which already anticipated the base of the new type of monument. This pyramid seems to have appeared for the first time about the period of the third dynasty with the tomb built for the Pharaoh Zoser by his architect Imhotep. The latter, who is thought to be the inventor of the pyramid-shaped building, was a kind of Le Corbusier of Ancient Egypt. He was both high priest of Heliopolis and prime minister to the king. Much later, about the time of the Saite Dynasty (seventh century B.C.), he was regarded as a divinity, son of Ptah, the builder-god, and the Greeks identified him with Asklepios, their god of medicine.

The Step Pyramid stood at Sakkara, facing Memphis on the other bank of the Nile. In its original form it consisted of a stone mastaba about 27 feet high and 180 feet square, on top of which Imhotep built four tiers or platforms amounting to a total height of about 120 feet, forming the symbolic staircase which the Pharaoh Zoser would climb after his death when he was reunited with the Sun God.

This building was merely the start of the edifice; since the king's life was happily prolonged, his architect more or less doubled the dimensions of the base of the monument and increased the height to 180 feet by adding two new tiers.

The interior consisted of several small rooms and corridors built over the tomb chamber as in the ordinary type of mastaba, and the pyramid was surrounded with a rectangular walled enclosure.

As the centuries passed the edifice became a ruin, but during the last thirty years eminent Egyptologists, including Lauer, have made a model reconstruction of the most immense complex of buildings ever discovered round a pyramid earlier in date than the Giza group.

However, before describing it and recounting its history, we should point out that there still exists a pyramid of an intermediary shape between the step pyramid and the pyramid with rectilinear or smooth sides; this is the pyramid with curved edges, which various writers have referred to as the "rhomboidal," "false," "blunted" or "bent" pyramid. This is the Dahshur Pyramid, the only one of its type, built by King Seneferu, and measuring 558 feet in length and about 300 feet in height. Wilkinson believes that this shape was caused by the speeding-up of the construction after the death of the Pharaoh, and that the height as originally planned was reduced by modifying the angle of the slope. Other writers consider that this change of angle was merely caused by a wish to reduce the weight resting on the base, after there had been some doubt as to its solidity. Apart from this difference in outline the building of the Dahshur Pyramid offers many points of comparison with the internal plan of the pyramids of Giza.

We should also mention another architectural singularity, the pyramid of Meidum, not far from Dashur, which was perhaps another tomb for Seneferu, consisting of a mastaba of eight tiers, covered, for reasons which have remained obscure, with a smooth coating of limestone.

The dimensions and shapes of the pyramids vary with each dynasty and even with each succeeding reign within these periods. These "lithomorphoses" or different stages of the finished building set problems for the archeologists which they then tried to resolve.

How for example did the Pharaoh Cheops, who chose the unprecedented area of twenty square miles at Giza for the building of his tomb, know that his reign was to be one of the longest in Egyptian history and that he would therefore have all the time he required to finish it?

If he had died a few years after his accession to the throne how would his successor have been able to finish this tomb in addition to undertaking his own? In other words, as we shall see, how would he succeed in finding the considerable labour force required?

Three eminent archeologists have given their answer to these questions.

"Each king," said Lepsius, in Baedeker's *Guide to Egypt and the Sudan*, 1929, "began to build his pyramid as soon as he mounted the throne. He began the work on a small scale, so that it could be finished quickly. If the gods granted him a longer life he continued gradually to enlarge the edifice by surrounding it with additional layers of outside stones until he realised his end was near. If he died before the work was finished it was then given its final form, and its dimensions indicated in this way the measure of his reign."

This "stratified" method of building is strongly contested by Sir Flinders Petrie who believes on the contrary that the building of each pyramid was carried out according to a plan that was carefully worked out in advance.

More recently Borchardt, who later supplied the internal plan of the pyramids, supported the theory of Lepsius, although with some reservations. The Pharaoh would cause his architect to draw up an initial plan for a pyramid of modest dimensions; this plan was then followed strictly in accordance with the first instructions but in a manner which enabled it to be completed very quickly after the king's death.

But it must be repeated that these are suppositions only and at this point we will leave the architectonic history which takes us from the mastaba to the Great Pyramid with its smooth sides, the final form assumed by the royal mausoleum in the fourth dynasty. This pyramid shape was to continue for ten centuries or so until the Pharaohs of the twelfth dynasty who then caused their tombs to be dug out of the rock in order to protect their treasures from the greed of robbers.

III

THE GIZA GROUP

The largest "true" pyramids were built between the fourth and twelfth dynasties (about 2900–2000 B.C.), that is over a period of nearly one thousand years. They all stand on the left bank of the Nile, on the west, the place of sunset and symbol of death, and divide into nine groups over a distance of 100 miles (Fig. 3). Today many of them have been reduced to ruins which are only discernible to the practised eyes of archeologists.

The Giza group, which we shall now examine, stands between the sacred city of Heliopolis and Memphis, capital of the ancient kingdom of Egypt. It was the first to be discovered and remains the best known of all the discoveries made since Bonaparte's expedition.

When the great general saw the pyramids he declined to go to the top, as some of the accompanying generals and scholars invited him to do, saying that he would do so later, on an occasion that was to remain famous. However, he measured them with his eagle eye and declared to those surrounding him that the mass of stone composing the group of three "seemed to him enough to build a wall one foot wide and nine feet high round the whole of France." The famous mathematician Gaspard Monge, who accompanied him, confirmed by means of a few measurements and simple calculations the exactness of this statement.

In *The Pyramids of Egypt* Edwards estimates that if all the stone making up the three edifices "were sawn into cubes measuring a foot in each dimension and these cubes were placed in a row, they would extend over a distance equal to two-thirds of the earth's periphery at the Equator," i.e. about 17,000 miles. It has also been estimated that the cathedrals of Florence and Milan, together with St. Peter's in Rome, could be easily lodged on the base of the Great Pyramid of Cheops alone.

It was Jomard, the geographer and archeologist accompanying Bonaparte, who provided some of the first descriptions of the pyramids, dealing mostly with their dimensions, and the explorations of his colleagues amounted to little. The descriptions that he gave however led the Italian archeologist Caviglia to undertake further excavations in 1817. The latter acquired proof that the subterranean corridors and chambers of the Pyramid of Cheops had been explored and plundered during Roman or even Byzantine times. The following year, Giovanni Battista Belzoni, another Italian, who had previously been a fairground "strong man," attacked the second pyramid, that of Chephren, where he discovered a granite sarcophagus with its lid half broken open, dating no doubt from the Hegira, for Arabic characters were found inside it. This important discovery proved conclusively that the pyramids were tombs, of which nobody had been certain since the time of Herodotus.

In 1836 Colonel Howard Vyse and his colleague J. S. Perring
explored the Great Pyramid again and after using a drill and weak
charges of explosives, they found the tablet of King Cheops, which
proved this to be his tomb and confirmed the definite assumptions of
the Greek travellers.

In 1837 Vyse visited the pyramid of Mycerinus and discovered the
king's sarcophagus, which had certainly been moved from its place.
He was able to remove the mummy-shaped wooden lid along with a
few bones of the Pharaoh's skeleton, wrapped in a coarse winding-
sheet. Like a good Britisher Vyse decided to send these relics to the
British Museum. Unfortunately however the "ka," which was no
doubt still watching over the king, prevented this sacrilege and the
ship carrying the remains to London sank off the coast of Portugal.

Working between 1842 and 1845 the German Egyptologist Richard
Lepsius produced a general plan of all the pyramids in Egypt, although
he did not succeed in listing all of them. His plan of the Giza group
remains a first-class document which we have reproduced here more
or less in diagrammatic form (Fig. 6).

The most complete examination and exploration of the Giza group
were undertaken relatively recently by the British archeologist
Flinders Petrie in 1880.

Between 1880 and 1915 the great French Egyptologist Maspero,
director general of the "Fouilles et Antiquités d'Egypte," was responsible for acquainting us with the famous Sphinx. He succeeded
Mariette, who was made a Bey by the Khedive of Egypt and, apart
from his eminent contribution to Egyptology, composed the libretto
of *Aida*.

Finally, nearer to our own times, the American G. A. Reisner
completed our knowledge of the pyramids with new excavations,
while the English scholar J. H. Cole made definitive measurements of
the buildings with the help of the most modern instruments, more or
less confirming the facts given by his eminent predecessors.

Such is the brief history of the fascinating return to the world of the
Marvels of Egypt.

The Giza group of pyramids can be seen a few miles from Cairo,
the city which is said to have been the place where the gods Horus and
Seth confronted each other in battle. The three pyramids stand on a
rocky plateau noticeably square in shape, measuring 4,500 feet along
one side. The faces of the buildings, like those of the classic mastabas,
are directed towards the four cardinal points, with the result that if
their diagonals are extended they enclose exactly the area of the Nile

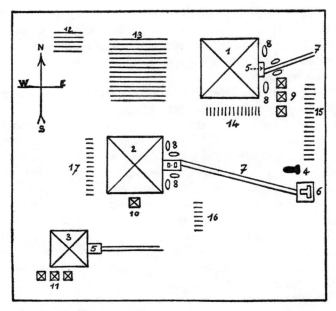

6. Plan of the Giza group (*after* Lepsius):

1. Pyramid of Cheops
2. Pyramid of Chephren
3. Pyramid of Mycerinus
4. Great Sphinx
5. Mortuary temple
6. Valley building
7. Causeway
8. Boat hollows
9. Small pyramids or mastabas (in the middle that of the daughter of Cheops: to the south that of Queen Henoutsen)

10. Pyramid of an unknown queen
11. Unfinished pyramids
12. Mastabas of the Fourth and Fifth Dynasties
13. Mastabas of the Fourth and Fifth Dynasties
14. Mastabas of the Fifth Dynasty
15 & 17. Mastabas of different periods
16. Tombs cut out of the rock

delta. This can only be a coincidence but it has led certain so-called "experts" to make endless dissertations on the secret "sayings" of the pyramids, attributing the architects of the pyramids with the most amazing geographical and cosmographic knowledge. (We shall not consider here the mathematical and esoteric propositions which are discussed and even distorted by eminent Egyptologists, including the Swiss Jéquier.)

At the foot of the pyramids, in addition to the Great Sphinx, stand other buildings which all belong to what is known as their complex: there are two other groups of three pyramids and all around are cemeteries of mastabas or tombs hollowed out of the rock, belonging to contemporary periods, for it was a tradition that the Pharaoh rewarded his servants and friends by building their tombs close to his own and at his expense.

These three pyramids, which belong in their entirety to the fourth dynasty (third millennium B.C.), were apparently built within a space of seventy years, a little longer than the time taken by Louis XIV to build Versailles.

THE THREE PYRAMIDS OF THE GIZA GROUP
COMPARATIVE DIMENSIONS, VOLUMES AND WEIGHTS

	Cheops	Chephren	Mycerinus
One side original base (feet)	755	707¾	356½
One side base today	753	689	356½
Original height	479	472	218
Height today	449	447	204
Original length of median of one face	609	574	278
Length today of median of one face	568	560	262
Original area of the base (square feet)	567,000	500,000	126,000
Original volume (cubic feet)	110,558,000	77,841,000	9,215,000
Theoretical weight (specific gravity = 2·5) in tons	6,250,000	5,245,000	662,000

The Great Pyramid, as the highest of the three is called, contained the remains of Cheops (the Greek form of *Khou-fou*), probably a son of Seneferu who, as we saw previously, built the pyramid of Meidum. This king, who seems to have been devout by nature, and disliked human sacrifice, reigned in peace for twenty-three years and saw the completion of his tomb.

The second pyramid is that of Chephren (*Khafrê*), his brother who succeeded him, after the reign of his nephew Didoufri, son of Cheops. Chephren also seems to have reigned for twenty-three years and was also able to see the completion of his tomb.

The third pyramid sheltered the remains of Mycerinus (*Menkaourê*) who also left a good reputation, although he was said to be somewhat prodigal. On his sarcophagus, the only one found in the three pyramids, the following inscription, which does him great honour, was deciphered:

"Mycerinus, eternally living, born of heaven, conceived by the heavenly goddess Nout, heir to the earth god Geb, her beloved. Thy mother Nout protects thee with her name of 'mystery of the heavens' and permits thee to live like a god that hath no enemies."

Generous fathers have mean sons, for the son of Mycerinus, finding the royal coffers empty, completed his father's tomb at little cost, and it was no doubt lack of funds which caused it to be relatively small in comparison with the two others.

As for the three little pyramids to the east of the Great Pyramid, one seems to be that of a daughter of Cheops and perhaps his "wife," Egyptian-style. The Pharaoh's eldest daughter was the legitimate heir to the throne, and during his lifetime he chose a male descendant, often one of his sons, who would then marry his sister in order to make his claims to the throne legitimate. According to Herodotus the second of these pyramids sheltered another of Cheops' daughters who was said to have prostituted herself in order to help with the completion of her father's tomb. The Greek traveller tells us that she asked her temporary lovers not for the traditional obol due to her as a prostitute, nor for precious jewels, to which, as a king's daughter, she was entitled, but for a solid block of stone; and he even adds that she worked extra hours, earning additional money which helped to build her own tomb.

The third small pyramid is that of the Queen Henoutsen, a half-sister of King Cheops, and thus completes the tombs of this Pharaoh's curious family.

To the south of the pyramid of Chephren stands the pyramid of an unknown queen, as well as three small pyramids next to that of Mycerinus, which seem to have remained unfinished.

Finally, to the east of this city of dead stones, stands the Hieratic Guardian, the solitary effigy of the Sphinx, its face weathered like that of some bulldog fixed immovably in the rock. The Egyptians called it also "Hou," the carved face. It was carved out of a natural spur of rock in the Libyan range and measured no less than 240 feet in length by 66 feet high, standing on a plinth more than 40 feet wide, while the face measured 13 feet 8 inches across. There are thousands of sphinxes in Egypt, and this is the largest of them all. There are more than a hundred of them between the temples of Karnak and Luxor, and it is thought that many more were placed in a double row lining the sides of the road that ran between these two holy places.

The Great Sphinx of Giza wears the royal emblems: the beard, the headdress and the sacred cobra on its forehead. Although its face has been damaged it resembles that of Chephren, and it stands in front of his tomb. Between the Sphinx's outstretched paws can still be seen a stele of red granite bearing an inscription relating to King Thoutmosis IV of the eighteenth dynasty. According to this text the prince, while out hunting, lay down to rest in the shadow of the Sphinx; while he was asleep the Sphinx promised him the double crown of Egypt if he would undertake to remove the sand which was gradually engulfing its statue.

IV

THE PYRAMID COMPLEX

This sphinx, or rather a pair of sphinxes (A, Fig. 7), were therefore the first to greet the mortal remains of the Pharaoh, which then journeyed through a series of buildings possessing as much ritual significance as the parts of a cathedral and together forming what the Egyptologists call a "complex" (Fig. 7).

Before it was placed in the stone tomb, its final resting place, the king's body was taken through the temples, the first one public, the second private or sacred, each of them distinct in function and symbolism, resembling the nave of a church where the congregation are gathered together and the choir where the priest officiates before the tabernacle, which is also subject to certain taboos.

Accompanied by his relations, friends and court dignitaries, the Pharaoh first entered the Low Temple or Valley Building (B) for the long and complicated rites of embalmment. The body was taken there through a narrow vestibule (a), carved with hieroglyphics, leading to the Reception or Purification Court (b). These ceremonies lasted at least several weeks and even several months, after which the wooden coffin was taken along the Causeway (c) to the Mortuary Temple (C). The Causeway was 1,200 feet long and 15 feet wide, with a well-paved floor, and walls carved with inscriptions; it was also roofed, no doubt in order to protect the carvings.

On entering the sanctuary the king's body, since it had been purified, belonged only to the priests. This new temple, which was 300 feet long and 150 feet wide, consisted of a vestibule (d), two galleries, one transverse (e), the other longitudinal (f), in which further ceremonies, different in type, but all essentially religious, took place, ending in the Sacrificial Courtyard (g) with the killing of some oxen.

Finally the sarcophagus crossed the gallery where statues represented the king under his various names (h), before entering the Sanctuary (i) where the symbolic layout, showing the Pharaoh as one of the immortal gods, can be easily understood. A group of priests specially chosen for this task went through a ceremony in his honour.

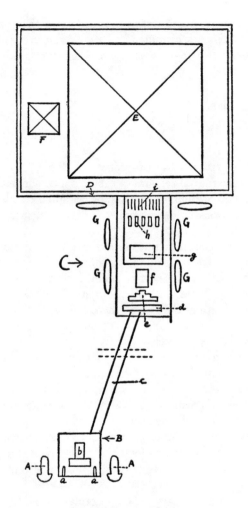

7. Diagram of the pyramid complex of Chephren:

A. Sphinx
B. Valley building
C. Mortuary temple
D. Pyramid enclosure
E. Pyramid of Chephren
F. "Satellite" pyramid
G. Boat hollows
   a. Vestibules

b. Entrance courtyard
c. Causeway to the mortuary temple
d. Vestibule
e. Transverse gallery
f. Longitudinal gallery
g. Sacrificial courtyard
h. Galleries with statues of the King
i. Sanctuary

Just before the sanctuary stood storerooms where offerings were placed in stone jars, ready for the dead man in case his priests should be negligent in bringing him refreshment every day.

The Valley Building was flanked by sphinxes and the Mortuary Temple by boat pits (G) hollowed out of the rock. The purpose of these oblong-shaped pits has never been exactly defined, but it is assumed that the boats were for the use of the king when he accompanied the sun in its daily course, by day in the brilliant sky, by night in the darkness beneath the earth.

From the moment when the king's body left the sanctuary and passed into the pyramid enclosure (D), the funeral ceremonies were practically complete. The body was to be sealed in the monument, the king's tomb properly speaking, and he would now lead there an existence which was to be secret, although not, the Egyptians believed, entirely disembodied.

The mastaba, as it was originally built, included shrines and offering-rooms along with the mortuary chamber, but the pyramid, with its two preceding temples linked by the causeway, only contained, strictly speaking, the royal vault, which was reached by passages arranged in a more or less complicated manner.

Of the three pyramids that of Cheops is the only one where the tomb is in the superstructure itself, whereas the mortuary chamber of Chephren was hollowed out of the base of the rock and that of Mycerinus lay in the subterranean depths of the pyramid, as in the classic type of mastaba. The pyramid of Cheops, which we shall now examine in detail, is the first of the group, it is the biggest, the oldest and the most complicated from a structural point of view.

This complexity was obviously designed to discourage, at least temporarily, the men who eventually robbed the tombs. In addition to the sacred remains, the pyramids contained treasures of all kinds and of incredible richness, but only in certain tombs in the Valley of Kings, such as that of Tutankhamen, were they found more or less intact.

The first problem was to find the entrance, which was concealed at a height of fifty feet beneath the exterior casing of the pyramid; when it was new this casing was quite smooth, and made any climbing almost impossible. Yet the Greek traveller Strabo believed, and both Petrie and Maspero were to confirm this eighteen centuries later, that this entrance had a removable door which slid open on pivots at the top, its existence being carefully concealed and the method of opening it kept secret.

Let us suppose that we know the "open sesame" and that in the company of Gaston Maspero we are following the tomb-robbers on an imaginary expedition through the secret recesses of the pyramid. There could be no better guide than the great archeologist[1] (Fig. 8).

"The first item for the robbers was to discover the entrance beneath the facing (T) which concealed it. It was situated about the middle of

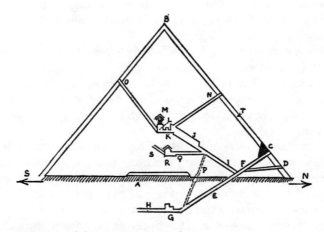

8. Cross-section of the Great Pyramid:

A. Base or rock foundation	K. Ante-chamber or hearse passage
B. Summit or pyramidion	L. Vault of King Cheops
C. Original entrance	M. Safety room
D. False entrance	N. Ventilation shaft (?) to the south
E. & F. Descending corridor	O. Ventilation shaft (?) to the north
G. Former original mastaba chamber	P. Shaft
H. Unfinished underground passage or cul de sac	Q. Horizontal corridor
	R. The "Queen's" chamber
I. Ascending corridor	S. Obstructed or unfinished corridor
J. Grand gallery	T. Original surface of the casing

the north face, but on a level with the eighteenth course of stones, about fifty feet above the ground (C). It was sealed by a block of stone which moved on pivots. As soon as it had been moved the robbers entered the Descending Corridor, which was 3 feet 11 inches high and 3 feet 5 inches wide (E, F), a larger version of the primitive tomb corridor, for example the traditional shaft of the mastaba, now going through the stonework. It went down to a depth of 300 feet, going beyond the old mortuary chamber (G) and terminating 345 feet

[1] Gaston Maspero, *Egyptian Archeology*. London, 1902.

farther on in an unfinished underground chamber (H). This was the first disappointment.

"If the robbers were not discouraged and examined their surroundings carefully they would notice in the roof, sixty-two feet from the door, a block of granite which stood out against the surrounding limestone. It was so hard that the exploring robbers, after wearing themselves out in a vain attempt to crack it or dislodge it, decided to force a way through the parts of the building constructed from softer stone."

The measurements of this block were larger than those of the descending corridor, and it is assumed nowadays, long after Maspero wrote these descriptions, that owing to the difficulties of inserting it and then lifting it again, the stone was brought inside the pyramid at the moment of its construction and placed in position after the body had been deposited in the vault. It is thought also that the workers who pushed it into place from the interior of the ascending corridor had contrived a secret exit so that they could get out of the monument after finishing their work.

This latter hypothesis has given rise to a film of the Hollywood type (in colour) which is full of anachronisms, and as a climax these last workers, who on this occasion are treacherous courtiers, are immured inside the pyramid.

Maspero now takes us further.

"Once this obstacle was passed the robbers entered the Ascending Corridor (I), which joins the first at an angle of 133° and divides into two branches. One branch descends horizontally towards the centre of the pyramid and ends in a granite chamber with a pointed roof, which is called, for no valid reason, the 'Queen's Chamber' (R), which is itself continued by a corridor which is either obstructed or unfinished (S).

"The other branch continues to ascend and its form and appearance change. It becomes a gallery (J) 148 feet long and 28 feet high, built of fine hard Mokattam stone, so highly polished and finely wrought that it is difficult to insert 'a needle or even a pin between the joints.'

"A further obstacle was encountered at the end. The corridor which leads to the Pharaoh's chamber was probably sealed by a single slab of granite; then came a small vestibule (K) divided into equal spaces by four portcullises. They have been so completely demolished that not a fragment remains, but they were probably made of granite. The royal vault (L) is a 'sepulchre' with a flat roof, 19 feet high, 34 feet long and 17 feet wide; there is no sculpture, no inscription, only a mutilated sarcophagus without a lid."

We should add here that in the royal vault itself, at a height of three feet above the ground, are the openings of two shafts (N, O), one going to the north and one to the south face of the pyramid. Their exact purpose is not known but they may have been ventilation ducts or they may have been the architectural expression of some religious or esoteric mystery.

"These," Maspero continued, "were the precautions taken against men.... But the very weight of the materials constituted a serious danger, and to prevent the royal vault from being crushed by the three hundred feet of stone which surmounted it five low hollow spaces were built over it (M). The first of these is protected by a pointed roof formed from two rows of stone slabs leaning against each other.[1] This device meant that the central pressure was directed almost entirely towards the side walls and the vault was spared. None of the stones of which it consists were cracked and if some have given way this must be due to the earthquakes which have so often shaken Egypt."

Although the precautions taken against over-weighty materials and the possibility of earth tremors seem to have been effective, neither architectural strategy, religious taboos, nor threats of terrible punishment were of any avail against the greed of malignant men.

These over-conspicuous monuments gradually attracted robbers as a magnet attracts iron. The Pharaohs of the New Kingdom decided therefore to cut their tombs out of the rock farther to the south in the valley of the Nile. In this way a vast necropolis was formed, known as the Valley of the Kings, which included both royal tombs and the temples of the gods. The discovery and exploration of this valley form another story, quite separate from that of the pyramids. We shall now describe the astonishing feat of the construction, a story in which hypothesis plays a considerable part.

V

KING CHEOPS BUILDS HIS TOMB

Today we understand Egyptian hieroglyphics and grammar fairly well, and even a few literary texts, but we know little about the art of building in the time of the Pharaohs. This is not the only lost civilisation where our knowledge of technique is based on conjecture, and the

[1] When Howard Vyse and J. S. Perring first explored this hollow chamber in 1837–38 they discovered on these rough-cut stones quarrymen's marks painted in red ochre, among which is the only mention of King Cheops that has been found in the pyramid.

mediaeval cathedrals, built much nearer to our own times, have not disclosed all the secrets of their construction.

Archeologists and technicians work together in an attempt to bring them to light, not without difficulty or conflict, and the pages that follow do not claim to include any startling new discovery.

Sculptors have left us many examples of Egyptian building, but apart from reliefs showing the transport of a colossus and a king granting an audience to his architect (Fig. 5), we have only one illustration of elementary work, the making and transporting of bricks. Between the brickmaker and the director of operations there is nothing at all. We can see none of the simple tools or machines, such as levers, scaffolding, accessory constructions or ramps, which we feel justified in imagining.

In the first place, the Egyptians of the time of Cheops, like the Incas, did not know the use of iron, or of the wheel, which was only to reach them a thousand years later, apparently introduced into Egypt by Jewish emigrants. Of the usual metals they used only copper, a soft metal which they succeeded in hardening by some process which remains unknown to us; perhaps they used ox-blood. Naturally they had stone-workers' tools, such as chisels or mallets with handles made out of flint or quartzite.

The methods of transport were also elementary, and the Egyptians carried small loads on yokes. Heavy loads, such as rough or dressed stones, were moved on sledges drawn either by donkeys, oxen, or more often by the men themselves, who either placed them on wooden rollers or else directly on the ground which they first soaked with water to make it more compact and smooth.

For their building materials they used bricks dried in the sun, the yellow limestone of Giza, and white limestone taken from the quarries of Tura which lay opposite Giza on the other bank of the Nile.

Granite was used mostly for the building of the temples in the complex, as well as for the doors of the pyramids, and certain interior details. In particular it came from Aswan in the Nile valley, which was 500 miles away, and the weight of some blocks reached 150, 200 and even 500 tons.

The stone was obtained either by surface—or tunnel—quarrying. The blocks were first of all attacked with chisels and then prised out of their bed by dampening the corners or perhaps by applying heat slowly and then cooling quickly. The quarrymen apparently worked in gangs, for inscriptions in red ochre have been found on these blocks: "Boat Gang," "Vigorous Gang," "Enduring Gang," "North Gang,"

"South Gang," which can be compared to the gang-organisation of today.

The stones were then placed on sledges, brought to Giza in flat-bottomed boats or barges of the necessary size and then dragged to the place of work. But how were they lifted when the building reached a height beyond the masons' reach?

At this juncture also the archeologists put forward two hypotheses, one of which had already been propounded by Herodotus, who writes in particular:

"The method employed was to build it in tiers, or steps, if you prefer the word—something like battlements running up the slope of a hill; when the base was complete, the blocks for the first tier above it were lifted from ground level by cranes or sheerlegs, made of short timbers; on this first tier there was another lifting-crane which raised the blocks a stage higher, then yet another which raised them higher still. Each tier, or storey, had its crane—or it may be that they used the same one, which, being easy to carry, they shifted up from stage to stage as soon as its load was dropped into place. Both methods are mentioned, so I give them both here. The finishing-off of the pyramid was begun at the top and continued downwards, ending with the lowest parts nearest the ground."[1]

Lauer[2] makes these very lucid comments on this passage from Herodotus:

"Herodotus assumes here that machines were used, after admitting implicitly that a mass of masonry in the form of tiers had already been built by another method; this could only have been done with the aid of a ramp system. It is possible however that Herodotus, who was not an architect, had interpreted the explanation wrongly, for if such machines existed one cannot see why they would not have been used for the entire building. . . ."

Other archeologists believe that the "cranes . . . made of short timbers" may refer to the "rocking hoist" system, for small-scale wooden models of a frame with a curved outline have been found; these belong to the New Kingdom, that is to say to a period one thousand three hundred years after the building of the pyramids. The German engineer Croon has suggested that the *chadouf* system was used; the *chadouf* (Fig. 9) was a sort of derrick which is still used in Egypt to draw water from wells. The *chadouf* could in fact have provided sufficient leverage to raise the blocks of stone the height of one tier and then slide them carefully into position (Fig. 10).

[1] Herodotus, *The Histories*. Trans. Aubrey de Selincourt. 1954.   [2] Op. cit.

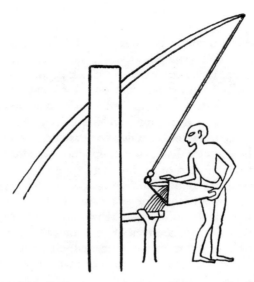

9. Ancient *chadouf* (from *Le Problème des Pyramides d'Egypte* by J. P. Lauer)

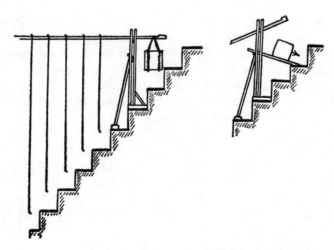

10. *Chadouf* system suggested by Croon

This ingenious argument is contested by Lauer, however, who points out how far this equipment would inconvenience the groups of workers and that its output would be small, in view of the fact that the Great Pyramid for instance contains 2,300,000 blocks of stone.

Then the ramp system was suggested, which has proved a stumbling-block for the experts in pyramid-building. They agree in assuming that the ramps consisted of mounds of earth reinforced by battens and bricks, but there is wide divergence of opinion about their dimensions, arrangement and method of functioning.

Croon assumes for example that on each of the four sides of the base of the pyramid ramps of the same width were built and, as the building went on, were raised gradually, by the addition of successive layers, almost to the top of the monument. If we assume that these ramps were built at an angle of 20° from the horizontal, each one would reach a total length of 1,200 feet. Such an undertaking was colossal, but feasible.

Lauer then suggested that there may have been only one ramp standing against one side of the pyramid at an angle of 20°. At the base it would have been only 300 feet wide and would have risen gradually along with the pyramid, growing narrower, obviously, but longer, until it reached a distance of 750 feet from the foot of the pyramid.

Finally, at each successive tier a kind of rectangular brick causeway might have been built all round the four faces of the pyramid, round which the workers and their sledges could circulate easily.

The system proposed by Lauer is supported by Edwards, who suggests that the foot-hold embankments were built of wooden baulks. "Let it be imagined," he writes, "that a pyramid has been built to half its final height. Nothing of the stonework already laid would be visible from the ground, because three of the outer faces would be entirely covered by the foot-hold embankments and the fourth face would be screened by the supply-ramp."

It is an undeniable fact that the architects of Giza used ramps, for Hölscher found traces of them set vertically against the south face of the pyramid of Chephren as well as at Lisht, about twenty-eight miles away. We can therefore conclude with Lauer that this discovery "proves that at least one ramp was used for every pyramid, and constitutes one of the strongest arguments in reply to those who rely on Herodotus and attempt to prove the absolute necessity of some raising equipment."[1]

The appearance of flying saucers however has made some people

[1] Op. cit.

believe that the building of the pyramids was a pure phenomenon of levitation, caused by music or magic incantations. This is at least the opinion of Kingsland:[1]

"When the King built the pyramids," he wrote, "the large stones were brought from a great distance. They were placed on pieces of papyrus bearing certain symbols. They then rose into the air and covered a distance equivalent to the flight of an arrow. In this way they finally reached the site where the pyramids were built."

This is not the place to discuss hypotheses of this kind, which may be attractive but belong more properly to the realm of occultism rather than the art of architecture, and needless to say we do not support them in any way.

The pyramid consists essentially of two elements: first, the internal casing, consisting of cubic blocks of yellow Giza limestone, cut to different sizes and then placed on top of each other without any bond between the joints, following the outline from which the pyramids take their name (unless the building gave its name to the shape); and second, a solid outer casing of other stones cut so as to incline inwards, thus giving the pyramids their smooth appearance. In theory this construction follows the same elementary method as that used for roadside walls where the stones are placed on top of each other as simply as possible. The same plan is adopted by a child building sandcastles or piling up stones at the seaside, for he chooses this method of building instinctively, realising that it provides the most stable form of equilibrium.

In reality the pyramids are a little more complicated, for they were built to last and their dimensions are larger than life. In the first place they have no foundations. They are set directly on the rock which was first levelled so that the base could be firmly established. The base itself consists of blocks measuring 4 feet 6 inches in height placed along the lines of the face, measuring about 700 feet in length. On this first layer of stones stand about 220 further layers consisting of blocks decreasing in height until the summit, which consisted of a small square platform.

On this was placed the final block, known as the pyramidion, which was apparently cut into the shape of a pyramid. It disappeared long ago, together with the last upper layers, with the result that the pyramid of Cheops is now slightly truncated in shape, ending in a platform thirty feet square, a resting place for tourists who have made the traditional ascent.

[1] Kingsland, *The Great Pyramid in Fact and in Theory*.

It is known that the pyramidion not only formed the architectural crown of the work but it also symbolised the *benben*, the sacred stone of the temples of Heliopolis, arranged in this way over the royal tomb. Edwards assumes that in order to keep it more firmly in place "a projection resembling a disk would be carved in the centre of the base to fit like a tenon into a mortise cut to receive it in the middle of the top course of masonry." Jéquier tells us that, according to an inscription he had found, this pyramidion was probably covered with gold leaf which symbolised even more strongly the brightness of the Sun God.

Lauer estimates that the number of blocks of stone making up the Great Pyramid amounts to 2,300,000, weighing altogether 6,500,000 tons with a specific gravity of 2·5 and necessitating the quarrying of at least 11,100,000 cubic feet of stone.

The interior casing blocks were merely cut while the exterior blocks were dressed with greater care and the joints between them were sealed with mortar. In its naked state, therefore, the pyramid formed a huge staircase of rough stone, as it is now.

Next came the work of dressing the faces, giving the pyramid the smooth appearance it possessed when it was first completed. It is estimated that the total number of these blocks of white limestone was 115,000; the height varied according to the height of the tiers, but the width varied from 4 feet 6 inches to 18 inches, and the heaviest of them weighed 15 tons.

One of the faces was dressed with an exterior angle of 52° and the higher face sometimes had a notch. Each block was set against the next one, joined by an extremely liquid mortar, achieving a joint of $\frac{1}{4}$–$\frac{1}{2}$ millimetre, an accuracy described by Flinders Petrie as "equal to the most modern optician's straight-edges of such a length."

Egyptologists are no more in agreement on the technique of dressing the pyramids than they are on that of raising the tiers. Some of them support Herodotus who states that the work was begun at the top; others believe on the other hand that the pyramid was dressed as it was built, but that the final surfacing and smoothing process was begun at the top as the ramps were demolished one after the other, liberating the entire pyramid, which was then revealed in its pristine whiteness to everyone who, in a humble or important capacity, had taken part in its construction over the years.

It is just as difficult to estimate the number of these workers as to say how they were recruited or the conditions under which they worked.

Modern opinion on this question seems to take into account once more the remarks of Herodotus, which impressed upon everyone the memory of the forced labour and the inhuman conditions under which the pyramids were constructed, for they are mentioned every time the actual building work is discussed. However, when the Greek traveller states that 100,000 men were employed for three months on this work, that is, 400,000 men per year, it should be realised that these 100,000 men were only occupied this way during the three months of the Nile floods (from the end of July to the end of October), when they could not work in their fields. The pyramids brought them seasonal work which was available close at hand and probably provided them with valuable extra money. It is hard to imagine that the Pharaohs would constantly empty the Nile valley of its population without running the risk of famine.

These temporary workers toiled either in the quarries or at the Giza site, where their strong limbs supplied the valuable energy needed to move the blocks of granite and then drag them to the foot of the pyramid.

They were essential to the operation, they were the machinery, the assistants to the specialists and artisans who were occupied unceasingly in quarrying the stone, cutting it and dressing it.

Sir Flinders Petrie has shown that the figure of 400,000 men employed for twenty years on the building of the Great Pyramid is exaggerated and we should bear in mind that on this occasion only one pyramid was being built at a time. The British archeologist estimated therefore that, in order to handle over a period of twenty years about 2,300,000 stones weighing on the average about $2\frac{1}{2}$ tons, a gang of eight men would only have had to move ten blocks every twelve weeks, which seems very reasonable.

Let us add also that from the mathematical point of view the volume of the building which remained to be constructed diminished rapidly each year in inverse proportion to what was already built. But it was also possible that hold-ups, such as shortage of funds in the royal treasury, wars, epidemics or unexpected Nile floods might have had a noticeable influence on the annual rhythm of work.

When the Egyptian fellahs returned to their fields in the Nile valley the experts had all the time they wanted for refinements without being surrounded by useless helpers whose presence had become embarrassing. It is therefore possible to imagine the Giza site from July to October crossed incessantly by sledges drawn by men or donkeys, straining hard on the ropes, moving rocks or wooden battens, whereas from October to July the quarrymen calmly excavated their blocks of stone in the Tura hillside while on the rocky plateau the stone masons dressed the blocks all round the monument according to the dimensions which had finally been calculated by the architect.

Did these workers live like slaves, as Herodotus said? Even Le Bon, the French social historian, stated in *Les Premières Civilisations* that the Pharaohs depopulated whole provinces, "conscripting even the old men and the children to spoil the mortar or carry away the rubbish, sending them back to their villages when they were exhausted and recruiting the inhabitants of another province in their place."

We do not believe this, but we believe with Weigall that cruelty is always remembered by any race that suffers it for a long time. Now apart from a few battle scenes Egyptian iconography includes no scenes revealing savage treatment of workers. Weigall tells us that on the contrary the Egyptians "carried out their work with a goodwill and an application almost unknown in the West."

In support of this optimistic assertion the historian translates for us an inscription from the time of Sesostris III, eight centuries after the building of the pyramids, it is true. It is the description, written by a governor, of the transport of a colossal statue:

"The road which the statue had to take when it left the quarries was very difficult and since the energies of the men would have been exhausted by dragging this enormous mass along it I caused a new way to be made. Then the strong men said, 'Now, we're going to take it away,' and my heart rejoiced at these words. The people of the town gathered together with rejoicing, and it was a fine sight, finer than any other. There were men with strong arms and weaker ones also, while *among the volunteers* there was even an old man leaning on a boy. Their valour was great, their arms became increasingly strong and each man worked like a thousand. Everyone shouted and applauded and when we reached the town a crowd of people were singing as they awaited us. It was a fine sight, finer than any other in the world!"

It is possible too to imagine that the Egyptian workers regarded themselves as building something that was much more of a temple than a tomb. It was the temple of their King-god, the resting place of the planet which brought them rich harvests. These workers, like those who later built our cathedrals, were performing an act of faith. They worked with enthusiasm, and not as slaves who had been regimented, cringing beneath the whip to satisfy the capricious cruelty of an inhuman satrap.

This is what we would like to believe when we look at the pyramids today.

III

THE GREAT WALL OF CHINA

The Great Wall separating China from the desert
Winds far away beyond the frontier.
There are no longer any towns,
Here and there a few scattered bones
Seem to express their eternal hate.
Three hundred and sixty thousand men
Are torn weeping from their families.
Since this was the King's command it must be obeyed.
But who now will work in the fields?

Li T'ai Po
(About A.D. 750)

Quoted by René Grousset in
Histoire de la Chine. Paris, 1942

"THE MOST WARLIKE BARRIER IN THE WORLD"

WHEN MEN BUILT the Great Wall of China to protect themselves from their earthly enemies, they succeeded in creating "the most warlike barrier in the world." At least this is how it is described on the stele which stands at Kiayuikwan, near Tibet, at the western end of the Wall. On the stone which stands at the eastern end, at Shanhaikwan, however, there is a more modest inscription: "Heaven created the Seas and the Mountains."

Certain astronomers have said that this stone reptile lying in the Empire of the Yellow Dragon is so vast that it could be seen from the Moon with the naked eye, just as we can see the so-called "canals of Mars" through the telescope.

The Chinese call this barrier "The Great Wall of ten thousand lis,"[1] but they exaggerate slightly. The *Encyclopaedia Britannica* gives its length as 1,600 miles. Geil, the American explorer, estimates that he covered about 2,240 miles when he went round it, including naturally the loops and spurs in Kansu and Shensi. This figure was confirmed exactly by Georges-Marie Haardt in his famous book *La Croisière Jaune*, where he described his journey and included maps. The shortest route consisted of 1,110 miles, and to this must be added a further 1,110 miles made up of the loops and spurs mentioned above, along with the double and triple walls which prevented access to them, without taking into account the mounds of earth braced up with bamboo hurdles which are no longer in evidence today, for travellers and weather conditions have worn them away.

"A complete plan of this immense undertaking," wrote M. G. Pauthier in 1937, "seems to have been made by missionaries in the eighteenth century and sent to France. It was drawn on silk, setting out the Great Wall in its entirety and showing all details. The original has disappeared but there is probably a copy in one of the national libraries in Paris."

[1] The *li* varies from 1,350 to 1,750 feet, depending on the author who mentions it. The term must be understood in a symbolic sense, meaning a great distance.

I have spent some time looking for this map, but unfortunately without success.

The Wall passes through twenty-two meridians, from 98° to 120° between the 35th and the 41st parallel. If we could imagine it rebuilt in Europe, its area would cover a rectangle drawn roughly round four points set in Paris, Minsk (Russia), Varna (Bulgaria) and Cape Créus near the French-Spanish frontier. In this way the Wall would include, either wholly or partly, France, Switzerland, Italy, Austria, Czechoslovakia, Jugoslavia, Hungary, Bulgaria, Roumania, Poland and Russia.

11. Stele at Shanhaikwan (from *The Great Wall of China* by W. E. Geil)

Much has been written about the Great Wall, half of it fact, half fancy. The Great Wall and the Grand Canal are the two most important constructional works of Ancient China, but unlike the legendary Tower of Babel and the ruinous Pyramids of Egypt this Asiatic fortification served an undeniably practical purpose.

The first travellers who visited the Empire of Cathay, especially the missionaries, wrote at length about the Wall, expressing wonder and surprise, and sometimes unexpected praise. Naturally one of them had to deny its very existence; the Abbé Larrieu, for instance, in a picturesque but absurd piece of writing, described it as "a low mound of earth," which is true of certain portions, but he made the grave mistake of basing his argument on the fact that Marco Polo does not mention it. The famous Venetian explorer returned to Europe through Kansu, where all he could see of the Wall were low embankments, judging from the few faint traces which survive today. Yet it is difficult to believe that during his ten years' stay in China Marco Polo was unaware of the Wall's existence. We must assume that the passages he wrote about this extraordinary edifice have been lost, which is most unfortunate. Father Tscheppe, a Hungarian priest who saw the Great Wall early this century, expressed the same regret. "I suppose," he wrote in his *History of the Kingdom of Ch'in*, "that descriptions of the Great Wall must exist, for the Chinese writers have written about everything. In spite of all my researches I have found nothing in this country. How glad I would be if I could find some somewhere else."

Although we possess few technical details about the building of the Wall, there is no end to the myths which circulate about it in China, for the legends have been faithfully handed down from one generation to another, ever since the days of the wonderful, terrible, colossal Ch'in Shih Huang Ti, first Emperor of China, who ordered the work to start, twenty-two centuries ago.

The Emperor's biographer, Ssu-ma-Ch'ien, left a not very flattering description of him during the second century B.C. "He had a snub nose," he wrote, "eyes like slits, and a bulging chest. He had the voice of a wolf and the heart of a tiger; he was crafty, mean and depraved." European historians go further and state that he was Nero, Caesar, Tiberius, Louis XI, Henry VIII, Richelieu, Louis XIV and Napoleon rolled into one. In more flattering terms he can be compared to Richelieu for his destruction of the old Chinese feudalism, to Caesar for his creation of the Empire, to Napoleon for his organising talent or to Louis XIV for his establishment of a royal court and the building of countless palaces. Finally he can be compared to Nero for he caused most of the books written in the Empire to be burnt. He had many more concubines than Henry VIII, and in fact there were such an incredible number of them that, according to one legend, "his temperament was so exceptional that it took him thirty-six years to spend a night with each of them." But his fantastic cruelty, which there is no room to describe here, made him a kind of Tiberius; Pauthier states in all seriousness that during his lifetime he ordered more than 1,400,000 people to be either decapitated or put to death with one kind of torture or another.

Such was the man who reigned over China from 247 to 210 B.C. and gave it his name, Ch'in. The Empire he founded lasted until 1912, when it collapsed and was replaced by the first Republic of Sun-Yat-Sen.

Prince Cheng-Wang, as he was then called, came to the throne in 246 B.C., succeeding his father Chung Siang, King of Ch'in. This kingdom was the area now known as Shensi, the province lying within the large bend of the Hwang-Ho, or Yellow River, a district nearly half as large again as Great Britain. Its other boundaries were formed by the Tibetan mountains and the two great rivers of China; the strategic position which it occupied as a result gave it supremacy over the feudal kingdoms which surrounded it, although they were not subdued until after a hundred and fifty years of bitter fighting.

We have little information about the tactical conduct of these immense holocausts, but we know various horrible facts about the way they ended: 80,000 prisoners decapitated in 331, 240,000 in 293 and 150,000 in 274.[1] When Tchovang-Siang captured Tchao (part of the modern province of Shensi) in 260 B.C. he ordered 400,000 prisoners to be beheaded, although he had promised to spare their lives.

These methods were modern and the arithmetic behind them was simple, for the Ch'in soldiers received no pay unless they produced the correct number of severed heads. Terrible tortures were inflicted before the ritual execution; one conqueror for instance turned a fat general into a human lamp for several days—he inserted a lighted fuse into his navel.

Cheng-Wang continued the work of his predecessors, brought the struggle to a victorious close and overthrew his great feudal enemies; in 221 he assumed the title of Ch'in Shih Huang Ti, meaning "Supreme Emperor of the Ch'in dynasty," or more simply, "Emperor of China."

After his bloody victory the young sovereign pacified the Empire and organised its internal life, but along the northern frontier there was a constant threat of invasion from the Barbarian Hung-No, or Huns, who were later to penetrate into Europe in the fifth century.

The Huns seem to have been established in Asia since the thirteenth century B.C.; there were many nomadic tribes, each with their different characteristics, but all of them were equally hostile towards the peaceable Chinese peasants, and razed their crops as soon as they were ready for harvest. Their horsemen and archers were unsurpassed and with lightning forays they laid waste the countryside or pillaged a town in a few moments, leaving only blazing ruins, corpses and famine behind them, while they disappeared into the desert to absorb their booty. Naturally they were greatly feared, as the age-old proverb shows: "Have no fear for the Tiger of the South, but beware the Cock of the North!"

[1] René Grousset, *L'Histoire de la Chine*. Paris, 1942.

Before the unification of China by the Emperor Ch'in, the feudal princes had already sealed the mountain passes with shaky fortifications or attempted to build walls in the enclosed valleys. Once he had consolidated his throne and given some thought to the defence problem Huang Ti gave orders for all these sketchy forts and improvised ramparts to be joined together in one immense unbroken line which was to become the Great Wall.

The Caesar of China did not prefer defence to attack, for he had immediately shown himself capable of forming an army of 300,000 men to subdue the invaders before starting work on the Wall. Under the command of General Mung-Tien the Chinese destroyed most of them and succeeded in keeping the rest well away from the frontier.

But this was merely a temporary expedient. The only way of dealing with these wild tribes was to "wall" them out of China, in an effective, definitive fashion which would overcome their primitive weapons and feeble strategy. The Emperor decided that this method was preferable to maintaining a string of garrisons, for they could never be strong enough. And the future was to prove him right, at least until the large-scale invasion of Ghengis Khan which shook the Wall—but that was fourteen centuries later.

II

FROM THE YELLOW SEA TO THE "ROOF OF THE WORLD"

Old Chinese documents and literary works have left us no reliable descriptions of the great enterprise, and we possess only scraps of information about how the Wall was built, how the work was organised, what techniques were used and even how long it took. Yet from every part of the rampart countless stories have been preserved which are unanimous in describing the Emperor's stern will and his incredible cruelty towards the workers.

General Mung-Tien, "Conqueror of the Tartars," was entrusted with the building of the fortress and the coordination of the armies of workers who were brought by force, in millions, from all the provinces which were now in Ch'in's power. It has often been said that 400,000 workers died during the operation, but since we do not know very much about the duration of the work it is hard to say whether this figurè is abnormal or to assert that the Great Wall became the longest cemetery in the world and that the sick and wounded were walled up alive inside it.

Ch'in's savage cruelty is not mentioned by historians but it has survived in legends, such as this one which is told in the East: "Ch'in, finding that the work was not progressing as fast as he wished, since there were not enough workers, went up to heaven and took 'the tree that froze the earth.' He shook it so hard that the countryside was soon covered in thick frost which destroyed the crops just before harvest time. The peasants were in despair and rather than die of starvation they were forced to work on the Great Wall."

In any case the Wall was certainly a prison, for all the jails of the Empire were cleared and their occupants sent to augment the peasants. There were still not enough workers, so all the redundant civil servants were sent, as well as the dishonest tax collectors—an army of clerks to reinforce the convicts. Finally, after he had destroyed nearly all the books in the Empire, for they seemed to perpetuate the ancestral cult of feudalism that he had only just suppressed, Huang Ti sent some of the unemployed intellectuals to break their nails in the mud and granite—the rest of them were buried alive.

At the same time as he built the Wall Mung-Tien built thirty-four fortified towns which were to act as command headquarters, supply posts and base workshops. All round the Wall and the towns the land was cleared, sown and harvested to feed the workers, but supplies were by no means certain and had to be requisitioned throughout the whole of China. Endless food convoys ploughed across the country, but most of them were lost. Father Tscheppe relates that out of 180 loads of grain coming from Shangtung only one reached the Wall, for the rest were eaten, sold or stolen on the way.

The workers were underfed and died like flies. Women took part in the work, naturally, acting either as beasts of burden or else doing the lighter work of weaving canvas for the tents in which the workers lived; the huge camps moved with them as the work progressed.

As they lay miserably awake in their tents the poor worn-out workers still had the heart to recount the delightfully naïve legends that can be heard even today near the Wall, from Korea to the Gobi desert. One story tells how the Wall came to follow a winding course. "After the foundations had been laid a fall of snow brought work to a stop, for the bricks became soft again. A dragon was passing that way and went to sleep where he was, leaning against the Wall. Since it was pliable it assumed his graceful shape. When the workers came back they took this as a sign and continued the curving outline."

But other stories mention the fearful shadow of the Emperor and his magic whip, which symbolised his absolute power, and the lash which whistled through the air and came down on the naked backs drenched with sweat. A legend from the Gobi desert area, where the Wall is built of mud, tells how Ch'in could not finish it because on this occasion he lost his magic whip. He frequently came to watch the work

12. The Dragon Wall (from *The Great Wall of China* by W. E. Geil)

and one day he fell in love with the daughter of a foreman and asked for her hand in marriage. The girl replied however that she was devoted to the poor suffering workers and added that she would rather die than become his concubine.

In the meantime another dragon who had come to look on was heard to reply that the powerful monarch was building the Wall with the help of his magic whip. Then the heroic young girl fell on her knees before the monster and begged him to take pity on the workers. The dragon returned to his lair and ordered his wife to come down to earth in her turn to seduce the Emperor. Since she was very beautiful

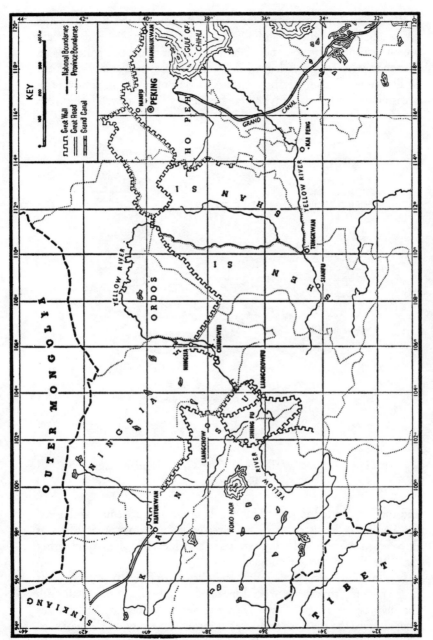

13. Map showing the Great Wall of China

she succeeded without difficulty, and at the right moment (you can guess when that was) she made off with the famous magic whip. This is the reason, the legend concludes, why the Great Wall was never finished and why in this district it is called only "the Wall of the eight thousand *lis*."

Whether the theft of the magic whip had anything to do with it or not, Huang Ti died in 210 B.C., before the Wall was finished. There is always some truth in legends which tell of miraculous events. The fearsome Emperor was buried beneath an enormous mound of earth which had been erected during his life time. Many of his wives, his best archers and many of those who had shared in the building of the tomb were buried with him.

The Wall as it exists today belongs to several different periods and very little remains of the first outline. Some parts which are still standing go back no further than the fifth century A.D., and the portions of the greatest architectural interest, as far as their proportions and beauty are concerned, notably in the Peking district, date only from the Ming dynasty (1368–1544). The Wall covers three areas of different geological type:

1. The desert, in the West, from Kiayuikwan in the Chinese part of Kansu, between the Tibetan frontier and the Gobi desert as far as Ningsia where Ghengis Khan crossed the Yellow River.

As far as Liangchow, in an area of low hills (between 3,000 feet and 6,000 feet), the rampart, which consists of unsteady embankments, is in a bad state. For long distances no trace remains at all, except for a few fortified towns, small advance forts, watchtowers and ways across.

From Lanchowfu to Chungwei the Wall includes a triple line of defence at the place where five rivers, all tributaries of the Yellow River, meet, for their valleys are danger spots from the point of view of invasion. Near Sining Fu, in the Ho Tao valley, a spur runs ninety-three miles to the south, parallel to the Tibetan frontier. It is in this reinforced section that the Wall climbs to 6,000 feet near the famous Koko Nor lake, which is ten times as big as Lac Léman and lies at a height of 9,600 feet, with "water that is soft as silk."

2. The mud region. This lies within the large bend of the Yellow River, across the Ordos steppes which consist of 40,000 square miles of loess and quicksands. It was here that pressure from Mongolia became strongest and finally caused a breach in the Wall in the twelfth century, leaving the way into China open to Ghengis Khan. There was fierce fighting here on both sides of the Wall and the nomadic tribes who still live there say that in the whistling of the wind across the dunes at night

they can hear the cries of the dying Chinese soldiers pleading for mercy and cursing their Mongolian attackers.

Local legend says that the line followed by the Great Wall across the Ordos was traced by Huang Ti's own white horse, which crossed the area with a saddle fastened to its tail to leave a mark on the ground.

3. The mountains. This section lies to the East, and after following the Yellow River the Wall goes towards Peking, providing for the defence of the town by a loop of some 250 miles. It is here that the Wall is in the best state of preservation, for it lies near the capital of the Empire which ever since the start of the modern era has been destroyed, resited and rebuilt. There are many defiles in this high region and the defences are reinforced, especially towards the north, by passes fortified by small circular sections of wall placed up the hillside, like that of Yang Kao which will be described later. A spur 250 miles long which separates the provinces of Shansi and Hopeh seems to protect the Grand Canal on its way to Nanking.

After Peking the Wall twists along towards the Yellow Sea as far as Shanhaikwan over a fairly high mountain range. It forms part of the ramparts of this town and runs along the river bank for several miles, opens out to form a citadel and ends in the Gulf of Liaotung, in the form of a jetty which rests, it is said, "on vast ships which were sunk voluntarily to provide foundations."

Not far away, at Chinwangtao, according to the American explorer Geil, there stands a small temple erected to the memory of Princess Yen. Her husband, Prince Yen, was defeated by Huang Ti and forced to work on the Wall. He died, and when the Princess found his body by the rampart she was heartbroken and flung herself into the sea. "This woman," runs an inscription in the temple, "will be honoured for all time, but the name of the Emperor Ch'in will be detested for ever."

III

THE ORGANISATION OF THE DEFENCE SYSTEM

In spite of the time spent on its construction and the different geological regions that it traverses, there is a high degree of uniformity about the way the Wall is built. Most of it consists of two walls built on foundations of between 6 and 12 feet in height and 4 feet 6 inches in thickness. The walls themselves measure 4 feet 6 inches at the base and about 18 inches at the top, rising to a height of 21 to 24 feet above ground level, including the parapets, which are 4 feet 6 inches high. The two facings are built of bricks cemented together with mortar made from lime, and Pauthier states that "the builders were forbidden, under pain of death, to leave any space between, not even enough for a nail to pass through."

The bricks were frequently made on the spot or nearby, but the big blocks of stone were dragged there by men, or, according to tradition, in the steep places, by goats which were specially trained and harnessed together for the purpose.

The space between the outer brick facings, which was about fifteen feet wide, was filled with clay which was sometimes brought from a great distance, especially in the mountainous districts, by vast numbers of coolies who carried two baskets suspended from a bamboo rod, a method which is still used everywhere in China today.

Once the clay was there it was filled in as the Wall progressed, pushed down either by the men's feet or by heavy tree trunks which were used as long rollers or else turned on one end and used as pile-drivers.

The clay filling was then covered by a causeway of bricks of roughly hewn stones, and the rainwater which accumulated there ran away through holes pierced in the parapets and leading to gutters with a semi-circular cross section.

There were battlements along the parapets, always on the outside and sometimes on the inside too. At the base of the parapets there were loopholes set at an angle which made it possible to shoot arrows almost vertically downwards, reducing wastage and preventing attackers from scaling the Wall.

When Earl Macartney came to China as Ambassador for George III his first sight of the Wall, in 1793, filled him with astonishment and led him to utter grave reflections. "Whenever a race of people who are civilised enough to cultivate the land," he wrote in his *Journey to the Interior of China and Tartary, 1792-1794*, "have as neighbours another race who are still merely hunters, possessing as it were the characteristics of highly developed animals, the first race builds fortifications and the second race naturally destroys them. . . . But . . . the fate of warlike nations today cannot be governed by barriers of this sort. The power of armies triumphs over every kind of obstacle. No fortifications are impregnable. But they can slow down the enemy's progress."

And so in two paragraphs the noble lord sums up the entire history of the Great Wall throughout twenty-two centuries.

Huang Ti and his successors produced ramparts of ever-increasing strength, which could be neither crossed by horsemen nor penetrated by arrows. The Great Wall eventually became a vast garrison, divided into countless barracks. But it was built not only as a precautionary measure, but as part of a deep-laid political plan.

After he had defeated the Huns, with the help of the valiant General Mung-Tien, the Emperor realised that he had on his hands hundreds of thousands of soldiers, mainly coming from distant provinces, some of them mercenaries, some soldiers of fortune, and it would have been dangerous to let them remain idle. What is more, if the vast communities whom he had subdued were now moved closer to the Wall, from north to south and from east to west, the Emperor would avoid the possible recurrence of Chinese feudalism, for he was determined to stamp this menace out, and this mass transfer of population would prevent its renewal.

He divided the mass of men, victors and vanquished, into two groups, who were now merged in the cause of national security: the workers would work while the defenders would occupy the Wall and maintain it while it was being built. There were to be three different defensive systems:

1. *Watchtowers* which allowed the enemies' movements to be observed from far away. The distance between them varies from 100 to 500 yards, and they are set closest together at the vulnerable spots, placed so that the enemy could be caught between two lines of archery-fire. The smallest of these towers accommodated about ten men who divided their time, day and night, between rapid scrutiny of the moving desert and the supervision of the peasants who came and went as they cultivated the land on both sides of the Wall. These small forts were about forty feet square and forty feet high, standing on top of the Wall and overhanging the edge, providing defence on the flank.

2. *Garrison-towers* which were much larger, some of them reaching a length of over sixty feet. They were usually built over the entrances to the Wall, and narrow gates opened inwards and outwards, leaving just room for a horse and its rider to pass through. They also served as arsenals, and along with additional arms they housed fuel stores, food and medicines calculated to last for a period of four moons.

These garrisons varied from 100 to 200 men and usually commanded an isolated camp or a group of villages. They were spaced out unevenly but carefully, standing farther apart over the hills than on the plains, while in the mountain passes they were reinforced by advance posts consisting of small isolated forts and other walls in the shape of a half-moon; sometimes there were ditches at the foot of the Wall filled with water, or hollow craters arranged in quincunx formation and spiked with sharp bamboo stakes, providing traps for the enemy soldiers whose horses would rush straight into them.

The Wall also formed part of the defensive system of the towns, which were reached through narrow, carefully guarded gates. Some of them were less forbidding, like the "Gate of Tongues" in the Yang Kao pass, near Peking, dating apparently from the fourteenth century, with a hexagonal frieze of white marble over its archway, carved with figures of the Buddha and bearing inscriptions in seven languages. It was after going through this pass that Genghis Khan first set eyes on Peking, which he attacked and destroyed. In addition certain important gaps were protected by iron gates, of which twenty-five or so still remained in the eighteenth century.

The Great Wall and its approaches were subject to continual inspections by the Emperors themselves or by their envoys, who sent them very careful reports. One of these, addressed to the Emperor Tse Tsong in the twelfth century, includes the following details:

"In a pastoral area the people must remain nomadic in order to maintain the Wall and keep watch. In agricultural areas on the other hand twenty families should be allotted to each fort; in summer they must dig the ditches which have collapsed during the winter. A one-roomed house will be built for each family and trees will be planted round them."

Some writers state that at various stages between A.D. 600 and 1000 the Wall was defended by three million men—a remarkable defence force which has hardly ever been equalled in modern warfare. It allowed one soldier to every hundred yards of the fighting line. At the end of the eighteenth century, when the defensive system seems to have been most complete, Father Magalhan, who died in Peking after living there for twenty-nine years, wrote that there were 3,000 towers of all types[1] manned by 902,054 soldiers, on whose behalf a remarkable cavalry force of 389,167 horses was kept in reserve, ready to charge the enemy.

3. This *light cavalry*, which was augmented by foot squadrons, constituted the last defence system of the Wall. Day and night the cavalry went round the ramparts where the couriers could gallop six

[1] Geil estimates that when the Wall was in its most highly developed state there were 40,000 towers and half as many when its defences were at their lowest. Two thousand fortified towns were partly encircled by the Wall.

abreast, giving orders for assembly or dispersal according to the tactical needs of the moment.

The watchmen posted along the battlements gave the alarm signal by means of gongs, trumpets, smoke, damp straw or banners of different colours. At night blazing logs sprinkled with metal oxides to make the flames burn different colours were used as rocket-signals. The Chinese are usually credited with the invention of fireworks.

When the alarm was given the soldiers—who were peasants at the same time, because they cultivated the surrounding fields and regarded the produce as their pay—left their ploughs or shepherd's crooks, exchanged their straw hats and linen smocks for helmets and armour, took to their posts, filled the quivers and tightened the bows, rushed up the ramps or the ladders leading to the ramparts and riddled the enemy with projectiles of a more or less effective type fired through the battlements, until during the fifteenth century artillery came into use on the towers and the raiders were repulsed with cannon balls.

IV

THE WALL THROUGHOUT CHINESE HISTORY

Although the Wall was unfinished at the death of Huang Ti and even on that of his successors this was no reason for abandoning the work. In fact the contrary was the case.

The Emperor Wu-Ti (140–87) and his lieutenant Wei Tsing organised the cavalry which was as light and rapid as that of the Tartars. It entirely replaced the heavy Chinese carriage system which had previously transported the troops. Wu-Ti then adopted the same rapid tactics as the Huns and was able to anticipate their forays; using the Wall as a base he took the war into their midst by means of counter-attacks and for a time he succeeded in keeping them outside the bend of the Yellow River.

During the third century A.D. the Emperor gave way to the barbarians and agreed to regard them as a federated people, allowing them to live within the bend of the river, outside the Great Wall.

The Emperor Yang-Ti (605–618) was almost taken prisoner by the Huns when he was making an inspection of the rampart. He was so upset and angry that he is said to have caused the work to be finished in ten days, with the help of a million men, of whom more than half perished. This figure must however be treated as legendary or at least greatly exaggerated. After his death, for nearly forty years, from 682 to 722, the Mongolian Turks came "like wolves" to ravage the frontiers, while the Chinese behaved "like sheep." "At this time," runs a Turkish inscription, "we had made so many victorious expeditions that our slaves became slave-owners themselves."

During the tenth century the K'itan, consisting of tribes from southern Manchuria, installed themselves within the Great Wall and endangered the unity of China, until it was finally restored once more by the Song dynasty.

Finally, from 1211 to 1213, came the tidal wave of the famous Genghis Khan invasion. For two years he was held back by the Wall, until he broke through triumphantly at Ningsia, came through the Yang Kao pass and captured Peking, where he installed the dynasty of his successors, who were then continued by the Ming dynasty (1368–1644).

Yung-Lo, the third Ming Emperor (1403–1424) restored the Great Wall magnificently and provided it with its first artillery. The cannon were made of iron or brass and installed at the loopholes on the fortresses or the ramparts; they were mounted on tripods or stands with wheels. The soldiers were full of admiration for the "Weapons of God," or the "Great Generals," as they called the new cannons, and lovingly bestowed names on them, such as "Flying thunder", "Slayer of horses", "Divine Mortar," or even "Goose-beak," terms which reveal both their effectiveness and their design.

During the fifteenth century and throughout the entire Ming dynasty, the Wall was continually maintained, restored, lengthened, even fortified on the outside with detached buildings and reinforced by powerful artillery which allowed the enemy to be cut off between two lines of firing.

The men who devised and built these local fortifications did not fail to leave an account of their work and their own bravery on tablets built into the interior walls of their forts or on the gates of the towns. Geil has quoted several of these inscriptions, such as the one from Hopeh, which informs us that this "third rate" wall was the work of Tsui-Tching-d'Er-Kuo, general of the light brigade, who supervised the work, and Liu-Tching, military engineer. Civilians also collaborated with them in a more humble capacity, such as the master-mason Chao-Yen-Mei and the local builder Lu-Huan. The inscription is dated on the ninth hour of the sixteenth day of the fourth year of the reign of the Emperor Wen-Li (1577) and informs us, what is more "with pleasure," that the work was finished during "the autumn guard." This is valuable information and means presumably that the soldiers were recruited by seasons; it shows too that private enterprise took part in the work on the Wall at this period, although under the supervision of the military leaders.

It was precisely this Emperor Wen-Li (1573–1620), one of the sovereigns who reigned over China longest, who was to do the most important restoration work on the Wall, in addition to completing the work, at the stage when the defensive system reached its height. In China the popular term for the fortification is still *Wen-Li Tcheng ching*, the Wall of Wen-Li.

After his death in 1625 the Manchus attempted to force their way through the Great Wall but were thrown back by cannon-fire. The cannon had been cast by the Jesuit Fathers, who, according to Father Ricci, had acquired a great influence at the court of the Ming rulers.

The Manchus were not discouraged; they attacked the Wall for twenty years and in 1644 they succeeded in breaking through and conquering China. On the other side of the world England was in the grip of civil war and in France a great king was about to come to the throne—Louis XIV.

The new Manchu dynasty lasted until 1912, but the upkeep of the Wall was never abandoned. Pauthier states that "strong garrisons were still maintained there about 1835, in the most open and best fortified mountain passes."

The Great Wall, which expressed the very spirit of its originator, does not seem to have failed in its task in any way. In modern times three great lines of fortifications, the Maginot Line, the Siegfried Line and the Atlantic Wall, which were built with amazing materials, did not resist more than a few days when under heavy pressure. The Emperor Ch'in had been far-sighted and imaginative, for the defences he built to withstand futile arrows lasted fourteen centuries. The Wall remained impregnable for another four hundred years until the Manchu invasion, and just like the Mongols who had passed victoriously through it, the new invaders did not fail to close the door behind them. What better way could there be of showing confidence?

In its present state the Wall can still inspire the Chinese with deep respect; every traveller who passes through it follows an ancient tradition—he throws a stone against the ramparts, and if it bounces back, he knows he will have a good journey. If it falls down in a lifeless way, the outlook is bad. Visitors to Peking always make an expedition to see the best preserved portions of the Wall and never fail to admire it.

The French traveller Louis de Beauvoir saw the Wall in 1870 and was impressed by this gigantic enterprise. "I was wondering," he wrote, "what the Great Wall itself could possibly be like, and as we penetrated further into the wild valley (Nan Keo) the rays of the sun lit up far ahead of us the battlemented lines of two other parallel walls, situated also on the highest summit, standing out like theatrical scenery against the distant backdrop. . . . The Great Wall is in a perfect state of preservation, and square towers stand at each high point as though measuring out the vast construction. . . . This fantastic serpent of stone,

14. Stele at Kiayuikwan (from *The Great Wall of China* by W. E. Geil)

its battlements without cannons, its loopholes without guns, its ramparts without a single man to defend them, these fortifications which give no protection and withstand no attack, will remain in my memory like some magic vision. . . ."

This magic vision which we have tried to bring to life through the ages is no longer the same Wall that was built by the redoubtable Huang Ti. Since he descended into Hell his work has undergone at least a dozen major transformations, caused as time passed by the needs of defence, the perfecting of weapons and the tactics they called for.

The vicissitudes of the frontier wars, from Turkestan to Manchuria, naturally caused some changes in the strategic points. At one period some portion of the Wall would be consolidated, or another abandoned. This is the explanation of certain strange aspects which seem incomprehensible to us today, from an aesthetic as well as a geographical point of view.

Yet in spite of everything the Great Wall has not failed in its task. First it consolidated the unity of China during its early stages by keeping the Huns at bay, then by hurling them back beyond the frontier that it constitutes. For this very reason the Wall seems to have acted as a kind of immense trap for the marauders, for its impregnable defences retarded Attila's barbarian invasion of Europe about A.D. 550. Five centuries earlier these Asiatic hordes might have destroyed or weakened the infant Roman Empire which was itself preparing for the conquest and latinisation of Europe. The Huns would have overrun it and annihilated it, thus preventing the birth of Christian Europe which was eventually to succeed to the Empire of the Caesars.

It may be an exaggeration to say that the Great Wall protected both Imperial and Apostolic Rome, but the possibility cannot be denied today.

The stele at Kiayuikwan, inscribed with the words "the most warlike barrier in the world," offers food for thought. Beside these words some well-educated traveller has scribbled in tiny characters the following sentences: "This wall is the ancient frontier between the Flower People and the Barbarians. The winds of spring and the soft breezes of autumn desire to reach the Barbarians of the West."

Unfortunately we do not know at what period this was written, but it seems to show that the writer wanted to know their civilisation rather than to combat it.

And lower down, written also by some unknown hand, but this time in prophetic vein, can be read the following words: "Without violence we should establish patriotism, and without sorrow we should awaken the ancient race."

IV

THE ROMAN ROADS

"Caesar has procured us a profound peace: there are neither wars nor battles, nor great robberies nor piracies, but we may travel at all hours, and sail from East to West."

(Epictetus: *Discourses*, III, 13)

A THOROUGHFARE IS a human phenomenon just as a watercourse is a manifestation of nature. Tracks, pathways, lanes and roads follow the same pattern as ditches, gullies, streams and rivers. First came the tracks used by huntsmen and warriors, then the paths that linked villages and towns together, and finally the roads leading to markets and fairgrounds which also saw the rapid passage of invading and conquering armies.

Thousands of years lie between the path followed by the Iroquois Indian on his way to attack the enemy Hurons and the "silk route" which linked Europe and Asia as far back as the fifteenth century; but only a few centuries separate the caravan routes from the concrete motorways of today.

When the Romans made their first conquests they obviously found traces of local roads nearly everywhere which they incorporated in a network of roads which still forms the basis of European overland communications.

The survival of the roads is due not so much to strategic or commercial traditions but to the carefully detailed plans which were drawn up in advance and the techniques that left nothing to chance.

The Romans were primarily colonisers and pacifiers and although their strength appeared brutal it was perfectly orderly. The *pax romana* lasted for nearly six centuries, and during that time the power of Rome spread all over Europe while civilisation followed in its wake along the roads of victory.

As soon as the Roman conquerors decided to make *Urbs romana* the centre of the Empire it followed logically that the roads would provide the means of commercial and colonial expansion. Gradually the arteries were to lose their peaceful character and became instead the instrument of new conquests, and the legionaries, like the conquering armies of any country, were to do as much building as fighting. They then built new roads for the tradesmen and dealers who later followed their cohorts and took their places behind Caesar in the conquered territories which so far had been barely defined.

I

ALL ROADS LEAD TO ROME

In the first century A.D. in the reign of Trajan, when the power of Rome was at its height, twenty-three roads radiated from the milestone set up in the Forum of the capital. This gilded milestone[1] marked the central point of a network of roads covering 56,000 miles.[2] To the north they crossed Lombardy, Gaul and Britain, going as far as the Scottish border, and farther east to what is now the Zuyder Zee; to the south they reached Cadiz in Spain and from there they followed the Mediterranean seaboard as far as the Pyramids; then they went along the Palestine border where different forks led to Byzantium, Smyrna, Persia and the Indian Ocean; to the west they reached farther still, going towards the Bosphorus across Greece, Hungary and the Dalmatian coasts on their way to the frontiers of Germany.

At various places they broke into infinite ramifications, forming 125,000 miles of secondary roads which penetrated into the hearts of the nations, the provinces and the *pagi*.

Such was the vast network of commercial roads, ringed by strategic routes, which fixed a voluntary limit to Roman conquests. Perhaps the milestones that surrounded their Empire caused the Romans to lose it, for they believed that the figures on them which proudly marked their distance from the capital were sufficient to damp the ardour of the barbarians.

H. G. Wells even maintains that the halt in building roads, the negligence in maintaining them, followed by the failure to take the frontiers beyond these limits which had been fixed once and for all, contributed to the decadence of Rome for, he says, "the armies and chargers of Marcus Aurelius advanced with difficulty along the same roads as Scipio Africanus had done three centuries before."

It is perhaps an exaggeration to state that Rome fell because she fixed her frontiers or lacked good road-menders, but it is quite possible to say that before the memory of her greatness had faded from men's minds all knowledge of her roads was lost, and centuries passed before the archeologists, notably the Abbé Bergier, rediscovered them, barely three hundred years ago.

[1] Constantine the Great, when he took up residence in Byzantium in 306 A.D., also set up there, in the centre of the *Forum Augusteum*, a milestone-column for the Eastern Empire.
[2] 8,700 miles lay in the Italic peninsula and 12,400 in Gaul.

People used them, it is true, but without knowing it, just as Monsieur Jourdain, Molière's *bourgeois gentilhomme*, spoke in prose, and the passer-by might bare his head before the crosses fixed on top of the old milestones, unaware that the "King's highway" had first been that of a consul or a prefect whose name could still be read through the moss at the foot of the Christian emblem.

For a long time everyone assumed, like Virgil and, later, like Isidore of Seville, that the Romans had learnt the technique of roads "built like a wall in the ground" from the Carthaginians. But it is now certain that the Romans merely took it, like so many other things, from their ancestors the Etruscans, as well as from the Greeks, at the time when the latter occupied "Greater Greece" to the south of Italy.

The few Etruscan roads which have been discovered are roughly paved and measure only six to nine feet in width; they even include ditches with drains running across the causeway to drain away the water from the neighbouring hills. The main roads between the Etruscan towns however reached a width of 45–50 feet, including the pavements. These roads were built on a foundation of pebbles overlaid with large paving-stones, sometimes scratched to prevent the surface from becoming slippery. In other words the roads were rudimentary and it must be admitted that the Romans improved these techniques considerably and used materials of a far better quality.

The oldest of the great Roman roads seems to be the Appian Way, built in 300 B.C. and named after its founder Appius Claudius Caecus. It was lengthened and re-built on many occasions, and then generally embellished; it was fairly rudimentary when first built but it was the most important road in Italy, for it was the route taken by the Roman cohorts leaving for Africa as well as by livestock and merchandise entering the capital. Then it was flanked by pavements and continually improved under Nero and Augustus, and during the last centuries of the Empire, thanks either to personal generosity or to taxes levied on those who used it.

The Appian Way entered Rome by a monumental gate, the Porta Capena, which has now disappeared. During the time of the Roman Empire it became a kind of promenade, a meeting-place for idlers, patricians, poets and lovers. It also became the fashion to be buried there in a costly sarcophagus or to set up a burial urn. Later on the early Christians met there and then buried their martyrs in the Catacombs, which were only disused exhausted quarries from which the materials for building the road had been taken.

The Appian Way does not seem very wide today, for we are used to gazing across motorways, but it is still well maintained and can easily recall the past, especially when peasants pass by riding little donkeys or idly goading the oxen harnessed to jolting carts.

Two other equally important roads started from Rome, the Via Latina to the south-east and the Via Salaria to the north. The former was named after Latium, the second after the salt that was taken from the Adriatic near the Sabine mountains.

The Romans used the profits they drew from the destruction of Carthage to build the Via Emilia, the Via Flaminia and the Via Claudia leading to the Po valley, from where they were later to cross the Alps.

The year 145 B.C. saw the building of the first "international" Roman road, the Via Egnatia, which extended the northern branch of the Appian Way through Dyrrachium (Durazzo) towards Thessalonika and the Hebrus. The Via Egnatia was the way to the East and it was along this road that Cicero went into exile and Pompey made his attempted flight into Asia.

In 123 B.C. Caius Gracchus undertook to complete the road network

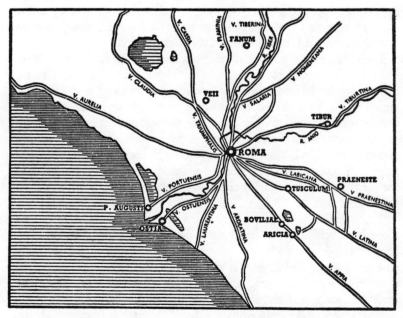

15. Map of the roads leading from Rome (from *Notes on the History of Ancient Roads and their Construction* by R. J. Forbes)

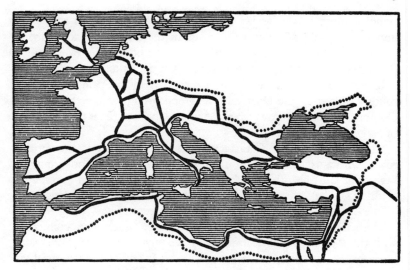

16. Map of the principal roads in the Roman Empire

throughout the peninsula from Capua to Messina by extending the Appian Way and then by linking Sicily to the mainland. Finally by completing the Via Aurelia and the Via Domitia in the north he made the latter run all along the Mediterranean coast of Gaul, cross the Pyrenees and go across Spain as far as Cadiz (Gades).

This is how many Spanish towns come to preserve the memory of their Roman founder or that of the road network which linked them together. Caesar augusta became Saragossa; Emerita augusta, Merida; Astarica augusta, Astorga, and Lucis augusti, Lugo.

The Domitian Way became the road to the copper mines of Rio Tinto (their shares are still quoted on the Stock Exchange) and the mercury and cinnabar of Almaden. The network of roads in Gaul joined the Appian Way at Nîmes and Lyons, passing through the valley of the Rhône; Lyons was the capital of Gaul and the meeting-point of all the roads leading to Britain (through Lutetia), the Bouches-du-Rhône, Brittany, Aquitaine (Bordeaux) and more directly still towards Northern Italy through Besançon and the Apennines.

The first road-system in Gaul was the work of Agrippa, son-in-law of Augustus. His successors, including Claudius, who was born in Gaul, enlarged it by a secondary network extending especially to the north and west in order to receive British merchandise more speedily, particularly tin, which was used in the composition of bronze, a popular alloy. Lastly Trajan linked the eastern section of the Gallic network to Strasbourg and the roads in the Rhine district, starting point of the frontier roads which marked the boundaries of Pannonia (Hungary) along the Danube as far as Roumania and the Black Sea.

In A.D. 42 Tiberius laid down a second road in Spain, the "silver route," following the Domitian Way and going farther through the Columns of Hercules towards the African Coast, as far as the Pyramids of Egypt and beyond.

After the defeat of Caractacus, Claudius undertook the British roads, with a *trivium* in London and two principal forks, one going to Liverpool and the other to Caledonia, where it came to an end by Hadrian's Wall, the artificial frontier which probably delayed the union of Scotland and England for sixteen centuries.

The roads in Germania and central Europe, which were connected with the Roman network in the way we have seen, were principally *limes* or boundaries, frontier roads, not so much commercial as strategic routes linking the fortresses or fortified camps which were scattered through the valleys of the Rhine and the Danube. Finally these highways were extended by a defensive "bulge" directed against Asia through Palestine and Arabia, one end on the Bosphorus, the other at the foot of the Pyramids of Egypt, with an offshoot going down the Nile valley. Asia Minor was traversed by two roads which started from Byzantium and Ephesus and met at Khorsabad, from where they continued as one towards the Persian Gulf, starting point of the Asiatic route.

This network was completed by Trajan, whose successors were little concerned with undertaking new thoroughfares and contented themselves with maintaining the old ones in a more or less mediocre fashion, particularly when they were of some economic importance.

So much for the chronological and geographical outline of this vast road-building programme which lasted six hundred years, from 400 B.C. to the end of the second century A.D. Later these roads formed the itinerary both of the apostles of Christ and the Barbarians who were to make them pass into oblivion.

II

TECHNIQUE AND ADMINISTRATION

Many fragmentary studies on every aspect of the Roman Empire have been published by scholars in different countries but they bring neither clarity nor unanimity to bear on the technical side of road-building.

There were three categories of Roman road, and the system used in most European countries today, especially in France, is still basically the same.

1. The main public thoroughfares, built at the expense of the State or by the generosity of rich or powerful individuals who wanted to see their names inscribed on a milestone, just as the municipal worthies of today like to have streets named after them. These roads were like the trunk roads of today, guaranteeing the public services between the home country and the provinces which had been conquered; they were used by civil servants, imperial messengers and the army. They were also called military roads because they were used for major troop movements and at first the army maintained them, under conditions to be described later.

But as scholars have pointed out, not every public road was a military road, even though all military roads were public.

2. Secondary roads which were connected to the main roads, by linking together towns of secondary status, including administrative centres, pleasure resorts or market towns of no strategic importance. This local road-system was enclosed within the main roads.

3. Private roads, forming the small units of a minor network linking the smaller towns and villages or serving the large estates of independent landowners or those presented to the "centuries." They were financed, built and maintained by the adjacent and local property owners and the municipalities.

Before describing the financial and administrative aspects of the Roman roads it should be noted that although their width and external appearance varied, their internal structure was more or less standard.

The Roman road surveyors first marked out the pre-arranged width by two parallel ditches, and then the loose ground was dug out to a considerable depth, usually down to the bed-rock. The bed was then beaten and covered with sand or mortar. On this foundation were placed four layers of different materials rising to a height of about

3 feet to 4 feet 6 inches (and sometimes higher), taken from local quarries and arranged in the following order:

1. At the base (D), several layers of flat stones (*statumen*) 1 or 2 feet deep and bound together with mortar or clay.

2. A nine-inch layer (*nucleus*) made up of small pebbles (C), broken stone, fragments of brick or tile pounded down closely together.

3. A mixture of lime and sand (*rudus*) spread in layers 6 to 18 inches thick (B) and carefully rolled.

4. Lastly, 5 to 12 inches of gravel or paving-stones (*summa crusta*) of considerable width and depth, reasonably well jointed (A); the surface was slightly convex so that water could drain down more easily into the ditches that ran along both sides of the road.

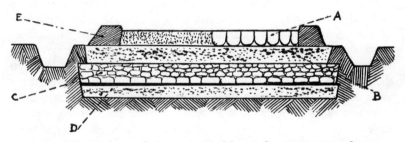

17. Cross-section of a Roman road (according to R. J. Forbes, as above)

The width of the roads was fixed in detail by a decree of Augustus, and varied according to their importance; some roads were 40 feet wide or even 60 feet on the outskirts of the big towns; the secondary roads were 9–22 feet wide and the private roads 4 feet 6 inches to 9 feet wide.

In the case of the main roads the width included two raised pavements (E) which were fairly narrow but each measured up to half the width of the carriageway (*agger*). These pavements were raised even higher at distant intervals by mounting-blocks used by riders.

All contemporary excavation carried out on the Roman roads has revealed more or less the same quality and type of structure, apart from differences in depth and materials. For example iron dross was used in the mining districts, basalt in Syria, lava in the volcanic areas, and fragments or even paving-stones of marble, like those which cover certain parts of the Appian Way near Rome.

Even if we imagine them taking heavy traffic these roads seem to have survived a much heavier load than was expected of them, especially since the movement of loaded waggons was regulated in the fourth century by the Theodosian Code, which laid down extremely severe penalties. (This was certainly the first "highway code" ever devised by humanity and many centuries were to pass before another one was brought into operation.) The heaviest load permitted was equivalent to about 9 cwt. or over 13 cwt. in the case of a four-wheeled chariot.

Given these restrictions, it is easy to imagine how much time and material was needed merely for the building of the roads, especially since the Romans were unaware of rational modern methods of harnessing horses. Presumably the materials were brought by bullock-carts or donkey-carts, or even by men, carrying them in hods or baskets, as is still done on the minor roads in Spain or North Africa.

Bearing in mind the slow rate of the traffic and the relative lightness of the loads "we are astonished," as the French scholar Jullian wrote, "by the size of such an undertaking, particularly when we think of the huge outlay in labour and materials that it made necessary, and we are almost   pted to say that the roads were built to last for ever."

The first work on the Roman roads was certainly carried out by the army, for in the early days the cohorts could not rely on assistance from the local civilians, who would not be able to adapt themselves to the rapid methods of the legionaries. In addition to the regulation *impedimentum* carried by each soldier the army took with it a set of engineering tools and camp equipment which we know was set up in exactly the same way anywhere. In addition there were the siege-engines, the ballistas, onagers and catapults which were probably taken to pieces when moved so that they could go through low tunnels or over unsteady bridges. It is possible that this heavy equipment forced the legions to build roads carefully so that they would last well, a system which was naturally found to be out of proportion after the achievement of victory.

Towards the end of the Roman Republic the High Command organised a separate engineer corps which was part of the army, although it marched ahead of the legions. The same system is still used by modern armies, and this is how the American engineers became largely responsible for the invasion of Germany during World War II, building bridges over the Rhine at lightning speed in the teeth of the enemy.

There were enormous advantages to the Roman innovation. Real technicians were now available and the roads were no longer built by soldiers who had to put down their swords and take up spades instead. This system had led to complaints and even to mutiny, as it did again during the reign of Augustus. The Roman engineers also used prisoners, slaves and even requisitioned local labour.

After a country had been conquered the building of the roads was taken over by the civil administration. The trunk roads were financed directly by the Emperor who paid a special *fiscus* to administrators who in their turn entrusted the work to specific contractors. The latter employed adequate workers, the *silicarii*, who lived in shanties or temporary huts built along the roads. Their itinerant existence was not unlike that of the steam-roller operator who owns his own machine and drives it along the road followed by his green-shuttered caravan painted with flowers.

The French scholar Grenier in his *Manuel d'Archéologie Gallo Romaine: les Routes* (1935) quotes figures showing that the cost of building a road was heavy. He states that the Emperor Hadrian paid out 1,157,000 sesterces to repair the Appian Way, without counting 569,000 more which he asked from the adjacent landowners, although a mere fifteen miles of road were involved.

The roads were not merely paved with good intentions. Some unscrupulous administrators, like the Consul Fonteius, who was responsible for building the Domitian Way, were accused in their time of not being too careful about the quality of the work, and they no doubt had their own reasons for it.

On the other hand it is gratifying to read in Tacitus that one senator was totally uncompromising with his contractors and ruined them unhesitatingly in order to make the roads as excellent as possible. The Emperor Tiberius attached so much importance to the upkeep of the roads that he tried to divert to road-building a sum of money bequeathed to the inhabitants of Trebia for the building of a theatre, but he was unsuccessful.

The cost of the secondary roads was guaranteed by the districts they went through, the local towns or the rich landowners. In A.D. 50 the Consul Sempronius suggested, unsuccessfully, that vehicles should be taxed in order to levy funds for new roads.

With the exception of a few roads where toll had to be paid there was complete freedom of movement everywhere, even on the military roads. Lastly, with the exception of the ground for the trunk roads, which was acquired forcibly as part of the conquest, the others were bought by friendly treaties or private contract. In any event the roads remained the property of the Roman people.

Generally speaking it can be said that the technical, financial and administrative aspects of road communication during the Roman Empire was not very different from the modern system used on the Continent.

III

MEASURING THE ROADS

Some of the most vital information about the Roman roads is provided by the monumental milestones which have survived the centuries. About 4,000 of them have been found in the countries that once formed the Roman Empire and as many again in Greece and the territories to the east. Six hundred milestones have now been discovered in Gaul alone, although only five were known at the beginning of the eighteenth century. They did not exist along every road, however, particularly in Asia and Africa.

Each milestone consisted of a column of stone 10 to 20 feet high and 18 inches to 2 feet 6 inches in diameter. As a rule each stone carried the following information, more or less in this order: the name of the Emperor who had built the road or caused it to be built or provided for its maintenance, unless the inscription was merely of a flattering nature; the number of years the praetor or local consul had been in office; the letter M (*milia*, mile) or L (league) followed by a figure indicating distance; and sometimes in addition was the letter P (*passus*, pace) followed by a final figure (Fig. 18).

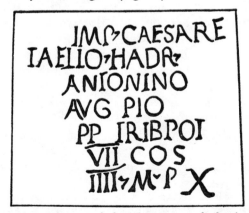

18. Inscription on the Mirabel Milestone, Ardèche (according to Ph. Pouzet, *Revue archéologique*, 1898, I)

The type of distance indicated varied considerably; sometimes the figure referred to a crossroad, or the proximity of a town (the number of miles being reckoned from the last houses forming its boundaries) or the nearest frontier. Sometimes there were additional figures on the milestone, referring to several towns or roads in the vicinity.

The Roman mile was almost equivalent to an English mile and consisted of 1,000 steps of about 4 feet 6 inches. The Romans sometimes preserved local units of measurement, however, such as the league of 2,222 metres in Gaul.

On the major roads tablets known as *tabellarii* were placed between the milestones, consisting of stones let into the edge of the pavement, bearing no inscription but indicating the tenth part of a mile or stage. They have often been confused with mounting-blocks and are more or less non-existent nowadays.

Sometimes hexagonal milestones were placed at important crossroads, like that at Tongres in Belgium, indicating which road should be taken to reach the neighbouring towns and stating the distance in each case. Lastly, in some large towns, stone or marble tablets were usually placed near the forum, with the names of the adjoining cities and their distance carved on them.

Surprising though it might seem, some travellers, including the Imperial post messengers, used guides, official routes drawn on parchment, or engraved on drinking goblets; these included valuable information, like the Vicarello goblet, giving all the distances between the towns situated between Rome and Cadiz (Fig. 19).

The French scholar Grenier disputes the accuracy of the figures given, but admits that "What we have here in fact is no longer an official or municipal inscription like that on the milestones or the column at Tongres, but a product of private enterprise, a kind of compilation like the other two important ancient documents, Peutinger's Table and the Route of Antoninus, which invariably include mistakes of the same kind."

These two documents however are more or less the only maps of the Roman road system which have come down to us.

Peutinger's Table,[1] a manuscript on parchment in the Vienna State Library, has often been reproduced with lengthy and superfluous commentaries. It is a copy, made probably during the twelfth century

[1] So named because it was discovered by the antiquary Peutinger early in the sixteenth century. It is clear that the original map was drawn up with the help of rough routes used by the Imperial messengers or perhaps made by individual travellers for their own use.

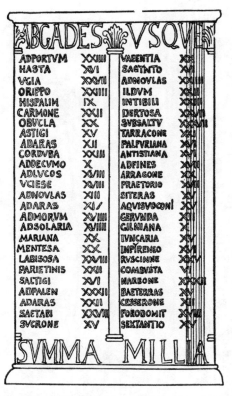

9. The Vicarello Goblet (from *Géographie de la Gaule* by Desjardins)

by a monk at Colmar, of a map drawn apparently at the request of Caracalla in about A.D. 210, and itself only a reproduction of the famous map of the Imperial roads made by order of Agrippa.

There are eleven maps in this "Atlas," but it is still incomplete, representing the Roman Empire of the first century B.C., but in a very sketchy fashion. Geographical contours are ignored and there is a complete lack of proportion; the directions of the rivers and the placing of the mountains are entirely haphazard. Jullian has described it severely as "one of the most ridiculously distorted and arbitrarily incomplete documents I have ever encountered."

Its inaccuracy, which is quite understandable, is certainly due to the interpolations which have crept into the copies of the original map, and we do not know how many there were. This is unfortunate, but

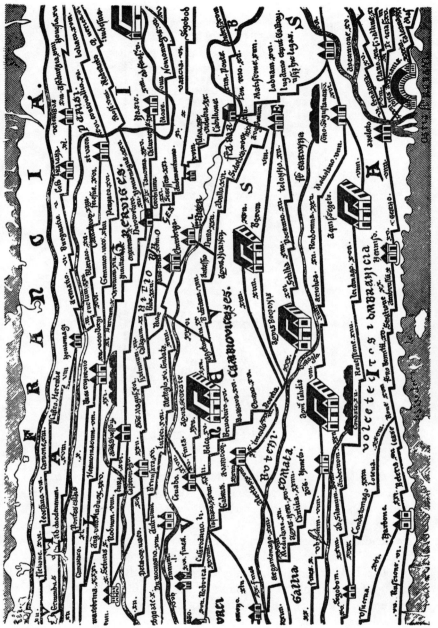

20. Peutinger's Table (photo Dubure-Plon)

the "table" still remains an indication of the degree to which the Romans lacked information about their splendid roads. And it should be remembered that map-making is a very modern science—the first reliable maps were not made in Europe until the sixteenth century.

The Romans had no maps whatsoever when they set out to conquer the world, but it is quite inaccurate to suggest that they were able to govern their empire without them.

The Route of Antoninus, which has no connection with the Emperor of the same name, and belongs to a later period than Peutinger's Table, is considered by archeologists to be just as inaccurate. But Grenier was quite serious when he stated at the end of his commentaries that "These are unreliable documents, deserving endless criticism and found to be wrong on every point, but they are nonetheless contemporary documents about the road network of the ancient world and therefore valuable."

IV

ARCHITECTURAL AND HUMAN ASPECTS

With the energy inherent in their race the Romans laid out their roads in their own image, covering the distance as quickly and directly as possible. They made little use of the natural features which had been used by the native inhabitants before them, and attempted on the contrary to overcome them with a boldness that still strikes us as astonishing, even in our age of mammoth technical achievement.

Roman thoroughfares go across rivers, wind over high hills, stride across valleys and plunge into mountain ranges, encountering the same difficulties as our trunk roads today.

The many Roman bridges which still exist are proof of the supreme skill of the men who built them. The army Engineer Corps were acquainted with pontoon bridges but they also built temporary wooden bridges (known as *sublicius*) such as Caesar's bridge over the Rhine. In other cases the bridge floor rests on wooden arches, their base resting on stone piers, like Trajan's bridge over the Danube which measured over 3,000 feet in length.

But Roman bridges did not reach their true perfection until their builders used stone, creating small hump-backed bridges, with one or more arches, or bridges supported on stone piers, either round or rectangular in shape.

Among the best buildings which have been preserved many deserve mention: in Italy, the Aelius bridge (now known as the St. Angelo bridge) built over the Tiber in Rome by Hadrian, its piers sunk more than fifteen feet below the bed of the river; in Spain, where the finest ancient bridges are to be found, at Cordoba, Merida, Alcantara, the latter consisting of blocks of stone without cement, jointed by iron clamps soldered with lead, and at Salamanca, where the bridge with a span of 2,250 feet is supported by twenty-seven arches each twenty feet wide.

In France bridges still exist at Argens, Arles and Saint-Chamas, the latter decorated at each end by two small triumphal arches, and at Sommières on the Vidourle river in the Gard region, consisting of seventeen arches alternating with smaller archways which allowed the water to pass through when the river rose.

There are viaducts too as well as bridges, at Narni in Umbria, at Rimini on the Flaminian Way, and the Ponte di Nona near Rome across the Pontine Marshes.

The Roman engineers were not daunted by mountain ranges and they tackled the road over the Saint Bernard Pass, which was eventually to be completed by Napoleon, as we shall see. They knew how to avoid tunnels by attacking the rock on the mountain-sides and making their way through it as they did on the road to Grenoble at the Col du Lautaret. At Aricia, near Rome, it is still possible to see a breast-wall over 130 feet high supporting part of the Appian Way. If the Romans were ever short of stone they did not hesitate to build wooden superstructures overhanging precipices, but they could not withstand avalanches.

In such cases the road went through a tunnel, and traces of one remain in the Dauphiné, known as the Porte de Bons. In Italy one can still see the curious underground passage connecting Naples with Pozzuoli, the tunnel on the Flaminian Way through the Apennines, measuring 1,000 feet in length, the tunnel of 125 feet on the Monte San-Angelo which still connects with the Appian Way, and lastly in Switzerland the famous Hagdek tunnel near Soleure which is 2,500 feet long and goes through the depths of the Aar river.

The roads were not only means of communication, for they also played their part in the survey of the subordinate countries, when the land was divided into "centuries." This division had two objects: first, it provided a reward for the victorious soldiers, and the fixed area of land which was granted to them kept them on the spot as settlers; secondly, it limited the property owned by the native inhabitants so that they would not encroach on each other's land and provide cause for dispute at a later date; for the Roman occupiers were extremely anxious to maintain peace throughout the Empire as well as over plots of ground.

The new sections of land were therefore carefully measured out by the surveyors in squares ("centuries") of about an acre, and then a country pathway about six to ten feet in width was planned alongside. This division of the Empire was not limited to the conquered countries and the Italian peninsula itself was subjected to the same treatment. It was not merely a formal administrative division but a practical and mathematical system of levying taxes on landed property which could be recovered easily.

The organisation of this vast survey was linked with the general plan of the great Roman roads which provided basic dividing lines. The survey and final plan were completed by Augustus in 27 B.C. by the careful census of the entire population of the Empire. The establishment of these population statistics caused two Nazarenes to make a famous journey back to their native village of Bethlehem, which in this way accidentally became the birthplace of Christ, about twenty-seven years after the Edict of Augustus.

"Agrippa's achievement," says Grenier, "was not limited to the laying down of roads, it was a financial, social and basically political measure. The plan for the road network in Gaul did not consist merely in coordinating and linking the old roads into a continuous system. It involved the application of the Roman *cens* to the whole area of land traversed by the roads, and the tax assessment of every property. The real conquerors of Gaul, those who consolidated the victory achieved by Caesar and his legions, were the labourers working on the survey, the men who, until the time of Claudius and perhaps even later, laid out the paths and at the same time established the *forma* of each property."

The new towns which were built after the completion of the survey were based on the geometic plan of the "centuries"; in particular they were divided by two bisecting lines, the *decumanus* (the origin of the word is obscure), which was about forty feet long and the *cardo* (or pivot) measuring about twenty feet, the intersection of these two lines forming the principal crossroads of the city.

This "chessboard" system of building was not invented by the Romans, for the Greeks and the Etruscans had used it long before them. The town of Pompeii, which was founded by the Oscans at the end of the sixth century B.C., had kept to this plan until the town was destroyed. When excavation work began on the buried city this geometrical plan and regular system of measurements made it possible to draw up a careful method of procedure, which was a masterpiece of archeological restoration.

Outside these two main arteries the secondary streets in the Roman towns were fairly narrow and the traffic was carefully controlled. For example heavy vehicles were forbidden to travel during the day, with the exception of those transporting materials for the construction of public buildings, or during certain feasts or performances of public games. Heavy transport had to be carried out at night, or at least ten hours after sunrise, even the collection of domestic refuse, which was taken every night to dumps established at the city gates. These regulations were not always obeyed and were often repeated, including the one which forbade riding through the streets on horseback, for mules and litters were the only permitted means of travel.

Outside the towns many watering places were to be found along the roads, offering treatment which was valued by all classes of society. There were particularly large numbers of them in Gaul, and Peutinger's map includes every single one. They were like the spas of today, pleasure resorts, providing hot and cold baths, gaming houses, or sports grounds where, according to some satiric poets, the games played were far from innocent.

Less attractive were the fortifications of varying importance which stood at strategic points along the road, usually on high ground from where the enemy country could be watched and signals sent when necessary.

The boundary roads swarmed with garrisons, usually established in camps, whose work was to police the roads and provide protection against brigands and sporadic invasions. When this supervision became too difficult the people living along the frontiers were persuaded to move within the road network.

Colonies of veteran soldiers were also established close to the countries which were either dangerous or not yet subdued, such as the mountains of Judaea or the Caucasus and the African deserts; their presence was usually enough to ward off incursions or mere raids. In this way small armed outposts were scattered along the African desert roads mounting guard over the water points which consisted of wells or cisterns, which were kept carefully filled on behalf of travellers.

Local orders were transmitted by signals from the camp towers, but edicts from the Emperor were passed on much more discreetly by the Imperial post messengers who went up and down the roads unceasingly.

This official post, which was severely restricted to the central administration, or the Prefects and Consuls, was very highly organised, especially from the time of Augustus who, according to one historian of the police, "provided himself in so doing with an easy way of governing the Empire without leaving his capital."

The roads covered by the *cursores regii* were compulsorily paved; their horses were carefully selected, both those they rode themselves and those who were harnessed to the light vehicles which transported for example government funds or perhaps civil servants who might be important but old and feeble.

The Emperor himself did not scorn to use this transport, and Tiberius for instance drove 250 miles in this way in order to reach Antioch where his beloved Germanicus met his death.

The Imperial post was placed under the direction of the prefect or *praetor*, and in the provinces it was controlled by the transport administrators. The latter delegated their authority to the master of the post (*manceps*) who had close control over every post officer (*stator*) in his station.

The messengers operated in the post-houses where the officials also stayed—consuls making a journey, special envoys, or ambassadors accomplishing a mission who, at least when the service was first instituted, had to provide evidence of their status by a letter of "evection," in other words a special passport which allowed them to demand any horse or vehicle which they might need.

21. A chariot of the Imperial post (from a bas-relief near Trèves)

As for members of the public, according to the price they were prepared to pay, they either sent their messages by a private messenger or asked some friendly traveller to help them. However, it is known that towards the end of the Roman Empire there were highly organised private postal services with horses and vehicles which could cover thirty-eight to fifty miles a day.

Gradually these relay-posts were transformed into administrative offices keeping not only the regulation forty horses in their stables but also stores of foodstuffs and even government money destined for Rome.

Later on, roadside inns grew up near these establishments, but they were equally noted for their dirty condition and their bad reputation, especially when they were close to any of the garrisons. However, they were also subjected to control by the police who ensured that the travellers had signed the public register, where it was compulsory to state their name, place of birth and profession. The lack of comfort in these inns meant that they were frequented by the poorer classes, for the rich and powerful preferred to stay quietly in private houses where there was a tradition of reciprocal hospitality.

The patricians and those who were religiously inclined liked to be buried in the tombs which stood beside the roads near the towns, such as the Alyscamps cemetery at Arles in the South of France, or the Appian Way. These tombs varied from simple sarcophagi to real monuments such as the tower-like mausoleum of Cecilia Metella, the daughter-in-law of Crassus, or the tomb shaped like an oven commemorating the rich baker Vergilius Eurysaces, on the Via Labicana in Rome.

For this reason certain places along the Roman roads became a kind of public promenade where the more worldly people liked to gossip and the devout meditated beside the funerary inscriptions or the altars dedicated to gods who watched over the road.

Among these monuments were the shrines of the goddesses Biviae, Triviae or Quadriviae, standing as their name indicates, at the meeting of two, three or four roads. It was no doubt customary—but more or less as a matter of form—to ask these deities which road one should take.

In many places along the Roman roads statues dedicated to Mars and Mercury have also been discovered, probably traces of votive shrines of varying importance built in honour of these gods. Was this by accident or design? There could be no better choice than Mars, the god of war, or Mercury, the protector of tradesmen, as "patron saints of the Road," while Venus also appears frequently, for the pleasure of travellers in search of amorous adventures.

V

THE TRADE ROUTES

The Roman roads were not only used by the legions and the Imperial post messengers. During the period of the *pax romana* the overland and sea routes combined to make travel possible in a way we can only imagine with difficulty nowadays. Both types of route had their advantages—sea-travel was less troublesome and more rapid but dangerous in winter, when land travel was preferred; road-travel took longer, certainly, but along the Mediterranean coast it was rarely very cold.

Sometimes journeys covered both sea and land, using the inland waterways. In this way goods leaving Syria for London for example first crossed the Mediterranean, then on reaching the port of Narbonne they went up the River Aude as far as it was navigable; then they were placed on carts and went as far as the Garonne district by road; they then reached Bordeaux where they were finally sent to Britain by sea.

The Romans called the Mediterranean *Mare Nostrum*, "Our sea," and its name was entirely justified, for it included the ports of Thessalonica, Brindisi, Ostia, Smyrna and Marseilles in addition to Cadiz on the Atlantic. It was the Great Lake, the Blue Carrousel where ships sailed continuously round and round, loading and unloading in the ports all the goods that finally jolted along the streets of Rome.

Rome, situated at the centre, was the control point where merchandise of all types was distributed according to the law of supply and demand, just as nowadays all the tea produced by the British Commonwealth is sold in London.

Trade was not only in the hands of the merchants; there were powerful trading companies, and all groups of Roman aristocracy, patricians, generals, tribunes, famous lawyers and doctors, were quite agreeable to investing their capital in them and receiving a share of the profits. Even courtesans, like Crispinella, Nero's favourite, took advantage of their temporary influence and brought off brilliant deals with the help of anonymous agents.

It is well known that the crafty Vespasian, the inventor of lavatories, married the daughter of a Roman knight who had made money by speculating in corn and that the Emperor Augustus himself controlled all the wheat in Egypt as well as such varied products as perfumes, bricks and *cervisia*, or barley-beer. This was no stranger at the time than the modern custom of appointing a general as director of a canal company or seeing some literary man draw dividends from the motor industry.

It is obvious therefore that the Roman roads had to be well maintained and that the important men of the time remained in favour by offering liberal amounts of money to keep them serviceable.

The western part of the Empire was the great producer of raw materials, such as tin from Britain or copper from Iberia, but the eastern part produced mainly manufactured goods—textiles, carpets, perfumes, glassware and pottery. This latter industry was a good instance of the remarkable exchanges of goods that went on throughout the Roman Empire. It is for this reason that vessels from Gaul have been found in Britain or Syria, Egyptian ware in Spain and Spanish ware in Germany. Such pottery was cheap and lent itself to all the decorative freedom of folk art, and it was particularly appreciated by housewives throughout the Empire.

The Roman patricians enjoyed an incredible variety of rich food; they had the best Colchester oysters and caviare from the Baltic; they preferred the dried plums from Damascus to the prunes from Spain, while their truffles came from Syria and what is now Auvergne in France. They consumed an incredible amount of rare spices, such as cinnamon, nutmeg and cloves, which were literally worth their weight in gold, and Pliny describes in all seriousness how Nero burnt enough spices on his wife Poppaea's funeral pyre—after he had kicked her to death—as "Arabia produced in a whole year."

The Roman ladies enjoyed many beauty products, such as perfumes, incense, unguents, essences of rare flowers and even aphrodisiacs such as rhinoceros horn, in addition to precious metals, tortoiseshell, amber, coral, pearls and precious stones.

Other remarkable goods included wild animals from Africa and Asia which were used in the circus games and in private menageries; there were also slaves and gladiators, strong men and dwarfs, and freaks with strange deformities who were brought to Rome either by fair means or foul.

The Romans were not the only people to engage in trade, and since every citizen of the Empire had the right to move freely round the roads, it was quite usual to see a Syrian seated in a British tavern or a Gaul weighing amber in Scandinavia, an Iberian resting in a Numidian's tent and, near the Red Sea, a Greek bartering weapons for Chinese silk which had been brought from Tibet.

There were of course many Italians living in the provinces of their

Empire, working either in colonial administration or commerce. When Mithridates engaged in bitter warfare against Rome he caused no less than 80,000 of them to be put to death in his kingdom of Pontus alone.

In this way a tide of humanity flowed over Roman territory, and Roman money enjoyed the same respect as Roman arms. Honesty was a generally admitted moral convention; promises were honoured and merchandise was accurately counted and weighed. However, certain Oriental people were traditionally regarded as unscrupulous, as indicated by the remark some Roman soldier carved on a rock in Asia Minor: "The Syrians are a rotten race."

This magnificent commercial expansion led Augustus to say: "Under my government a great number of countries with whom we had not previously had any diplomatic relations have thus had the opportunity to appreciate the good faith of the Roman people."

And he added:

"I am surprised that Alexander did not regard the organisation of the Empire that he had conquered as a more difficult task than the conquest itself."

It is understandable therefore that all Roman subjects were intensely occupied in trading and as a result remained friendly and peaceful. But it is unfortunate that the Romans, in becoming merchants, forgot that they had been soldiers. They lost all caution when the Barbarians began to look around and cast covetous eyes upon their raw materials and manufactured goods.

It is possible that unwise bartering, like Esau's pottage of lentils, was one of the causes of the invasions which annihilated the Roman world. There is no doubt that the quality and administration of the roads made conquest more rapid; it was also possible that in the words of the Bible, "the hour was at hand."

But humanity certainly never knew such peace and prosperity, which lasted longer and more satisfactorily than at any other time. Perhaps we can say with Pliny the Elder, one of the noblest and most intelligent writers of Rome:

"The might of the Roman Empire has given unity to the world; all must agree that human life has benefited, both in the general intercourse made possible, and in the common enjoyment of the blessings of peace."

V

THE PALACE OF VERSAILLES

"Thirty-five years of scaffolding, ladders, plaster, labourers, marble-sawing, trundling carts, waggons stuck in the mud, the air full of dust. You have to enjoy building to condemn yourself to such a life; the amazing thing is that the result is so fine! It consists of bits and pieces added on all sides round Louis XIII's little château, which no one had time to knock down, so that it disappeared in the midst of everything, like a truffle in some splendid pâté!"

Georges Lenotre
Versailles au Temps des Rois

THE POOR LITTLE CHATEAU

SUPPORTERS AND ADVERSARIES of Louis XIV, the Sun King, both contemporaries and biographers, all agree about one thing—he was a star whose brilliance has never faded from the sky of history. God of his kingdom by divine right, Louis XIV raised his own altar at Versailles and the democratic régimes that followed him were impressed in spite of themselves by the incomparable brilliance of the "vanished monarchy."

Just as Athens went to Delphi, so Paris would consult the oracle at Versailles. There the French Republic, like the monarchy before it, suffered the humiliation of defeat or dictated its conditions to the vanquished.

This tradition will probably last as long as Versailles or France itself. France is a land of pilgrimage and France itself makes the pilgrimage to Versailles along the *Pavé du Roi*.

The way to appreciate Versailles is to listen, as you lie in bed, to the ring of marching footsteps over the ground when the bugle sounds in the garrisons on clear summer mornings or misty evenings in winter.

At these times the *Pavé du Roi* seems to echo again to the sound of the gold-headed cane striking the marble threshold as the voice of the Chamberlain silences every sound beneath the Mansard archways: "Gentlemen! The King!"

The entire past of the magic, royal town can be heard in these echoes.

Once upon a time—for this is a fairy tale—there was a little village five leagues from the centre of Paris, and its name was Versailles. It was lost among tall trees interspersed here and there with a few corn-fields and marshy ground teeming with game of every kind. Here there stood "an old ruined castle with five large rooms, two small towers over the entrance gate, two courtyards, a garden, a close, a dovecote, a sheep-fold, the whole comprising a little more than four acres." This is more or less how it is described in an old deed. It does not mention, unfortunately, the "carriage wheel leaning against a milestone, its spokes crumbling into dust," as the French poet

Théophile Gautier described, symbolically, the faded splendours of the manor of the Lord of Sigognac. This was the first Château de Versailles, resembling some Callot print or Doré woodcut.

Opposite stood a windmill on a hill, and below it lay the village, carefully described during the second half of the sixteenth century, with its forty or so thatched cottages, a few craftsmen, and a church dedicated to St. Julian. Finally there were three poor inns, the "Image Saint Antoine," the "Image Notre Dame" and the "Ecu de France," this unusually large number being explained by the fact that the village lay on the road followed by the cattle-drovers taking their animals from Normandy to Paris; the inns also provided shelter for members of hunting expeditions who were kept late by a stag at bay. There was also the scrivener's house—presumably less rough than the others, and on that glorious day of April 8th, 1632, the scrivener lived through, or rather traced on a piece of parchment, stamped with fleur de lys, the finest moment of his life.

It was not surprising that the good man was completely bowled over. The King of France, paying the vast sum of 66,000 livres, had

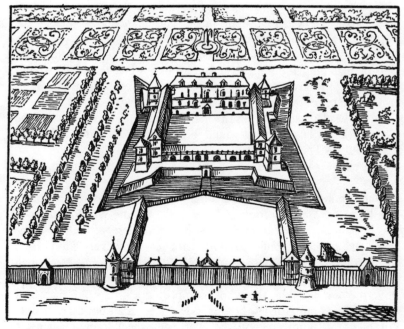

22. Versailles at the time of Louis XIII (according to Gomboust)

just acquired once and for all the entire village and its land, formerly owned by Monseigneur Jean-François de Gondi, first Archbishop of Paris; until then, surprisingly enough, Paris had been only a bishopric.

King Louis XIII was by no means unknown to the peasants of Versailles. From the time he was six years old he began to go there on hunting expeditions with his father. After the death of the worthy Henri IV a week never passed without Louis escaping from the intrigues of the Louvre and the iron control of Richelieu to return to the scenes of these childhood memories which he prized most of all. He hunted the stag or the boar, or went pheasant-shooting. Versailles is only an hour from Paris but on some evenings the young king was too exhausted to return, and flung himself fully dressed on a bed in the "Ecu de France" while his attendants spent the night in revelry with the host. It was very uncomfortable, even though at this period comfort was still neglected, even in royal palaces.

During the winter of 1623 Louis XIII asked an unknown architect to build near the old château a small hunting lodge which he paid for out of the funds voted for the *menus plaisirs*, or royal pocket money. When he bought the de Gondi estates in 1632 he caused the ruins to be demolished so that he would feel more at his ease. The hunting lodge then became his country house; it was a large two-storey building with four square towers, surrounded with an old-style moat. Since it was a royal residence it was politely called a "château"; the Marquis de Sourches refers to it as "a small gentleman's château" and the Maréchal de Bassompierre christened it, most impolitely, "the poor little château."

On May 14th, 1643, Louis XIII lay on his deathbed in the Louvre. The good Vincent de Paul came to visit him and the King made his confession to Father Dinet.

"If God restores my health," he said, "as soon as the Dauphin comes of age I will put him in my place and I will retire to Versailles. I will think only of spiritual things and the salvation of my soul."

A few days later, a new tomb was opened in the royal church of St. Denis and the impressive royal funeral took place with all its traditional ceremony. The Duc de La Trémoille, King-at-Arms, came up to the grave and repeated three times:

"The King is dead."

Then he added:

"Let us pray to God for the peace of his soul."

Everyone knelt, said their prayer and rose.

"Long live the King!" cried the Duc de La Trémoille. "Long live

King Louis XIV, by the grace of God, King of France and Navarre. Let us all cry: Long live the King!"

The tomb was closed. With the new King Versailles was to come into its own.

We do not know how the young King felt when for the first time, on April 18th, 1651, he went hunting at Versailles. He was twelve years old, a not very happy adolescent boy who was fed on coarse soup and dressed in clothes too small for him. Presumably he hunted with that same enthusiasm which as a baby had led him to "devour his nurses." The King had a hearty appetite all his life, and Versailles was to be his favourite dish.

In 1651 also the wars of the Fronde were at their height and from the outskirts of the town to the Louvre Paris was rife with intrigue. At the royal palace both fabric and etiquette were in a state of collapse. Louis' mother, Queen Anne, was a "distant princess" whom he saw rarely; she was completely under the influence of Mazarin, the lean Cardinal who regarded the King as stupid.

Versailles stood for the country, fresh air, the excitement of the hunt and the little château haunted by the memory of Louis' father with his sad eyes and little colourless beard. For the time being it was a large abandoned building given over to frogs which croaked in the moat. Towards the end of his life Louis XIII built two wings in the great courtyard which was separated by a minute colonnade. Some ornamental pools had also been made and avenues laid out in the woods which, with the addition of trees transplanted from St. Germain-en-Laye, were gradually changing into a park. The château was furnished in a bare rustic manner, with six or eight tapestries, two pictures and a few games kept in a closet to while away the long candle-lit evenings.

1661 was an important date in the life of Louis XIV. His honeymoon had come to an end, and the hated Mazarin had just died, leaving him in power at last, and bequeathing him Colbert and Fouquet.

The latter was a scoundrel with good taste who had just built the Château de Vaux, whose splendour was intended to eclipse the finest and most ancient of the royal palaces. It is true that Fouquet was Financial Secretary, which meant that most of the official funds were at his disposal.

The magnificent fête that he gave in honour of the King on August 17th of the same year to inaugurate his palace has been superbly and unforgettably described for us by Madame de Sévigné. The Château de Vaux was built by Le Vau, and the interior decoration designed by Le Brun; the gardens were laid out by Le Nôtre and it was here that the genius of Molière first came to light. This fête was the crowning achievement of the minister's career, and his downfall too; the King was not too pleased for he was apparently somewhat jealous, and through Colbert, who had made no secret of the fact, he knew the source of the money which was thrown about so lavishly in order to impress the new monarch. The King even thought of having his host arrested in the midst of the celebrations, but his mother persuaded him with great difficulty not to do so, in the name of propriety, for which the King always had the deepest respect. But as soon as the lights were put out Fouquet was arrested and condemned to life imprisonment. Vaux was confiscated and some of the finest things it contained were later to adorn Versailles. According to Georges Lenotre Louis XIV "also confiscated Le Vau, Le Nôtre, Le Brun and Molière."

At the end of that same year he undertook the transformation of his father's domain. The apartments were decorated in the taste of the day and the two wings in the forecourt were demolished. An apartment was prepared for Queen Marie-Thérèse who, on November 1st, 1661, had given birth to her first son, *le grand Dauphin*, who would not come to the throne any more than would his brothers. She was the first Queen to haunt Versailles, the first of many from both sides of the royal house.

For in spite of what has been written or said, Versailles was not built for Louise de La Vallière. Louis XIV took her there while she was his mistress and gave magnificent fêtes in her honour, but his plan was conceived on a loftier scale. He was already thinking of a royal town and palace and the idea of Versailles soon crystallised in his mind. It was in his blood—the Bourbons had a mania for building, just like the Valois who preceded them, and who, in order to escape from the troubles of the Reformation, created the delightful string of châteaux along the Loire. In the same way we owe the building of Versailles to the Wars of the Fronde. On the other hand, Napoleon, who was a child of the Revolution, built no palaces.

There was nothing about Versailles from a geographical, economic or political point of view which singled it out as a new capital of France: its woodlands were unattractive, the ground was marshy, it was no better than any other site in Beauce and there was not even the smallest of rivers—nothing like the Thames at Windsor, for instance. St. Germain-en-Laye, with its fine terrace overlooking the Seine, would have been much better, provided the uncomfortable château, which reminded Louis XIV of his unhappy childhood during the Fronde, was demolished. Without a truly royal will-power Versailles would never have come to life among the marshes and the woods.

Between 1661 and 1663 500,000 écus were spent on it; 330 labourers "worked hard carrying away the soil from the Orangery," under the direction of Le Nôtre, while Le Vau organised an army of carpenters, painters and iron-workers inside the "poor little château," the outside of which was left intact at the King's wish.

Le Vau was responsible for the delightful Hôtel Lambert, on the Ile St. Louis in Paris, the Institut and the central pavilion of the vanished Tuileries. He was the first architect of Versailles and his death in 1670 did not hold up his plans in any way. His son-in-law, François d'Orbay, was first his assistant and then his successor, until the arrival of Hardouin-Mansard, who, with his personal genius, was to finish the Versailles of Louis XIV.

Among the architects who were suggested to the King, Le Vau had all the qualities likely to please him: he had built the Château de Vaux which the young sovereign admired, but he still retained the slightly heavy Louis XIII style for which the King had a certain affection. It was odd, therefore, that it should be he who was to transform the last château built in the mediaeval style, with towers and moats, built on the site of a Don Quixote windmill, and prepare the masterpieces of the new style, that of "Le Grand Siècle," which attained perfection under Mansard.

The Versailles of 1668 was not in any case entirely the work of Le Vau. Other artists and architects, such as Claude Perrault, Jacques Gabriel, Vigarani, Le Pautre and Blondel, introduced distinctive elements of their own, based on the wishes or commands of the King, and carried out in accordance with instructions which were as precise as military orders:

"The King wishes the Cour de Marbre to be kept clean, with a fountain in the centre; no carriages may enter it. He wishes the four views from the centre of the courtyard to be opened up; the view from the entrance to be opened from the centre, that facing the garden by arcades in the low gallery and that on the two sides by vestibules with windows. On the side facing the courtyard there are to be two large wings. In the one on the right of the entrance will be the Great Staircase all in marble. In the one to the left will be the Chapel and the staircase. The two pavilions will both follow the same symmetrical plan. Above will be the King's large apartment, guard-room, ante-room, large bedchamber, large study.... On the Queen's side will be her large apartment looking on to the gardens; a bedchamber and a dressing-room overlooking the courtyard, for her convenience. The remaining space will be an apartment for the Dauphin."

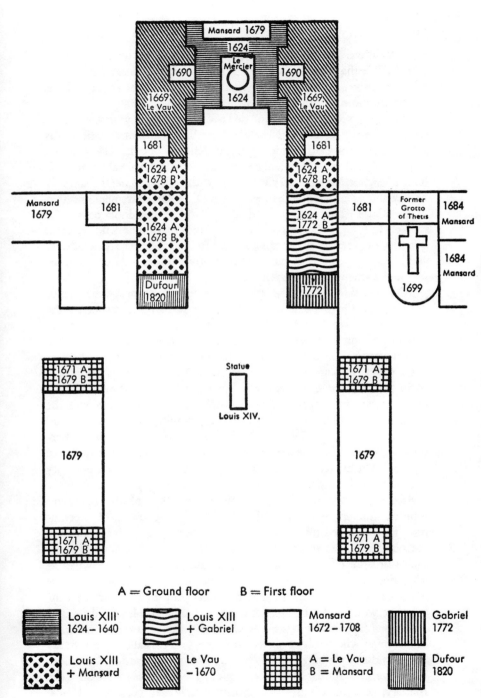

23. Versailles: different stages in the building of the Château,
1624–1820 (from a plan by Questel)

Le Vau went to work immediately, following the King's plan strictly. But the King's obstinacy earned him the discreet disapproval of his courtiers, expressed somewhat basely but not without style in the posthumous writings of Saint-Simon:

"The King's love for Madame de La Vallière, which at first was kept secret, gave rise to frequent visits to Versailles which at that time was a little house of cards built by Louis XIII.... Louis XIV enjoyed tyrannising nature, dominating it by artistic and financial means. He built every section one after the other without any general plan, and beauty and ugliness could be seen side by side. His apartment and that of the Queen have many disadvantages since they look on to the thickets in the grounds and all the dark trees that lie beyond. A great quantity of water has been found and brought together from all sides and it runs green, turbid and muddy; it gives off an unhealthy dampness and a smell which is even worse. . . .

"On the side facing the courtyard the vast wings extend into nothingness. On the side overlooking the garden one can enjoy the beauty of the whole, which looks like a palace destroyed by fire. . . . The impression everywhere is of a vast catafalque. The workmanship is exquisite in all respects, but there is no plan whatsoever. . . ."

Of course this unfair criticism refers to Versailles in its unfinished state, but it expresses every adverse remark made* about it while building was in progress. The class-conscious Saint-Simon was the mouthpiece of all those who thought they would lose caste if they did not hand over any building work entirely to their architect. Fortunately Louis XIV, the greatest lord in the kingdom, was capable of laying down his sceptre and taking up the plans, for which posterity will be eternally grateful.

After the criticism of the courtiers came that of the bourgeois minister Colbert, who based his remarks on the question of expenditure. He was asked for funds rather than for advice, he was jealous of the authority given to Le Vau and Le Nôtre and he was alarmed to see such vast sums of money paid out. But later, as we shall see, when he was appointed Minister of Works, he put his heart and soul into the royal building, so much so that the work killed him. For the time being he wondered if he had not another Fouquet on his hands.

"Your Majesty," he wrote, "will observe that you are in the hands of two men who hardly ever see you except at Versailles, that is to say in the midst of pleasure and relaxation; their type of mind, their social status, various motives of private gain, their desire to please Your Majesty, combined with the authority which they possess, will cause them to lead Your Majesty from one plan to another, if you are not on your guard against them. . . ."

But Colbert need have had no fear; if his designers had *carte blanche* the King was in control of operations. When he was told that his father's castle was not solid and should be demolished, the son, without even raising his voice, replied:

"I see what you are coming to: if the château is unsatisfactory it must certainly be knocked down, but I warn you that it will be rebuilt just as it is now."

This was how the château of Louis XIV came to be built entirely round that of Louis XIII, "like a truffle," says Lenotre, "in some splendid pâté."

II

THE HOUSE OF CARDS

The King knew what he wanted. His consciousness of heredity and his dynastic inheritance dominated all other feelings; he wanted to set the date of the historical and royal beginnings of Versailles as far back as possible, even if they were relatively recent, and he forced his descendants to show the same conservative respect. Napoleon and Louis-Philippe, who were his successors but not his heirs, did not fail to observe the tradition.

In 1663, the *Allée Royale*, which later was to become the green expanse known as the *Tapis Vert*, or "Carpet of Green," was laid out and stretched almost as far as the future *Bassin de Neptune*. Four hundred men carried out this work, while the orange-trees from the Château de Vaux were brought into the first orangery, which was not yet the fine building that we know today.

The King visited Versailles every day, usually coming before he left for the hunt. The royal carriage would arrive without warning, turning round in the entrance courtyard and stopping in the *Cour de Marbre*, where it was the only conveyance allowed. Two lines of men stood at attention, and while the drums beat out *Aux Champs!* the King made a detailed inspection.

"A broken window pane or sash-bolt," wrote Colbert, "is enough to excite a great number of overseers and upset His Majesty, who appears, however, to be satisfied when he comes here."

When the King was away with the army or elsewhere, he maintained careful daily contact with Colbert, and then with Louvois, who succeeded him. Each one of their reports was taken to him by dispatch rider, carefully annotated in the royal hand and returned to Versailles at once. The style of the notes was brief and dignified: "The only important thing is to lose no time.—I should be very pleased if this were done by the time I arrive.—This would only mean a delay of a few days. No great matter.—You were right to use longer screws.—All that can be done is to open the windows and light a fire to remove the smell. See that this is done.[1] It is important that this should be done. At the worst the delay will amount to a few days."[2]

Beneath the master's attentive eye "all this chaos was resolved." The King held his Council at Versailles for the first time in October 1663, among the fresh paint and stucco, the first symbolic meeting which foreshadowed the end of the Louvre, which for centuries had been the seat of government. According to Colbert it was too much neglected, in spite of Perrault's magnificent colonnade which completed it.

This abandonment of the Louvre was a great sorrow to the Secretary of State, who wrote to his sovereign in straightforward terms:

"How sad it is that the greatest and most virtuous King of all, possessing that true virtue which makes the greatest princes, must be judged by Versailles! And yet there is reason to fear such a misfortune!"

The fête entitled *Les Plaisirs de l'Isle Enchantée*, given on May 16th, 1664, in honour of the affectionate La Vallière, celebrated the completion of the first part of the building programme, but there is no room here to describe all the magnificent spectacles which, between 1664 and 1680, brought each successive stage in the building of Versailles to a brilliant close.

In 1665 the great park began to take on the aspect which can be seen in the plans drawn up at the King's command. With the help of heavy trailer-waggons invented specially for the purpose of the Abbé Truchet, great trees were uprooted and brought there from almost all the royal châteaux. The yews and firs came from Normandy while trees from the inexhaustible nurseries of Vaux flourished along the paths in the groves planted closely round them. The exceptionally magnificent flowers were changed each season and sometimes as often as twice a day, with the help of thousands of flower-pots transported by an army of gardeners. The colour combinations depended on the weather or simply on a command from the King, sometimes intended to gratify the whim of one of his mistresses.

---

[1] Louis XIV was very susceptible to smells and could not even bear the smell of snuff; he refers here to the paintings in the royal bedchamber, which had recently been decorated.

[2] P. de Nolhac, *La Création de Versailles*. Paris, 1925.

Work was begun on many ornamental basins, which were soon filled with mythological figures in bronze, lead and pewter from whose embraces there spurted out the delightful water symphony known as *Les Grandes Eaux*. The famous expanse of water which mirrors the Orangery was named after the Swiss Guard—*La Pièce des Suisses*. Thousands of workmen, known as *ristons*, worked for ten years on the excavation of the Grand Canal. Later on splendid galleys sailed along it, manned by sailors or real convicts, ships fitted with cannon and even Venetian gondolas with authentic gondoliers.

In spite of the severity of religious observance the gardeners and navvies had the little sought-after honour, granted exceptionally by the Curé of Versailles, of working on Sundays after Mass, to the greater glory of the King.

The *Cour de Marbre*, the tabernacle of the royal sanctuary, received all the solicitous attention of the architects and artists. In the centre was a white marble fountain; on the three brick and stone façades were sculptured piers and busts on corbels, while the first-storey windows had wonderful carved balconies; from here the King could see the aviaries which were full of twittering birds of paradise. In 1689 the *Cour de Marbre* was flanked by two short wings completed by d'Orbay.

Lastly, in the grounds, Louis XIV built some innovations which are even more representative of the style of the period.

First was the *Ménagerie*, a delightful octagonal building with balconies from where one could watch the valuable game which was used for the hunts, as well as the ordinary poultry served at the King's table. Louis often visited the Pheasantry where the birds were trained to entertain him by coming for their food to the sound of drum beats. Later on gazelles were brought to Versailles, Barbary sheep, pink flamingoes and valuable birds; further additions included a camel, an elephant who became very famous and very vicious in his old age, and finally lions and tigers. At the end of the next century the royal *ménagerie* was torn down by men of equal ferocity acting in the name of Liberty, Equality and Fraternity.

Another building which we were not to see was the *Trianon de Porcelaine*, a magnificent pavilion designed by Le Vau with gardens by Le Nôtre. It was a one-storey building decorated with Delft porcelain in the Chinese style of the period; the King used to come here for supper parties in feminine company.

Seventeen years later Louis XIV caused the porcelain pavilion to be

24. Versailles: the water tower (from an engraving by Silvestre)

demolished and in its place Mansard built the *Grand Trianon*[1] in the form that we know today. When the King grew more sober he enjoyed staying there with his family to escape from the strict etiquette of the palace. During a recent visit I searched in vain for the famous casement which displeased the King so much, to the great disgust of Louvois, who dared to say that it was very fine; Louis XIV went white, which was his way of seeing red. The King and the Marquis were not on speaking terms for several days. Saint-Simon recounts that in order to settle his nerves Louvois unleashed war and caused the Palatinate to be devastated. It is a far cry from the delightful Trianon to such horrible events.

About 1670 work was begun on another of the fantastic projects which the King liked so much, the Grotto of Thetis. This was the holy of holies where the Perrault brothers paid homage to the star which was shining more and more brightly. The grotto was decorated with rocks and shells among which was an "organ driven by water imitating the song of the birds." There were also many marble statues representing mythological figures paying homage to Apollo the Sun King "on his way to the couch of Thetis," as Charles Perrault says, "after making his journey round the earth; this was intended to

[1] Louis XV asked Gabriel to lay out the *Petit Trianon* grounds. Louis XVI gave it to Marie Antoinette who in her turn built the "Hamlet."

represent the King coming to rest at Versailles after working for the good of all humanity."

It is comforting to learn that this pagan magnificence disappeared in 1689 to make room for the permanent Chapel, which was dedicated to St. Louis and the Christian religion. In 1775 the central group from the grotto was placed among the rocks in the Baths of Apollo where Hubert Robert, an artist who specialised in ruins, arranged the statuary in the way in which we know it today.

In 1668 the *Parterre d'Eau* (Water Garden) was laid out and many magnificent ornamental pools were placed along the garden façade, with bronze statues representing symbolic figures. Louis XIII had merely planned a series of lawns, but his arrangement was changed many times up till the death of Louis XIV, since when no further changes have been made. Another magnificent piece of work was the *Allée d'Eau* which led northwards towards the *Bassin du Dragon*, flanked by fourteen little fountains each supported by a group of children.

It is fascinating to think how the day passed for everyone working at Versailles. Le Nôtre could usually be found early in the morning either in the vegetable garden, or near the Orangery, or perhaps in the *Bosquets des Dômes* or trimming a yew tree in the Maze. He did not look very different from the gardeners who worked round about him, for he usually wore sabots and a black apron with a large pocket; he would carry a hoe in his hand and a pair of pruning-shears would be slung round him. When the King came he would grumble slightly as he put on buckled shoes and a wig. He was as self-contained as the great elms that he looked after so well. The King bestowed a title on him in spite of himself and even devised an eloquent coat of arms for him: "A chevron of gold with three snails argent on a field of sable." He was said to act entirely on impulse and when he visited the Vatican he dared to embrace the Pope. There was much gossip about it in the salons of Versailles. One duke wagered 1,000 louis that the story was pure fiction. At that moment the King passed by and heard the remark.

"Don't make any wager," he said. "When I return from the country Le Nôtre embraces me. It's highly possible he embraced the Pope!"

It is easy to imagine the painter Le Brun standing on a ladder, with marks of blue paint on his habit and gold dust on his wig, while the King, with flakes of plaster falling on his shoulders like snow, would raise his cane to point out some detail that needed highlighting or some colour to be made darker.

Although the eighteenth century produced so many prints of everyday life among ordinary people etiquette and prejudice were so over-whelming that no scene showing work in progress has survived, not even a slight sketch by some amateur of the scaffolding. The King's presence caused the very paint to freeze on the palettes.

The ornamental basins and fountains were built by workers brought specially from Italy, known as "Francine." The King showered them with money and honours, for the fountains were of special importance to him, and he took care every day to ask to what height the jets of water rose.

"The *Francine*," wrote Pierre de Nolhac, "had to create effects which were superior to any achieved previously, and they worked far from any abundant water supply, on marshy soil full of stagnant water which was ill-suited to this experiment."

The same men built the Pump and the Water Tower which stood on the site of the present Hôtel des Réservoirs, and many other miraculous water devices which will be mentioned again later.

Nicolas Petit, Controller-General of Buildings, whom one can easily imagine dressed in moss-green or stone colour, acted as Colbert's "private eye" at Versailles. He never left the Palace and every day he sent a detailed report to his superior, who returned it with severe comments. This correspondence forms one of the richest documentary sources for the history of the building of Versailles.

Alexandre Bontemps could be described as chief personnel officer. He was first Gentleman of the Bedchamber, "possessing the keys to this room and sleeping there himself," and he was also superintendent of the Château, the grounds, the town and the estates of Versailles. The way in which he carried out that obscure and thankless task caused him to be equally feared in the Château and the town, but he did not weaken during forty-two years of faithful service to the King.

In fact he was second in command to Colbert. Although he was not actively concerned with the gardens, the fountains or the stonework, he could be seen everywhere at every hour of the day. Along with Nicolas Petit he took care to see that the orders coming from the King or the supervisor were properly carried out; he willingly counted the spades, picks and trowels with immense care. Colbert's orders were like those of a military commander. Here is how he described the duties of the inspector of works: "Monsieur Lefèvre should take care to begin his inspection of all work at five o'clock in the morning; he should see how many men are working on each job and write it down on the forms and notebook which he should have in his pocket, so that he can give me an exact account every time I come here."

Or this was his "decision" about the boy fountain-workers:
"They will be housed in the pump buildings, and whenever a man or boy is not at his post when work has been allotted to him óne écu will be deducted from the money given to Denis (master fountain-worker) and he in turn will deduct thirty sols from each boy."

The great architects and artists worked directly for the King or for Colbert, but the craftsmen or labourers worked in groups according to their trade under the direction of contractors, mainly from Paris, whose contracts were set out in careful detail and registered with a notary. The contractors were then formally described as "Officially sworn in as builders and building contractors to His Majesty." It was a great privilege to work for the King of France and very remunerative too, for private clients were impressed by it. Sometimes these contractors styled themselves, on their own account, "architects to the King," a description which looked well in their daughters' marriage contracts, when they married into some wealthy or noble family, but led to violent protests from the group of architects who were members of the Royal Academy.

The official contracts were written in a fine flowing hand, but the printed specifications set out plainly enough the work to be done within a fixed space of time; this was generally short, for the King was extremely impatient. The materials were described with exact details about their place of origin, such as hard stone from St. Cloud, or soft stone from Meudon; the thickness of the timber was carefully stated and everything was paid for at so much a linear, square or cubic yard or foot. The price was left blank and was finally written in by hand after fierce discussions. Then everybody signed, and a copy of the estimates, initialled by Colbert, d'Orbay and Louvois themselves, was placed in the files of Maître Debeauvais, the King's notary.

These documents are couched in terms so exact that contempoiary architects would be astonished. They include page after page of building technicalities and set out exact delivery times with dates of payment, but also with a strict system of fines in case of delay:
"All this will be paid for at the price to be agreed and on condition that the requisite number of workers are allocated to this work to the stage when the timber can be put in place; that is to say: half of one side by St. John's Day (June 24th), the other half by July 15th and the last roof-timbers of the other half by the last day of August, all this year, all expenses and damages payable.

"Payment: 10,000 livres on account and the same amount at the end of the month (of March); 15,000 in April and the same amount in May;

25. Architect and workmen in the seventeenth century, engraved
by Lagniet (*photo Richard Blin-Plon*)

12,000 in June; 11,000 in July, 10,000 in August, and the remainder as the work progresses. To be deducted in case of non-completion in the stated time: 10,000 livres."

But in certain circumstances Louis XIV's remarkable love of speed led him to offer good bonuses for work carried out without delay. In 1682 therefore the masons Vignaux, Lecoeur and Martin, after carrying out work worth 720,000 livres, received a bonus of 120,000 livres "in consideration of the exceptional haste and expense necessary to finish the work perfectly in the time commanded by His Majesty."

The contractors in their turn kept a record of their work, but unfortunately these documents are extremely rare. One of them which was discovered in the Versailles Library deserves to be quoted in entirety. It was drawn up by the master-builder Villard when working on the Rocquencourt viaduct and states day by day the level of the water in the building, thermometric and barometric readings, the amount of rainfall, the strength of the sun, the direction of the wind, the amount of snow falling, and the phase of the moon, which made it possible to forecast frosts.

In order to carry out the indoor and outdoor decorative work at Versailles Colbert created manufacturing concerns under royal patronage and the majority of them outlived him; he also attempted to introduce a "controlled economy" with the intention of strengthening the workers' guilds. The guilds in their turn preserved traditions and practices by means of rules which all their members had to obey, and the quality of their work was subject to continual inspection.

Some craftsmen of high reputation, such as decorators, gilders, wood carvers, bronze workers, marble cutters for example, worked directly for the Château. All the building trades were represented at Versailles; most of the work was carried out in the Paris workshops or studios and then placed in position or completed at Versailles under the supervision of the artists or contractors.

The masons and stone-carvers, who formed the largest group of the workers at Versailles, mostly came from the Limousin district in the south-west of France, lying round Limoges, and in the seventeenth century Limousin was synonymous for builder. They left their homes with the first fine days, but many went back again with the swallows. At Versailles they lived in tents, cabins or huts, and in the town they had hutments which gave their name to the present Rue de Limoges, a dreary street full of military barracks.

The vast amount of excavation work necessary for the foundations, ornamental basins and lakes was carried out in exceptional cases by regiments of soldiers who were not needed for fighting, but mostly by poor wretches who found their way to Versailles from the four corners of France, following the dishonest promises of unscrupulous contractors. They went from site to site, without any contract, living from week to week, going wherever their fancy took them and existing as best they could on poor wages. Their pay was meagre. A master jobbing-workman received from twenty-five to fifty sols a day but the actual labourers themselves received six to twelve sols, which barely bought a few loaves of bread or a few ounces of low-quality meat. Nobody knows where they lived, for the records of the period give no information—probably in some tent taken over from the army, some cottage, barn or corner of the building site which they had to leave every morning; or else, when their wounds, crippled limbs or chilblains became too gangrenous to be tolerated by their comrades, they would sleep in groups of three or four in the bedroom of some wretched almshouse.

Accidents were inevitable on this vast building site, which employed as many as 36,000 men; in addition large gaps in the ranks of the workmen were caused by illness, bad weather and especially the fearful miasma which rose from the Versailles swamps and gave even the King a fever. These scourges of nature, especially during the terrible winter of 1678, almost brought the work at Versailles to a standstill; from October onwards the weather was terrible, as Madame de Sévigné informed her cousin Bussy-Rabutin:

"The Court is at St. Cloud; the King wants to go to Versailles, but apparently God wills otherwise, for the buildings cannot be got ready to receive him and a fantastic number of the men are dying; cartloads full of corpses are taken away every night, as from the Hôtel-Dieu.[1] This sorrowful journey takes place in secret, to avoid frightening the other workers and so as not to decry *this favourite without merit*. Have you heard this witty description of Versailles?"

Bussy replied to this famous letter from his provincial retreat:

"I did not know that Versailles was described as *a favourite without merit*; nothing is more apt nor better expressed. Kings can transform the ground by spending money, but they have no power over the quality of the water and the air. It would be strange and sad if after the expenditure of 100 million livres Versailles were to become uninhabitable. . . ."

During the terrible winter of 1684 the sites at the Château were

---

[1] The large hospital in Paris; during that winter cartloads of dead were taken from it every morning and buried in quicklime in the Cemetery of Clamart.

deserted and the Limousin workers abandoned the building of the enclosure to the park *en masse*, for the frost had made work impossible, as Louvois wrote pathetically to Louis XIV:

"The bad weather continues, and the worst thing concerning the park is that the Limousins are deserting every day, *although we owe them two weeks' pay.* I have sent word round the park today to promise them thirty-five sols per six feet completed. This is thirteen sols more than they are given in summer. If this does not keep them it will not be possible to finish the park completely before the spring. . . ."

"It is somewhat strange," comments Pierre de Nolhac, "to see the all-powerful minister, whom Saint-Simon was later to describe as so harsh towards the poor soldiers working on the aqueduct of Maintenon, held up, along with his clerks and his money, by recalcitrant plaster-workers who refuse to touch the King's wall."

In 1688 financial difficulties followed the bad weather. The King had to send his silver dinner services to the Mint so that they could be melted down and turned into money to allow the work at Versailles to proceed . . . and the Dutch War had just broken out, close to the frontiers of France.

There was a great deal of poverty, too, both in country cottages and Paris houses. In the centre of Paris leaflets were published protesting against the King's excessive expenditure, and they were posted at night in the public squares, on the walls of the churches, and insulting remarks were scribbled even on statues of the King; the leaflets and inscriptions were removed during darkness by the archers of the night-watch.

In the town of Versailles steps had to be taken against the rapacious shopkeepers, who had not failed to grow rich by selling food at exorbitant prices. The village had suddenly become an overpopulated town, attracting hordes of beggars and even criminals who came from Paris to settle there, living on the lavish royal leftovers and engaging in frequent disturbances which, at night especially, transformed the lawless town into a real death-trap.

To remedy this situation the King appointed a governor and a magistrate who made sure of their authority by issuing strict orders. In the first place, since everything had to be brought from a distance, the shopkeepers had had the chance to monopolise food supplies, speculating over prices and cheating over weights and weighing scales. As early as 1672 therefore the magistrate issued a set of regulations, "following complaints by the craftsmen and labourers working on His Majesty's buildings."

Bread, meat, wine, straw and hay too, which were usually no more than the workers' beds, were carefully priced and taxed. The opening-times of shops were also published in order to stop the "cornering" of supplies, and to prevent drunkenness, the curse of all building sites, the taverns were closed during working hours.

In 1688, almost thirty years after work had begun, Versailles was still without a hospital. Anyone who was badly injured or seriously ill was transported to the hospitals in Paris, in conditions one hardly dare contemplate. Louis XIV then remembered that he had recently built Les Invalides in Paris adorned with a majestic sun carved in his honour. In 1689 therefore he rented the house of a certain François Lespée, and in 1707, for 10,000 livres—the cost of one statue in the grounds of Versailles—he bought this large house, "consisting of several bedchambers and ground floor rooms, attics and cellars." Then he allocated 25,000 livres per year to the Sisters of Charity; and yet at first the only patients admitted were the poor people from the town, and servants working for the King and the princes. This charity was not established as a royal hospital until the time of Louis XV.

Sometimes Colbert took an interest in a particular case, involving for example some poor but outstanding craftsman. The King was most punctilious in the exercise of his prerogatives however and the Controller-General had to give full details before anyone could hope for any special assistance.

Examples of royal generosity towards workmen are rare in the annals of the building of Versailles. Louis XIV was not soft-hearted and at every level, from the apartments to the gardens, work was carried out under the threat of the whip.

Charles Perrault, the famous French writer of fairy-tales, was also a civil servant working on the administration of the royal buildings. In this capacity he often had to lay down his pen and spend several months at Versailles, from where he sent daily reports to Colbert, who was as impatient and severe as the King.

But work carried out with such haste sometimes leads to mis-judgement and errors, like that noticed by Huyghens when, in the company of Perrault, he looked over the Pump built by the *Francine*.

"The expense of raising the water in this tower was quite un-necessary," said the famous Dutch scientist; "a pump could easily have taken it from the Pool of Clagny into the reservoirs."

When Perrault reported this to Colbert the latter threw up his arms in fury:

"What can you expect, you have to pay for experience!"

For the unfortunate man paid for the experience with sleepless nights and public money. It was not merely a question of an unnecessary pump; he had a tidy mind but he was unable to grasp the haphazard general plan which involved building sites scattered over the fifty square leagues of the royal estate.

Colbert strove his hardest to make order out of this chaos, but only the King with his remarkable instinct for building could understand it. He did not need even a rough sketch to direct for thirty years the most highly organised dream-castle in the world. Colbert was a native of Champagne, where everyone is realistic, but he tried in vain to work out a vague plan on his own accord. There would have been no point in it. The next day a command from above would have destroyed it completely.

"Everything the King does," he wrote, as far back as 1665, "is on the same scale as his greatness, that is to say it achieves monstrous size"; but he admits that "the monster is well-proportioned."

Le Vau died in 1670; d'Orbay succeeded him, with neither a definite appointment nor a great deal of originality, for ten years. Then in 1680 Mansard finally came on the scene, and it was he who gave a design to the monster, and completed it.

III

THE WELL-PROPORTIONED MONSTER

When the King died, in 1715, only a few years after the great architect, the Palace of Versailles was completed by Mansard's brother-in-law, Robert de Cotte, financial Under-Secretary. The building looked more or less the same then as it does now.

During the eighteenth century the interior was transformed by improved arrangements for comfort, which people had now begun to appreciate, and the changes in contemporary style during the reigns of Louis XV and Louis XVI. The former established his small private apartments on the site of the vast Ambassador's Staircase, a joint masterpiece by Mansard and Le Brun, and its disappearance is a great loss. The furthermost pavilion on the right of the royal courtyard was added by Ange Gabriel at the command of Louis XV, and that on the left, built in the same style, was carried out by Dufour for Louis XVIII.

When the monarchy was restored in 1814 Louis-Philippe made

Versailles into a museum and arranged an intelligent collection of artistic masterpieces in the palace that had been completely emptied by the Revolution; the Convention had sold the furniture over a period of three years and it had been dispersed all over Europe. When the third Republic was instituted in France Versailles became a memorial to the Monarchy.

The jewel remains therefore intact in its case, just as it was abandoned by Louis XIV when, on a September evening in 1715, he went to join his ancestors in a mediaeval crypt, on a gun-carriage drawn by eight horses, preceded by members of the poor on foot, bearing torches.[1]

Le Vau had extracted the gem of Versailles from its matrix and under Mansard it was polished continually until it shone in many-faceted splendour.

The great architect was barely eighteen when he worked at the Château de Clagny, built for Madame de Montespan, then in all her glory as mistress to the Sun King. The building lasted ten years, almost as long as the lady's ascendancy, and cost ten million livres; contemporary accounts describe it as magnificent, but not one stone of it remains. Louis XV had it demolished and the entire materials were sold to a contractor for 400,000 livres.

Mansard was responsible for the delightful buildings of the Château de Marly (which disappeared during the Revolution), the Place des Victoires, the Place Vendôme and the dome of the Invalides in Paris. His life was relatively short and devoted entirely to the glorification of Louis XIV and his times; he dedicated his last thirty years to Versailles.

Mansard was the true architect of the period, for his talents fitted him more than anyone else for carrying out the vision of Louis XIV; the date of his appointment as minister officially in charge of buildings, following Colbert and Louvois, is of the greatest importance, for now this lofty function was discharged by an artist instead of administrators. This appointment led to the programme which completed the work.

Contrary to the frequent assertions made by his most eminent biographers it is by no means certain that the King regarded Versailles as his future residence and the seat of government as soon as he acceded to the throne. It looks rather as though this decision was forced on him as the work progressed; when, for example, he began to be concerned about the amount of public money that it consumed, while he was also being forced to supply extremely costly weapons for wars of prestige. Then he could not stop, he had to build and he had to fight.

[1] Pierre Narbonne. See Bibliography.

He realised that the tyrannical power of etiquette had surrounded him with a vast and voracious court. First came a wretched succession of descendants who died either in their cradles or as soon as they reached manhood. He was to die at seventy-seven, leaving one solitary great-grandson who never had the benefit of his advice.

As he grew older, his mistresses became more demanding. The King granted their every wish, not from love and not from charity, but simply because it was only proper for a royal mistress to have, as we would say nowadays, a royal standing. And this was not all—a dozen bastard children were legitimised, thereby becoming princes who had to be brought up in royal style.

Finally there were three thousand parasites at court, so many poor relations, as it were, who had come up from the country "carrying their châteaux on their backs," as they have often been described.

Where could all these people be housed? The King's despotic attitude kept them round him, and they enjoyed it. Paris was out of the question. The town of Versailles was now being built, but it was still too far away. In any case it might have been necessary to give everyone a palace, and this would have led to difficulties about precedence and even perhaps to secret royal jealousy. Louis XIV would not have built a whole town to house these people, as manufacturers today build houses for their workers. Everyone had to live at the Palace: the family, the relatives in law, the mistresses, the illegitimate children and all the dignitaries, from the greatest equerry to the humblest, excluding the military staff and the servants. The King had to have his secretaries of state, his ministers and his controller-general constantly at his side, so that he could speak to Louvois, give orders to Mansard or talk to Le Nôtre at a moment's notice. Although they did not live in the Palace, their office staff did.

Versailles crystallised gradually therefore in the royal mind. The accounts which have been preserved in the Versailles library make this quite clear, and the expenses over the years 1664–1690 speak for themselves. This period can be divided into three shorter periods of more or less equal length showing a continuous rise in expenditure.

The first period goes from 1664 to 1670 (death of Le Vau), and the annual expenditure varies from 200 to 800,000 livres, forming a total of 6 million. The second period goes from 1671 to 1680, and the latter date was important for the King, for Versailles and the kingdom: the King gave up Madame de Montespan, Mansard was appointed first royal architect and the treaty of Nijmegen in 1678 marked the zenith of the Sun King's reign; the annual expenditure varies between

900,000 and 6 million, amounting to a total of 27 million livres. The third period (1681 to 1690) was the most costly and saw the completion of Versailles (with the exception of the Chapel, completed in 1710), but the expenditure rose to 48 million livres, the annual cost varying between 1,300,000 to 11 million livres.[1]

When the Palace was completed Louis XIV decided therefore to make it into his residence and the seat of government, for without realising it he had become a slave to his own grandeur, which kept him there, as Talleyrand said: "Because his fame . . . had restricted all his ideas within the limits of Versailles." And when he had finally made his decision he carried it out in a firm, implacably inhuman way.

Versailles was officially inaugurated on May 6th, 1682, when the King "dragged the Court out of Paris for good," to quote Saint-Simon's memorable remark. And he made no distinction between family and government. This decision involved housing problems which in ten years' time increased the living space in the Château and the town by four times.

The Dauphine gave birth to a son on May 6th among the building rubbish and the sound of hammering, and this event was highly significant. In future the royal princes born during the reign of Louis XIV were born at Versailles, near the royal apartments. Their baptisms were recorded at the Church of Notre Dame de Versailles[2]—in a special register, it is true, but that register was kept in the sacristy and so was the one in which the curés showed how the same water had been used for the sons of the bourgeois or the parish porter. This was the royal parish now, just as St. Germain l'Auxerrois had been the parish for the Louvre, before it was abandoned.

The Court took up residence. The princes lived in the South Wing, known as the Princes' Wing, built between 1684 and 1690, and in the North Wing, which also included privilege apartments destined for important servants of the Crown. The ministers and secretaries of State lived in the four large pavilions in the royal courtyard. The remainder of the entourage, lords or dignitaries of secondary import-ance who carried out their duties for free living accommodation, felt cramped in the second-floor attics which were as uninhabitable in winter as in summer. The Great Apartments of the King and the Queen, as well as the State Rooms, were on the first floor, and from 1700 onwards the King's bedchamber, which was at first in the *Salon de Mercure*, looked over the *Cour de Marbre*, situated, needless to say, at the central point of the Château.

---

[1] See Appendix I.   [2] Also built by Mansard, finished in 1684.

The Hall of Mirrors looked on to the terrace and linked the two magnificent salons, the "Salon of Peace" and the "Salon of War." An old gallery linked the two square towers of the "poor little castle" and on top of it Mansard built the famous room which is 230 feet long, one of the world's architectural masterpieces, and decorated by Le Brun. It was the shrine of Paris, so much so that in 1871 the Germans created their Emperor there, as though they needed the blessing of the Sun King. In 1919, however, the elderly Republican Clemenceau removed the last memory of Germany from it.

The military successes of the century supplied the subjects for the vast painted ceilings, and Racine and Boileau drew up simple inscriptions which were added beneath them. The French Republic extolled its own fame in the same way when Paul Valéry, the poet, was asked to write the inscriptions for the pediments on the Palais de Chaillot. Unfortunately the gallery at Versailles no longer includes the royal throne, which has disappeared, nor the furniture inlaid with precious metal, which ironically enough was melted down at the end of the reign to pay for the disasters of the recent wars.

The Most Christian King completed the work of Versailles by paying solemn homage to his Creator, and the Chapel which replaced the Grotto of Thetis—the fifth in the Château—was not finished until 1710. The roof rises higher than the roofs of the Château in a curious way, but not in the shape of a steeple. This was the only concession that the King made to God, well-deserved homage from the eldest scion of the Church who was granted a long life by divine dispensation. If Louis XIV had died prematurely Versailles would probably never have been finished.

The new Chapel replaced the last but one which had been built in 1682 and was to be entirely lined with marble columns and plaques. But shortly before it was completed in 1699 the King realised, or was perhaps informed, that such an expanse of marble, although satisfying to the Deity, would make the Chapel too cool and extremely damp. He had the walls and pillars taken down therefore and substituted in their place the stone which in the yellow light from the windows gives this fine building an atmosphere of dignified and unpretentious magnificence.

Mistakes of this kind, which would also have been unforgivable lapses of taste, occurred frequently during the building of Versailles but were skilfully rectified in time. The materials used were often too fragile, and would have been more at home in the mild air of Rome than in the harsh climate of the Ile de France. They provide a constant element of risk in the preservation of the Château, which fortunately continues to attract the generosity of the whole world; the maintenance of Versailles has certainly cost more than its construction.

The use of over-porous stone or unseasoned timber necessitates costly restoration work which is made unobtrusive by the ingenious conservators of Versailles and the skilful craftsmen who assist them. I have been able to see the extent of the invisible damage caused by persistent haste, dangerous "conversions" during later reigns, occasional shocking bad workmanship and time, all of which undermine the Palace like a termite.

Some of these weaknesses were noticed even while the Palace was being built. This is why the rich marble floors exist no longer, for when it was noticed that the water used in cleaning them had rotted the wooden flooring, the King had them removed. A wooden parquet floor was laid instead, the famous "Versailles parquet," and the marble was left only round the outer circumference on the thresholds and the surrounds to the windows.

It is impossible to describe the vast quantities and the many types of marble used at Versailles, or the subtle hierarchy of the scheme in which they were employed.

"The rarest and most valuable," said Félibien, "were used in the places closest to the King, so that anyone passing from one room to another would see increased magnificence either in the marble or in the paintings which graced the ceilings."

This fine stone came from the Bourbonnais, Languedoc and the Pyrenees, in unending convoys along the wretched roads or else following the new canals. Colbert deplored the shortage of marble-cutters, and he brought them from the provinces and even from Italy. The marble statues and groups of figures were naturally carved in the artists' studios. Pierre Puget carved his famous "Milo de Crotone" in Marseilles and it was transported from Le Havre by boat. This fine group is now in the Louvre, but it stood formerly in the *Allée Royale* and it is said that when the good Queen Marie-Thérèse saw the famous Greek athlete being devoured by the lion she cried "Oh, poor man!," a remark the statue must have heard many times since then.

Some ancient marble statues, both originals and copies, came from Italy, leaving from Cività Vecchia, and going to Le Havre by way of Marseilles; from there they came up the Seine to St. Cloud where they were placed on carts and taken to Versailles. In Rome the Royal Academy, which had been founded not long before on the initiative of Le Brun, had bought these works in the greatest secrecy, for the Pope had forbidden them to leave the country; however, penniless noblemen had no objections to selling the finest statues from their palaces at a high price to the King of France.

Colbert ordered an equestrian statue of Louis XIV from the famous Italian sculptor Bernini. It was executed in the purest Carrara marble and finished twenty years later, but it did not have the good fortune to be approved by the King, who ordered it to be destroyed. Louvois pleaded for it to be retained, especially perhaps because of the 100,000 livres it had cost. The sculptor Girardon was asked to change the figure of the King into "Curtius casting himself into the flames." In spite of this metempsychosis it never pleased the King, and he had it placed at the south end of the *Pièce des Suisses* where its only admirers today are the young firemen who carry out their exercises round it.

One can imagine the state of the grounds over a period of thirty years: derricks, winches, ladders and scaffolding more or less everywhere; workshops here and there with mountains of stones and forests of beams over which passed carts and waggons drawn by some of the 6,000 horses which were kept entirely for use at Versailles.

The *Place Royale* had become one of the depots for these materials, which spread like leprosy into the very courtyard of the Château, with the result that an order was issued several times to the effect that "the said stones must not be unloaded less than twelve feet from the pavement."

Mention has been made of the 100,000 livres paid to Bernini, for if the craftsmen and labourers received mediocre pay the King did not restrict the fees of his artists in any way. Since Colbert "thought nothing of asking the greatest painter of the time to design a lock or a door-knob" the artists were paid 4,300,000 livres over a period of nearly thirty years, without counting occasional gifts of land or jewels. Yet the total amount of money paid to the workmen over the same period—and there were as many as 36,000 men—only came to 1,381,000 livres.

On the other hand the inspectors of buildings, administrators, clerks and other supervisory staff alone received more than a million livres. The sculptor Tuby was paid 14,000 livres for the Apollo group; the painted ceilings in the Hall of Mirrors brought Le Brun a fee of 80,000 livres, without counting the payments received by his numerous collaborators. In addition, during the one year of 1685, the painter received 20,000 livres to "build a house on the site His Majesty has given him at Versailles." Puget only received 15,000 livres for his Milo, but he lived at Marseilles and was rarely seen at Court.

The King was alarmed to find costs mounting up, and at the instigation of Louvois, who, apparently, spent less when he built fortresses, he ordered Colbert to reduce expenditure. Perrault, in his Memoirs, tells how the controller-general, worn out, old and overworked, "ordered that in future all building work would be carried out at reduced prices; so that this would be widely known he wanted notices posted at the street corners in the hope of receiving offers from all workmen, but this was not helpful in any way; on the contrary it created a great deal of difficulty, for the bad workmen, who gave lower estimates, supplanted the better ones and those who were more capable of rendering service. There were carpenters who had only poor quality timber in their workshops and carried out such bad work at Versailles that when the frames for the casements were put together, they showed almost as much light as when they were open. . . .

"Monsieur Colbert said, 'Building is like a bottomless pit; the longer I work on it the more problems I find. In comparison the finances of the country gave me no trouble at all'."

There were so many people at Versailles that thieves stole lead ornaments from the grounds and even gold fringes from the King's bedroom; visitors came to the sites from Paris and the provinces every day, full of curiosity to see how the work was progressing. Famous people from all over the world went to the Château, which had begun to acquire an international reputation. Puget was taken round by Le Nôtre and Madame de Sévigné willingly acted as guide also.

In the autumn of 1668 a memorable visit was made by Boileau, La Fontaine and Racine, who came as a group; Molière should have joined them, but not even the affectionate insistence of Boileau could persuade him to see Racine again, for they had quarrelled over an actress. His place was taken by the good Chapelle. They saw everything that could be seen at that time, from the beginnings of the Grand Canal to the Chariot of Apollo, where the fountains were already playing, and La Fontaine described them as lyrically as he praised the Nymphs of the Château de Vaux.

Even the King himself enjoyed showing his work to visitors. "Madame de Lafayette was at Versailles yesterday," wrote Madame de Sévigné. "She was very well received, extremely well received, for the King invited her into his carriage with the ladies and enjoyed showing her the beauties of Versailles just as some private person shows you his country house. . . ."

The King himself was the first Conservator of Versailles and even wrote in his own hand a "Manner of showing the gardens at Ver-

1 en sortant du chateau par le vestibule
~~de la cour de marbre~~ sous la chambre du
roy on gra: sur la terrasse on
s'arestera sur le haut des degres
pour considerer ~~la situation du jardin~~ les parterres
les pieces d'eau et les fontaines
des cabinets

2 apres on tournera a gauche et
l'on descendra par le degré des ~~~~
en arrivant sur le haut on fera
une ~~~~ pour voir le ~~~~ du
medy et apres on ira sur le haut
de l'orangerie d'ou l'on verra
le parterne des orangers et le lac
des ~~~~

3 on tournera *a droit* pour ~~~~ monter
~~~~ la terrasse et l'on ~~~~ au ~~~~
a droit d'ou l'on voit les ~~~~
~~~~ de bacus et de saturne

26. Instructions for showing the gardens at Versailles, written by
Louis XIV in his own hand

sailles," a true guide describing briefly how to proceed when some great personage came to present his respects. Here is the first paragraph: "As you leave the Château through the vestibule to the *Cour de Marbre* you will go on to the Terrace; then you will pause at the top of the staircase to look at the placing of the flower-beds, the ornamental pools and the fountains in the clumps of trees." The visit continued and ended in this way near the Grand Canal: "Go past the *Bassin de Neptune* once again, go round the outskirts and arrange to meet the carriages at the gate leading to the Trianon."

The King then tired of writing and went no further, but no Versailles guide has ever surpassed him.

Louis XIV was delighted when anyone liked his château, but we would not have believed him capable of the bourgeois vanity expressed in this anecdote:

The Duc d'Antin, the last director of Building during the reign, sent a report to the King daily, as instructed. In one of them he described how Father Anselme, the famous historian of the French Monarchy, had visited Versailles. "I can still see Father Anselme standing at the foot of the Waterfall; he was almost in a state of ecstasy."

In his own hand the King made a note against the report: "This is due to his good taste!"

IV

THE FALL AND RISE OF VERSAILLES

The Marquis de Dangeau describes the Sun King in old age, going round the gardens in a wheel chair, accompanied by Le Nôtre. When the King noticed that the elderly gardener found it difficult to keep up with him, wrote the Marquis, he "had him placed in a wheel chair like his own." He took him through the entire gardens, and Le Nôtre said:

"If my poor father were alive and could see a poor gardener like his son going about in a chair beside the greatest King in the world, my happiness would be complete."

None of the great trees that witnessed this memorable tour are standing now. They have all been replaced at least twice, under Louis XV and Louis XVI, and again under the Second Empire. They will soon have to be replaced once more or they will all die.

It is sad to think that the magnificent fountains at Versailles could not have existed without the wholesale destruction that was found necessary before adequate water supplies could be obtained.

The trees which had been brought at great expense from Vaux or other royal nurseries and planted along the avenues, began to grow. Among them were built the ornamental pools with their innumerable fountains, but it was then realised that the water taken from the neighbouring pools would not be sufficient for them to work properly. The King was inordinately fond of water displays and without them the park would have been a failure; various suggestions to remedy this defect were therefore put forward.

The first, and the boldest, came from the famous engineer Riquet who had just completed the Languedoc Canal. He suggested that water should be brought to the Satory hills by diverting the Loire between Briare and Sully-sur-Loire. At the command of Colbert the Abbé Picard began the levelling operations in 1674. The scheme was abandoned however for it was realised that water could not be brought from the Loire without a sufficiently steep gradient and this meant bringing the supply from La Charité, which was more than fifty miles from Versailles.

The romantically minded Le Nôtre was very sorry to see this project abandoned, for he told the King, according to Perrault, that "it would be a fine thing to see ships sailing down the Loire, descending the hillside (Satory) like sledges and coming to float along the Canal." Then a vast machine, devised and built by the hydraulic engineer Sualem Renkin, from Liége, was installed at Marly. It operated 221 pumps which raised water from the Seine to a height of 400 feet in the Marly aqueduct and brought it to Versailles in canals. The work lasted seven years and cost nearly four million livres. The machine made a fearful noise and prevented the riverside dwellers from sleeping; but when the water reached Versailles it was still inadequate. The water was kept for the Château de Marly, a newly built residence where Louis XIV enjoyed staying in the company of courtiers whom he wished to honour in some special way.

Yet there was still a shortage of water and everyone tried to devise a way of getting it there. Finally it was decided to divert the River Eure to bring it to the royal residence. The work was begun and carried on near Maintenon which had recently become the property of the lady whom the King addressed respectfully as "Your Solidity," and to whom he was to ally himself by the secret marriage that is supposed to have taken place in 1684.

A canal of twenty-five miles long was made therefore between

Pontgouin and the little village of Berchères-la-Maingot in Eure-et-Loir. Racine went to see it in 1687, as he reported to his good friend Boileau:

"I have been to Maintenon and I am very pleased with the work I saw there. It is wonderful and truly worthy of the King's magnificence. The rows of arches which are to join the two mountains are almost complete, and there are forty-eight of them; they are built to last for ever. . . . There are more than 30,000 men working there."

Vauban directed this peace-time work, but as we shall see he was less successful than in the art of fortifications. He worked out that even if all the horses and oxen in the Beauce area were requisitioned they would not be able to transport all the materials needed for such a gigantic enterprise. At first therefore he dug a canal seven miles long with nine locks. It went from Epernon to Maintenon, through the valley of the Guesle river, and barges went down it carrying vast quantities of limestone which were taken from the surrounding quarries; the limestone came along another canal over twenty miles long from Saint-Priest to Maintenon.

Since bricks were needed also, coal was needed to bake them, for wood did not give enough heat. France produced the raw materials but the coal was sent from England. It came from Newcastle and was landed at Dunkirk, then brought in barrels, which made for easy handling, on barges as far as Rouen where large dumps were set up. Then the coal was taken up the Seine as far as Mantes and finally brought to the Eure valley by road.

Certain very old feudal rights meant that the King was not entirely master of the kingdom, and Louvois, like Colbert before him, had to forbid anyone to whom revenues from bridges, toll-gates and ports were due to demand payment for the passage of the materials.

There has been much discussion about the cost of this attempt to bring the waters of the Eure to Versailles. It probably amounted to 9 million livres, but it is only fair to point out that the work was not entirely wasted, for the water was also intended to supply the 20,000 inhabitants of the town of Versailles, who were rather short of it at that time.

Unfortunately this operation led to difficulties much more serious than the waste of money, which was now being thrown away by shovelfuls for the sake of completing the Palace. 22,000 men were occupied on the work in 1683, and all the labourers in the kingdom would not have been enough; according to Madame La Fayette it was then decided to use "troops for this vast undertaking *in order to hasten the King's pleasures by a few years* and it was done at less cost and in less time than might have been hoped." Moving large quantities of earth always causes many kinds of illnesses, and as a result the troops in camp at Maintenon, where the heaviest work was in progress, were incapable of doing any more; but this "drawback," concludes the Countess, "did not seem to merit any attention *in the midst of the peace and quiet which we enjoyed.*"

We can only assume that the noble lady was referring to the seven unhappy years of peace enjoyed by France after the Treaty of Nijmegen, during which the King, after the revocation of the Edict of Nantes, allowed his wrath to devastate the Protestant cottages of the Cevennes.

Historians have attempted to interpret this as a means of keeping the troops in training for the forthcoming siege operations. "There are nearly 30,000 men working there," wrote Racine to Boileau, "all fine people who, if war were to break out again, would much prefer to be digging somewhere near the frontier than on the plains of Beauce."

The great writer of tragedy deserves praise for his relevant and truthful remark. The author of these lines was himself a modest trooper in the Court of the King, engaged in cultivating the royal garden; he knew how much sappers disliked digging, particularly when it served no useful purpose, unlike Rostand's Cyrano de Bergerac who said, during the siege of Arras:

"No, no! Beauty that has no use is finer far!"

In addition to the terribly high mortality rate among the workmen, who were also undernourished, further hardship was caused by the iron discipline introduced by Louvois to speed the work, reduce desertion and stop the drunkenness and rivalry between the regiments which often led to bloodshed. Desertion began when efforts were made to use the soldiers for loading and unloading the boats. As much as four écus—equivalent to a huge sum of money—were given to the peasants as an incentive to make them denounce deserters. And when they were caught the punishments inflicted were terrible.

"The deserter appeared before the military tribunal," wrote F. Evrard.[1] Whenever several soldiers were to be executed, the King ordered Huxelles, the camp commandant, to make them draw lots, so that only one or two would be shot. Those who were sent to the galleys were condemned to have their noses and ears cut off and fleur-de-lys branded on their cheeks. One captain cut off one soldier's

[1] F. Evrard, *Les Travaux du Canal de l'Eure sous Louis XIV.* Revue de l'Histoire de Versailles, 1933.

nose so short that he could no longer serve in the galleys. "Since it is *the King's intention,*" Louvois pointed out to the military commissar, "that only the tips of their noses should be cut off, please make this clear to the officers, so that they will not be so severe."

These atrocities came to an end when war broke out again and all troops were concentrated together against the coalition of Europe. Most of the men were bravely mown down by the Duke of Savoy's cannon, but they must certainly have preferred it to the charnel-houses on the Beauce cornfields.

The removal of the troops ended the work on the River Eure. A plan on a more modest scale was adopted and in the end it was more or less successful. Water from the pools on the plateau between Versailles and Rambouillet was brought to the Château and the town by means of a vast system of trenches and channels.

When it was first built the town of Versailles was little more than a dependence of the Château, its parish in fact. Without it, today, it would probably be a pleasant little administrative centre, suitable for the transaction of agricultural business, or else, because of its lofty trees, a pleasure resort like those found near capital cities. In 1671 the King issued an edict granting building privileges and the property involved was exempt from seizure. Narbonne recounts that this latter privilege "meant that most of the middle-class never paid any of their debts, when it was a question of bread, wine, meat or clothing." It was revoked on March 6th, 1713.

In addition to these unfortunate abuses there was also speculation in land owned by the crown, which changed hands again and again as the town developed, and fetched exorbitant prices. But since the privileges could be revoked by the King when he wished, many warrants were abolished because their beneficiaries, wittingly or otherwise, had failed to build within the specified time. The last houses of the de Gondi estates bought by Louis XIII disappeared along with the modest church in 1673. In order to compensate for this "interruption of enjoyment," Louis XIV exempted the inhabitants from the "tallage" and other taxes, although he imposed on them the duties of carrying out "haymaking in the park, filling the ice-houses, cleaning the courtyards at the Château and joining in the hunts (as beaters) when asked to do so."

"From 1666 to 1670," wrote Fromageot, "in spite of some houses which had recently been built round the Château, Versailles was no more than a large overcrowded village, with the addition of a vast workmen's camp and a great number of huts where the small shopkeepers lived. An engraving by Silvestre shows that the future Rue des Réservoirs looked like a building site."

After 1671 the whole town, like the Château, looked like a building site, on a gigantic scale. In front of the Palace, three large avenues were soon to be built, going towards Paris, Sceaux and St. Cloud. Many houses were demolished at Sèvres and the hill at Chaville was levelled. A veritable army of workmen and soldiers stretched from Versailles to the gates of Paris building a good wide road, the likes of which had never been seen in France, for the carriages and messengers, whose horses' hooves struck sparks night and day along the "Pavé du Roi."

The buildings at Versailles were of two kinds. First, the royal buildings, including the Great and Small Stables, which housed as many as a thousand saddle- and carriage-horses, without counting the conveyances of all types in the King's service, as well as the staff and vast quantities of hay and straw. Then in 1683 the *Grand Commun* was built (today the Military Hospital), on the exact site of the old village church. This huge, square, somewhat inelegant building was principally a vast kitchen with cellars, storerooms, bakeries, and the excellent Perrault certainly had it in mind when he described the kitchens of Riquet à la Houppe in one of his fairy-tales.

Close to it is the Hôtel de la Guerre (now a barracks) and nearby is the Hôtel des Affaires Étrangères—today the delightful Versailles Library—built in less than a year, where on September 3rd, 1783, the famous treaty of American Independence was signed. My learned American friends always make a reverent pilgrimage there.

Lastly, apart from the royal buildings, private houses of all types, both princely and bourgeois, as well as the tradesmen's shops, sprang up like mushrooms throughout the town, which was planned on harmonious lines approved by the King. Here lived the great noblemen and officers of state, finding life more comfortable than in the attics at the Château where they followed their calling; the courtiers, too, who hoped to please the King by carrying out building work; the high officials, senior clerks, contractors, merchants and craftsmen who had dealings with the Court; and lastly all those whom the King liked to reward by gifts of land, and sometimes also by paying for the buildings erected on it.

These personalities included Daquin, the King's doctor, the musician Phillidor, "Trumpet-marine" of the Great Stable, La Quintinie, who in the royal kitchen garden supervised the growing of the pears that the King enjoyed so much, Le Nôtre, who also had a house in Paris, the great contractors Bergeron and Mazière, Marinier, chief clerk of the

Works, Desgranges, secretary to the King and other common satellites who revolved round the Sun King.

The speculation in land was quickly followed by demands for incredibly high rents, for sub-letting was carried out at Versailles in a way that far exceeds the situation today—the smallest attic or the darkest closet was inhabited. When Perrault left Versailles after selling his office he let his house for 1,400 livres a year, while the Comte de Toulouse, who also had a house in Paris, let his Versailles residence for 2,000 livres. "Average" rents varied between 50 and 500 livres.

The population of Versailles increased so much that the houses which had been built were insufficient. Wooden huts were put up for the small manufacturers and craftsmen—wood-turners, cooks, hair-dressers, etc. These huts were so much sought after in their turn that a certain Sieur Crocquoison, who built them, sold one of them for the sum of 4,000 livres.

Building was the leading industry of Versailles, and hotel-keeping came next. From the three modest inns of Louis XIII's time, the number grew to sixty-eight in 1678 and 120 four years afterwards, without counting the cook-shops, taverns, lodges and other places for drinking and sleeping.

The town had become a vast hotel in itself. Everyone offered food and wine, from the King in his Palace to the Swiss in the princely hotels and the porters at the middle-class houses who had serving-counters in their lodges or let rooms in their attics. The old church of Versailles had been dedicated to St. Julian, who was known particularly as "the hospitaller," and he seems to have had a good influence in the new royal town. Inn-signs could be seen everywhere, and in the Rue du Vieux-Versailles there was even an Hôtel du Juste, in memory of King Louis XIII (the "Just") whose bust appeared on the façade. The Emperor Joseph II, brother of Marie-Antoinette, stayed there in 1778, for even sovereigns visiting Versailles did not stay at the Château —it was a royal sanctuary which could not be shared. When the Revolution broke out the shrewd hotel-keeper removed the royal bust but called his establishment "Hôtel of the Just Innkeeper," a subtle move typical of the period, but not very charitable towards his colleagues.

Such is the story of the Palace and town of Versailles, up to the death of their founder. The finished whole is so perfect that it is difficult to imagine all the vicissitudes described in this chapter. It is not for us to pass judgement on the man or the work, to give an appraisal of the Sun King, criticising his faults or praising his virtues, absolving or condemning him in the light of modern principles which were unknown during his times.

Clemenceau described the French Revolution as "a solid block," and in the same way it is impossible to separate the King from the Château, the Château from the town or the town from the kingdom of France.

But Versailles deserves well of France. It brought fame to her artists and manufacturers of luxury goods. Under royal protection they created a French style completely free from the foreign influence which had been so marked during the preceding century. This style is so individual that it has lasted until today, manifesting itself in all kinds of different ways. The royal industries include Gobelin tapestries, Savonnerie carpets, Sèvres porcelain,[1] Alençon and other types of lace, the quick-silvered mirrors of Saint-Gobain, and the silks and brocades of Lyons.

Versailles is not only a permanent exhibition of French artistic production, but several pages of French history. The Sun King and his Palace were closely united in both honour and misfortune and together they achieved the "consecration" of the monarchy barely a hundred years before it disappeared.

Versailles therefore is the superb testament of France, signed by her most magnificent representative.

[1] Madame de Pompadour took under her protection the former Royal factory at Vincennes and moved it to Sèvres.

VI

THE TRANSATLANTIC CABLE

Puck: I'll put a girdle round about the earth in forty minutes!

A Midsummer Night's Dream
Act II, scene 1.

I

ENGLAND MEETS CALAIS

JUST OVER A hundred years ago the world entered the age of electricity, just as we have recently entered the Atomic Age, and there was a whole galaxy of incomparable physicists: Wheatstone, Lord Kelvin, Davy, Faraday and Wollaston in Great Britain, Morse and Spencer in the United States, Oerstedt in Denmark, Ohm and Gauss in Germany, Gramme in Belgium, Volta in Italy and Ampère in France.

Their joint work in the field of electricity had led to the development of telegraphy, and overhead wires and cables had begun to run across Europe and America, but just as there are seven towns in Greece which claim to be the birthplace of Homer, two countries where telegraphy was more or less unknown came to use it first. According to the scholarly Humboldt it was in Spain, as long ago as 1798, where the first telegraph line was installed, linking Madrid and Aranjuez. Then in 1834 Baron von Schelling apparently suggested to the Tsar Nicholas I that he should install a line between St. Petersburg and Peterhof, but the monarch refused to do so because of opposition from the Muscovite "experts."

The telegraph rendered immense services to commerce, industry and international diplomacy, but the pinewood telegraph poles and copper wires stopped dead when they came to streams, rivers, lakes and seas, for these expanses of water were liable to act as conductors for the electricity, which was of a fairly low potential, since at that time it could only be generated by batteries.

All that was needed was an insulating cover capable of retaining the current, which was inclined to escape. Not only humans take the line of least resistance. The value of rubber was very much appreciated but nobody yet knew very much about using it effectively. However, in India and Malaya the merits of *isonandra gutta* were beginning to be known; this is a tree yielding a resin which acts as an admirable insulating medium and resists the action of alkaline water. In 1839 Sir William O'Shaughnessy had used it with success in India to insulate an electric cable which crossed the Ganges.

When Sir Charles Wheatstone heard about this he suggested to the House of Commons the following year that they should install a submarine telegraph line linking Great Britain to France, going from Dover to Calais. But the time was not yet ripe either from a technical or from a political point of view for anything, least of all a telegraph line, which might remove England from her "splendid isolation."

During the same year Samuel Morse, the great American physicist, laid down a cable in the Port of New York, while Colonel Colt, who incidentally invented the famous revolver, linked together Brooklyn, Long Island and Coney Island by means of three other cables which were already giving excellent results.

Eventually, in 1849, England, now in the midst of the Industrial Revolution, realised that without the means of establishing rapid communications she was in danger of losing economic control on the Continent, and she jealously wanted to keep it. With the agreement of the French Government, therefore, a Franco-British Company was formed under the direction of the engineer John W. Brett for the purpose of laying a telegraphic cable which would eventually join Britain to Europe, with the cooperation of her traditional enemy.

The cable was manufactured in London and measured twenty-eight miles in length; it was merely a thin copper conductor encased in 6 mm. (·236 inches) of gutta-percha. It was taken to Dover and there wound round a huge wooden bobbin. It was placed on the deck of the *Goliath*, a paddle-steamer specially equipped for the purpose. On August 28th, 1850, the *Goliath* weighed anchor, after first attaching one end of the cable, protected by a lead covering, to the coastal telegraph station at Dover. Led by another steamer, the *Widgeon*, which left floating buoys to mark out the direction to be taken, the cable-ship reached Cap Gris-Nez the same day without any difficulty. The conductivity of the cable was good and communication was established at Dover without any trouble, but a few hours later absolute silence fell, causing total consternation. The cable had parted suddenly. It was thought to have been driven on to the rocks, and the tide was to blame.

Unfortunately this was not the case at all. During the night a fisherman from Boulogne had caught it in his nets and cheerfully cut it into pieces. He proudly brought his trophy back to Boulogne as a unique specimen of seaweed full of gold threads.

It was essential to give more publicity to the operation and to find a better method of protecting the wire. The engineers then thought of twisting the insulated conductor round lengths of plaited hemp and binding the whole thing with a strong tarred yarn, thus achieving an armour-plated effect by a thick outer casing of galvanised wire. This was an excellent device and every submarine cable laid since that time has, with the exception of a few details, been prepared in the same way.

A new cable made in this way was coiled and placed in the holds of the *Blazer*, sister ship to the *Goliath*. It measured twenty-five miles in length with a diameter of 32 mm. ($1\frac{1}{4}$ inches) and weighed 175 tons. Early in the morning of December 24th, 1851, the frigate sailed for France, which she reached in the evening after having paid out the cable into the sea in the normal way. But when the ship was about half a mile from the coast the crew found to their dismay that the hold was empty, although the English Channel was only twenty and a half miles wide. A navigational error and the currents had transformed the cable into a capricious kind of serpent.

Eventually it was decided that the cable would have to be abandoned; a buoy was attached to the end and, not without a certain amount of apprehension, the whole thing left to go down to the bottom of the sea. Finally, on December 31st, after the necessary extra length had been added it was possible to proceed to the official inauguration, in the presence of personalities who were equally unhappy on both sides. Lord Palmerston, Prime Minister of England, had just fallen from power because he had approved too strongly the *coup d'état* which had led to the installation of the Second Empire in France. And the French officials naturally felt somewhat new to the game.

On the same day the electric current, starting from Calais, ran through the cable and fired a cannon placed on the ramparts of Dover. This is certainly the only cannon shot ever fired by France in England, and it was in fact the last to be fired between the two countries, since Queen Victoria and the Emperor Napoleon III were soon to conclude, in opposition to Russia, the first Franco-British Alliance.

From then on telegraph wires crossed rivers and seas. England was then linked with Ireland, Belgium, Holland and Denmark. In October, 1853, the Rhine was crossed at Worms, and in 1854 Turkey was provisionally linked with the Crimea across the Black Sea, a great help with the tactical operations which were being conducted along its coasts. Finally, in 1855, the Mediterranean was crossed in turn from Italy to Corsica, from Corsica to Sardinia and from Sardinia to Bône.

But the Atlantic Ocean still remained to be conquered.

154

II

ANGLO-AMERICAN CONVERSATIONS

The British engineer Frederick N. Gisborne had seen with his own eyes the success of the Calais–Dover cable, and in 1852 he went to the New World in an attempt to link Newfoundland to Canada by an electric cable which would speed up the transmission of despatches brought by steamers from Europe.

First of all he set up an overhead line between St. John's and Cape Ray, covering an area of 311 miles over the large island. Then he laid a submarine cable between the Canadian mainland and Prince Edward Island in the Gulf of St. Lawrence. It was still necessary, however, to link this island to Cape Breton Island and the latter to Newfoundland. Unfortunately he could not succeed in this because his company was on the verge of bankruptcy. Also the line across Newfoundland was, for some unknown reason, several times sabotaged in deserted areas where supervision was difficult.

Early in 1854 Gisborne left for New York in the hope of raising money, but there was little chance of this, for American investors were more inclined to invest in the new railroad industry. Yet the misfortune which forced him into such a difficult undertaking led him to meet, in the hotel where he was staying, the man who unexpectedly was to be the moving spirit behind the first transatlantic cable.

This man was Cyrus West Field, a typical American capitalist and a most fascinating individual. He came of a British family which had been installed in New England since 1629 and belonged to the best society of Massachusetts. His mother was a Somers, one of four attractive sisters from Boston who were called the "Somers Beauties." Field himself had an astonishing likeness to Lincoln.

Field was born in 1819 and felt less inclined towards pure mathematics than his grandfather, the astronomer John Field; at the age of fifteen, therefore, he left school with $8 in his pocket to learn the less abstruse mysteries of the retail and then the wholesale grocery trades. Perhaps he was inspired by the art of folding paper bags for his goods, for at eighteen he became associated with one of his brothers-in-law in a paper business which went bankrupt just when he reached twenty-one.

Nine years later, in 1849, after a visit to the Old World, Field returned to New York and went into business again after conscientiously paying off all his debts. He was now worth $250,000, a tidy sum at this period. His business had developed in many ways and he was particularly occupied with financial speculation. By 1854 he had become one of the most respected members of the New York Stock Exchange. It was at this juncture that some chance miracle brought him into contact with Gisborne, who was sitting gloomily in the lounge of his hotel. A famous conversation then took place between them.

"We must lay a telegraph cable between Newfoundland and Maine," said Gisborne, going straight to the point.

"I agree," replied Field.

"Then we must organise a line of steamers between St. John in Newfoundland and Galway in Ireland."

"Agreed."

"Then, using my telegraph line in Newfoundland, we could receive important news from Europe and gain four or five days."

"But suppose," interrupted Field, "that we laid a cable across the bed of the ocean, linking Newfoundland directly to Ireland?"

Gisborne was left breathless as the financier went on:

"Your plan is a bad one from any point of view if it cannot link America directly to Europe. Your line of steamers has no great advantage, for in the near future we shall certainly attempt to lay a submerged cable between the two Continents. It is only a question of time before this can be carried out successfully. We must attempt it now. If the problem is not insoluble I will undertake to bring it to a successful conclusion. I will buy over your charters and take over operations from you. You will have my reply in a fortnight."

At that point Field got up, indicating that the conversation was over. He had two important letters to finish.

The first of these was addressed to Lieutenant Maury of the United States Navy and Director of the National Observatory in Washington. He had just distinguished himself by a remarkable report on underwater currents in the depths of the Atlantic and Field was writing to ask if he thought it possible to lay a telegraph wire safely at the bottom of the ocean to link the New and the Old Worlds together. The other letter was to Samuel Morse, who was universally famous for the alphabetical code to which he had given his name. Field wanted to know if he thought it possible to transmit an electric current across the 1,864 miles which separated Newfoundland and Ireland.

In less than a fortnight Field received two affirmative replies. Lieutenant Maury believed that enough was known about the ocean bed between Newfoundland and Ireland to be certain that the cable could lie on it without any danger from floating icebergs, anchors, tidal currents or any other means of destruction.

As for Morse, he was absolutely convinced that a steady electric current, of a potential to be examined, could cross this distance, provided that the cable was well insulated.[1] Two high authorities, therefore, showed that they had faith in an experiment which had never yet been tried out anywhere in the world.

However, it was not a question of mere theory, for the scientific adventure had to have the support of some industrial enterprise with solid financial backing. The New York capitalist now showed himself to be an outstanding organiser.

In March, 1854, that is to say about two months after the famous Gisborne–Field conversation, a Transatlantic Cable Company was formed. In the first place it obtained a charter from the Canadian Parliament for the development of aerial and submarine telegraphy in Newfoundland, Labrador, Nova Scotia and Prince Edward Island. Then Gisborne received $40,000 for handing over to the company his Newfoundland enterprise and his cable.

But it was also necessary to have some official support from Great Britain and the United States. This was achieved without too much difficulty, for the two Governments agreed that they would each provide $70,000 a year for twenty-six years as soon as the line was installed. After that the hydrographic services of the two nations would organise, first of all and at their own expense, the laying of the cable over a distance of 1,864 miles through depths varying from 6–12,000 feet between the two coasts.

All these negotiations, the taking of soundings and laying of buoys, then the installation of the various cables in the Gulf of St. Lawrence, took two more years. Finally, in order to establish a greater degree of safety a memorable experiment was carried out. During the night of October 9th, 1856, all telegraphic traffic was suspended throughout the whole of the British Isles and one single charge was made to pass through the entire 5,000 miles of telegraph wires. The results were conclusive—the current could cross the Atlantic.

On November 6th the Atlantic Telegraph Company was formed, an Anglo-American company with a capital of £350,000, issuing 350 shares of £1,000 each. Field acquired one-quarter of them and within

---

[1] It must be remembered that the dynamo had not yet been invented, and electric current was produced only by batteries. Experiments carried out later showed that the current produced by a battery the size of a thimble could easily cross the Atlantic.

a month all the shares were subscribed. The financial question was now solved and the great work could be put in hand without delay.

The manufacture of the cable presented problems which needed to be solved with care. In the first place such a length had never been undertaken before—2,547 miles, that is to say 630 more than the actual distance between Valentia in Ireland and Trinity Bay in Newfoundland. The cable weighed about 88 lb. per mile, although the diameter was only 18 mm. (·7 of an inch), infinitely less than any which had been used previously. The conductor core, which was manufactured at Greenwich between January and July, 1857, weighed 2,600 tons and cost £225,000.

III

SILENCE IN THE ATLANTIC

It now remained to devise a means of embarking and transporting such a weight. The company asked for the cooperation of two steam frigates which had been constructed in a special way. One of these was British, the *Agamemnon*, and the other American, the *Niagara*, and each of them took into their respective holds half of the cable already coiled; it was to be paid out from the stern by a steam-powered winch operated by a team of skilled men. Further, each ship was accompanied by auxiliary vessels which acted as pilots. The *Agamemnon* was preceded by the *Leopard* and the *Cyclops*, which were both British, and the *Niagara* by the *Susquehanna*, which was American.

The *Niagara* was to lay the cable from Valentia until it came to an end. The *Agamemnon*, which followed, was then to splice the cable at sea and take it as far as Newfoundland.

Just as the ships weighed anchor it was noticed that one section of the cable had been coiled from left to right, whereas the rest, naturally, had been coiled in the opposite direction. It was decided to leave this as it was, an unfortunate decision, as time was to show. On August 5th, 1857, a great ceremony took place before the final departure of the expedition. It appeared that the whole of Ireland had decided to come to this rocky creek, which was to see the departure of a flotilla comparable only to that of Christopher Columbus when he left Palos de Moguer more than three and a half centuries earlier, taking with him the hopes of two great nations.

In order to house and feed this multitude tents had to be set up and

27. Coiling the cable in concrete tanks (from *The Atlantic Telegraph* by W. H. Russell)

tons of potatoes brought in and cooked in the open air in huge cauldrons. While the Irish ate their potatoes and danced jigs to the sound of bagpipes the officials gathered together at a great banquet presided over by Lord Carlisle, Lord-Lieutenant of Ireland. For the first time in the world the Union Jack and the Stars and Stripes appeared fraternally side by side in a coat of arms, while Lord Carlisle delivered the main speech, ending with the words which were unfortunately prophetic, "It is a rule and condition of final success to fail the first time."

On August 7th the squadron weighed anchor, and the same day the cable broke, ten miles from the coast. It was repaired hastily and the ships sailed towards the open sea. On August 12th, however, 311 miles from the coast, the cable broke again, following a navigational error, and sank to the bottom in 10,000 feet of water.

This first catastrophe in no way discouraged the shareholders, who, without waiting for the expedition to return, ordered another cable, so that, with the lengths which were still in the factory, they would be ready for the next campaign to be undertaken during the summer of the following year.

On June 10th, 1858, operations began again, but this time a completely different technique was employed. The two ships each took half of the cable on board again, but they sailed to the middle of the ocean half way between the two Continents, spliced the cable on the spot and then each sailed in different directions, the *Niagara* towards Newfoundland, the *Agamemnon* towards Valentia. In this way they were able to communicate with each other.

But on June 20th the *Agamemnon* was caught in a terrible storm followed by a waterspout. She was so badly tossed about that the cable was thrown out of the holds on to the deck and uncoiled like some gigantic serpent, seizing hold of the sailors and imprisoning them within its endless rings. Some men were seriously injured, with broken arms and legs, but nobody was killed. The crew, however, were completely demoralised and tried to throw the accursed cable into the sea, and only the active intervention of the officers prevented them.

During this time the *Niagara* was proceeding on her way. Finally the *Agamemnon* was able to meet her and the cable was spliced again. It broke on two more occasions and by the fourth time 500 miles had been lost. The ships had to return to Ireland once more.

However, the operation was able to start again immediately, for enough cable remained on board the ships and in the factories. On July 27th the *Agamemnon* and the *Niagara* (with Cyrus West Field on

28. The winches used for paying out the cable into the sea (from
The Atlantic Telegraph)

board this time) again met in the Atlantic, each accompanied by a convoy ship. On July 29th a huge whale was caught in the cable and had to be chased away by shots from the cannon.

As usual, comedy and tragedy mingled together. The convoy ships were following a maritime route and passed many other ships which came dangerously near the cable out of pure curiosity. As the log of the expedition reports:

"About three o'clock on Tuesday morning all on board were startled from their beds by the loud booming of a gun. Everyone . . . rushed on deck to ascertain the cause of the disturbance. Contrary to all expectation, the cable was safe; but the *Valorous* could just be seen in the grey light—rounded to in the most warlike attitude—firing gun after gun in quick succession towards a large American barque, which, quite unconscious of our proceedings, was standing right across our stern. Such loud and repeated remonstrances from a large steam frigate were not to be despised; and evidently without knowing the why or the wherefore she quickly threw her sails aback, and remained hove to. Whether those on board her considered that we were engaged in some filibustering expedition, or regarded our proceedings as another outrage upon the American flag, it is impossible to say; but certain it is that—apparently in great trepidation—she remained hove to until we had lost sight of her in the distance."

Apart from a few incidents of this kind all went well, thanks to uninterrupted calm weather. The *Agamemnon* reached Valentia on August 3rd and the *Niagara* came to Newfoundland two days later; after the necessary arrangements had been carried out in the two coastal telegraph stations it was possible on August 18th to send the first cablegram from America to Europe, and it took only thirty-five minutes to arrive. The text was not a work of genius but it had been composed with great emotion:

"Europe and America are united by telegraphy. Glory to God in the highest, on earth peace, goodwill towards man."

For the first time a Queen of England and a President of the United States exchanged congratulations. "It is a triumph more glorious," President Buchanan telegraphed to her, "because far more useful to mankind than was ever won by a conqueror on the field of battle."

In the general elation it seemed as though an era of universal peace was about to open. The Crimean War, in which more than half a million men had been pointlessly killed, had just ended. Queen Victoria was at that moment in Cherbourg where she was being ceremonially entertained by Napoleon III. She was the first British Sovereign to set foot on French soil since the end of the Hundred Years War.

At the same time in New York the "Cable Carnival" was celebrated, a demonstration unique in the annals of the United States. Cyrus West Field was carried round the streets of the town for sixteen hours accompanied by 25,000 people, who eventually took him back to his house at night by the light of thousands of torches. During the celebrations the illuminations set fire to the Town Hall but there was such a display of general excitement that hardly any notice was taken of the incident.

Unfortunately, after the telegraph had been in service for twenty-three days, during which more than 400 cablegrams were sent, silence fell over the Atlantic. This "death" of the cable caused utter astonishment and speculators naturally took advantage of it to buy shares in the Atlantic Telegraph Company very cheaply, for their value fell at once.

But during the three weeks when it had functioned the trans-atlantic cable had twice proved its undeniable usefulness. On August 28th two steamers, the *Europe* and the *Arabia*, came into collision in the middle of the ocean. It was possible to learn by despatches that there had been no loss of life. The following cablegram was telegraphed immediately both to Europe and America:

"Collision between *Europe* and *Arabia*. No lives lost. All well."

On another occasion a message despatched from London in the morning reached the 62nd Infantry Regiment, who were to leave Canada that day for Europe, and told them not to embark. The arrival of this message in time saved the War Office the expenditure of £50,000.

However, a Commission of Enquiry was set up at once and made a report which soon restored confidence to the directors of the undertaking, for the cable had not broken. The following year, when it was possible to lift some sections of it along the Newfoundland coast, it was seen that the metal covering had not been strong enough to resist the rocks, the oxidisation process and the shellfish which had clung to it.

What is more, by means of electro-magnetic apparatus, it was found that the conductor, with its metal threads, acted as an immense Leyden jar which discharged its electricity into the sea water.

The following anecdote, if it is authentic, would provide a good illustration of a phenomenon which had already been known for a hundred years. In the presence of Faraday, an Englishman, out of pure enthusiasm, wanted to kiss the Atlantic cable. No sooner had his lips touched the end of the conductor and brought together two surfaces, each electrified in their different way—for the human body is a wonderful conductor—he received a terrible shock which threw him down on the ground.

The shock experienced by Cyrus West Field when the cable fell silent was of a very different nature.

"Don't worry," he said to his shareholders. "We'll begin again, and, even if we fail a third time, we'll go on until we finally succeed."

Cyrus West Field always kept his word and on this occasion he kept it superbly well.

IV

THE LEVIATHAN AND THE REPTILE

Unfortunately the humanitarian wishes of the President of the United States were not fulfilled in any way and it was in his own country that the terrible scourge was to appear in its most ugly form, namely, the Civil War, which lasted from 1861 to 1865.

However, these six years of silence over the Atlantic were used to good effect for the perfecting of the cable. It was at this time that the British physicist Thomson (later Lord Kelvin) invented the galvano-meter which bears his name, based on a theory put forward by his compatriot Charles Wheatstone and called "Wheatstone's Bridge."[1]

The report of the Commission of Enquiry had made two important points, one to the effect that the cable had been manufactured too quickly, and secondly, that the paying-out machinery had not been adaptable enough. However, it was recognised that the insulation and, in particular, the gutta-percha were in no way to blame.

Finally, a paint made from cyanide was discovered which would poison any shellfish that might presume on the cable's hospitality.

Even during the Civil War Field was constantly at sea telling his friends in both countries not to give up hope, nor to lose any time when the war was over. These were his genuine feelings, although we do not know exactly where his sympathy lay in the Civil War. He probably had no preference. He was first and foremost a financier

---

[1] This apparatus consisted of a small metallic mirror fixed on a magnetised needle If a fine ray of light was directed on to the mirror the slightest movements of the needle produced by an extremely weak charge of electricity were considerably amplified.

and the failure of the cable meant that he would lose his money, which was already endangered by the hostilities.

Newspaper campaigns against the cable persisted. It was said, or rather the very people who had carried the gallant Cyrus on their shoulders on the famous day of the Cable Carnival were made to say, that the cable had never even been put into the sea and that messages had been sent for the sole purpose of increasing the value of the company's shares. The final misfortune, or accident perhaps, came in 1859 when Field's offices and factories in New York were destroyed by fire, the cause of which was never discovered.

In London George Seward, Secretary of the Atlantic Telegraph Company, obtained from the British Government an annual guarantee of £20,000 which replaced the former subsidy of £14,000 promised in 1857 as an expression of gratitude and in memory of the services rendered by the timely cable sent to the 62nd Infantry Regiment.

The manufacturers of the cable, Glass, Elliott & Company, were quite happy to be paid in shares of the company. This time the Company's capital amounted to £600,000 and since the United States could not play its part Great Britain guaranteed the interest to the shareholders.

It needed six years, therefore, to replace the capital which had sunk to the bottom of the sea. In May, 1865, just as the Civil War came to an end, the cable was completed after a year's work and this time it measured 3,000 miles in length, allowing a safety margin of 40 per cent. It weighed 5,000 tons and cost £500,000. Now that it was ready to be cast into the sea once more, the two Continents were full of apprehension, and Cyrus West Field even more so.

The cable technicians as well as the sailors had always considered it a drawback to divide the cable between two separate ships. The problem was where to find a ship large enough to absorb this gigantic serpent. A ship did exist, providentially enough, and she was completely new. She was about to be sent to the scrapyards when the directors of the Cable Company thought of her; this was the famous *Great Eastern*, who had first been named *Leviathan*.

This monster, with her Biblical name, was an immensely large ship for the period. From stem to stern she measured 635 feet and her deck was 75 feet wide. She was a craft of 22,500 tons and was driven by a screw, with two paddle-wheels 55 feet in diameter. In addition she was equipped with six masts of a good height which could carry the necessary sail if her 3,000 h.p. engines should cease to function.

This ship had been built by Kingdom Brunel, the famous British

29. The *Great Eastern* and her auxiliary ships (from *The Atlantic Telegraph*)

engineer who came of an old family in Normandy. She was so **extra-ordinary** that it had taken five years before she could be launched **and** then only with enormous difficulties.

The *Leviathan* had been designed to take 3,000 passengers or an equivalent cargo to Australia in less than five weeks, without making any stops. The fifth Continent of the world was open for emigration at this period and the descendants of the convicts, who, in spite of themselves, had founded this Dominion, were short of equipment and especially of people.

When the ship was finally ready to take to the water the Eastern Steam Navigation Company, who built her, were bankrupt. They then sold her for a fifth of her value to a company who put her into service on the Atlantic. She was furnished with incredible luxury and her main lounge, decorated in Louis XVI style, measured more than 36,000 square feet. The cargo was carried from one end of the deck to the other on a little railway with trucks which were pushed by hand. There was even a lithographic printing press on board which was to publish the ship's daily paper, *The Leviathan Newspaper*.

Just as she weighed anchor a pipe burst in the boiler with a terrible explosion. This frightened everyone to such an extent that when the ship made her maiden voyage to New York only forty-six people dared to entrust themselves to her. There was at least one French passenger among them, Jules Verne, who has recorded all his impressions for us in the novel *The Floating City*.

These two monsters, the cable and the ship, both of them under an evil spell, were therefore to meet and one would lead the other, rather like the blind leading the blind; this was not the least astonishing aspect of this Atlantic epic.

Naturally the *Great Eastern* had to be specially fitted out to make room for three tanks, each of which were fifty-five feet in diameter and took one-third of the total length of the cable carefully coiled on a concrete floor. Then at the stern special machines for immersing the cable were installed along with all kinds of other equipment. These included grappling hooks, anchors, buoys and marking beacons which would be used if the cable had to be abandoned.

There were 500 people aboard, including the crew, under the direction of Captain Anderson, the engineers, presided over by Field

30. Lowering a buoy into the sea for the recovery of the cable
(from *The Atlantic Telegraph*)

in person and the cable technicians, who took their orders from Samuel Canning.

On May 24th, 1865, the Prince of Wales, the future Edward VII, went over the ship in detail and sent in Morse the following memorable cablegram:

"I wish success to the Atlantic cable."

The cable certainly needed it.

On June 24th the *Great Eastern* left Liverpool for Ireland and the serpentine wire was connected to the coastal cable. Then during the night of July 24th the giant ship weighed anchor and sailed for America. She was accompanied by the *Terrible* and the *Sphinx* in order to avoid any untimely encounters, although any such incident seemed improbable, for a ship of such vast tonnage was rarely seen in the Atlantic and would no doubt imbue any inquisitive ship with the greatest possible caution.

The same day, at a distance of nine miles from the coast, the test galvanometers suddenly stopped dead. Fifty-three miles of cable were retrieved and it was found that a length of wire a few inches long and cut with pincers pierced right through the cable. This section was cut out, the two ends were joined once more and the ships went on their way.

On Wednesday, July 26th, the ships lay about 430 miles from the coast of Ireland and the next day at 547 miles. The *Great Eastern* held the water magnificently and ploughed through the waves as though ironing them out. The cable was paid out from the holds as smoothly as from a distaff when suddenly on the 29th at one o'clock in the afternoon all communication stopped again. Once more the cable had been pierced with a short length of wire, which this time had been carefully concealed within the hemp covering.

This could not have been an accident. There was obviously sabotage. It was noticed also that the incidents occurred at the same time, caused perhaps by one or more men in the particular shift who were at that time on duty to uncoil the cable in the holds. In spite of their protests these men were given other duties. Everyone on board, from the ordinary seaman to the captain, was highly indignant, and if the guilty party had been discovered he would certainly have been assaulted and thrown overboard. From that time onwards armed volunteers mounted guard over the whole length of the cable from the winches in the holds to the place where it went into the sea. It was regrettable that devoted and courageous men had to be humiliated in this way, but the entire crew admitted the necessity.

Enquiries into the sabotage were not pursued. However, it was easy to see how the laying of a cable across the Atlantic could have harmful effects on certain kinds of business, especially on ocean-going liners. Through skilled seamanship, these delivered despatches in all weathers and at record speed, and in the case of important and secret messages they often received high rewards. It must also be added that certain cable companies were anxious for the expedition to fail. The vulnerability of the cable and an accomplice among the crew achieved the rest.

But unfortunately, although it was possible to take precautions against human malevolence, nothing could be done against the elements and against fate. On August 2nd, at half-past two in the morning, the cable broke a few yards behind the screw and sank in 10,000 feet of water. There was anguish and heartbreak on board. The machine had stopped and the entire crew were in a state of silent dismay. After so much care and effort everything was lost in one moment.

To restore confidence to the crew it was at once decided to try and raise the diabolical cable from the water. For ten days, in fog and bad weather, with the help of grappling irons or anchors fitted with 12,000 feet of chains and ropes an attempt was made to drag the elusive cable from the depths of an ever more tenacious ocean. On three occasions the men thought they had got it, but all the mooring ropes broke one after the other. It appeared on the surface like some ghostly demon and then plunged down again to the bottom. After the fourth attempt there was not a foot of chain or rope left on board.

It is easy to imagine the men's state of helpless anger as they left a buoy on the spot where the cable had been seen for the last time. Then the ships sailed back to Liverpool in the hope of returning during fine weather, bringing equipment capable of lifting and holding the enormous weight of cable which had now sunk into the mud.

There was great concern in both Continents and the state of unease was maintained by Press campaigns and countless letters asking for news of the *Great Eastern*. Despair and sarcasm mingled together. Some people began to believe that the ship and its fated cargo had gone down with all hands, although it was unlikely that the *Sphinx* and the *Terrible* had shared the same fate.

Finally, on August 17th, news spread through England like lightning that the giant ship had been seen docking at Liverpool with its two faithful pilots.

When it was known that the failure was due merely to the shortage and insufficiency of the mooring ropes, and that a buoy had been left at the exact spot where the cable could be lifted again, there was a complete change of opinion, like that which occurred when the multitudes of Israel saw Moses reappear with the tables of the law.

Cyrus West Field, the man from the New World, revealed himself to the Old World like the famous Old Testament figure. This is no exaggerated way to describe the confidence with which Field again stirred up enthusiasm among his valiant collaborators and shareholders, who immediately made preparations for a fifth expedition.

v

CYRUS WEST FIELD
GAMBLES AGAIN AND WINS

The subscription opened by the Atlantic Telegraph Company sur-passed all hopes. Ample capital was immediately available to them through the sale of 60,000 shares which, it is true, carried a 25 per cent. interest plus half the profits after interest on the shares in the cable of 1857 had been paid. Without waiting for all the money to be available Glass & Elliott, the cable manufacturers, had begun work on the new cable. 1,242 miles of cable manufactured in 1865 still remained in their workshops and they added 2,174 miles of new wire, that is 25 per cent. more than the total length required. For the first time the famous Chatterton adhesive (named after its inventor) was used, which improved the insulation of the cable, increased the diameter to 27 mm. (1·06 inches) but added considerably to the total weight.

On this occasion it was not only a question of laying the bewitched cable but also of raising the old one, lengthening it and taking the two of them finally to Newfoundland. Experience had proved that it was possible to raise the cable from great depths, but also large quantities of raising equipment were necessary—winches, marking beacons, chains and ropes, which had to be both long enough and strong enough. In addition, the ship had to carry the remainder of the first cable and the coastal cable for Newfoundland.

In spite of her enormous capacity the *Great Eastern* could not carry everything. The remaining sections of cable were therefore loaded on steam frigates, the *Medway* and the *Albany*. Then large-scale alterations were carried out on the colossal ship; her two paddle-wheels were made to work independently so that she could turn round more rapidly. It was the same principle as the caterpillar wheels on tanks.

In addition all kinds of improved grappling irons were provided; some were simply to raise the cable, others were to grasp it with pincers and a third set had cutting edges for dividing it up.

Infinite precautions were taken in recruiting the crew. The former crews were re-allocated and to achieve greater security the men who were occupied solely on the cable had to wear overalls with linen trousers buttoning at the back and made entirely without pockets in which any small objects could be concealed. Finally, each member of the crew had to sign a special agreement stipulating that anyone found causing damage to the cable would be immediately thrown overboard without trial.

Further attempts at damage were not thought likely, however, for detailed examinations of the cable had been made from the time of its manufacture and were to continue to the moment of its going into the sea. The drastic safety precautions had been given all possible publicity.

On June 30th the *Great Eastern* took the cable on board in the Thames Estuary, in addition to 7,000 tons of coke and all kinds of provisions, including a herd of cows and a flock of sheep, along with a hundred hens, all of which made her look somewhat like Noah's Ark.

Finally, on July 13th, 1866, which was a Friday, at 13.00 hours (these details are given especially for superstitious readers) after the cable had been soldered at Valentia, which in the meantime had become a small town, the five ships weighed anchor. The squadron now included also the *William Cory*, which transported the coastal cable destined for Newfoundland, and the *Terrible*, which went on the previous voyage, and, as her name indicates, was the watch-dog of the expedition.

Work went on steadily. News of the Old World was received regularly by the cable. The printing press on board was used and each morning it produced a newspaper relating episodes from the Prusso-Austrian War along with incidents on board and the gossip from the fo'c'sle, for the sailors themselves took part in its preparation.

In this way, for the first time, incidents taking place the day before anywhere in the world were recounted in mid-ocean. They included a fire at Portland, cholera in Liverpool and the failure of a bank in Birmingham. All this was much less important for one of the Irish sailors who, on July 21st, heard that his eleventh son had made his entry into the world. Field, who was on board, was immediately chosen as godfather and the sailor himself telegraphed to his wife the name he had chosen, which was Cyrus.

The work went on day and night with the help of powerful acetylene lamps which stood alongside the cable, while supervisors gave orders which nobody cared to disobey.

On July 23rd at midday the ships were half way across the ocean. The crew were working with complete confidence and calm, encouraged by magnificent weather and a sea like glass.

On the 26th they caught sight of an iceberg which seemed to be heading towards the cable route, and its extent below water, calculated from what could be seen, looked as though it might reach to the bottom of the ocean. Possibly the mountain of ice was frightened by the *Leviathan*, or perhaps some current diverted it; whatever the reason it disappeared and everyone breathed again.

Finally, on July 27th, the *Great Eastern* dropped anchor in Newfoundland in the Bay of Heart's Content, a symbolic name if ever there was one. On that day, with all her flags flying, the valiant ship proved the effectiveness and utility of her immense size, which had caused laughter in both the Old and the New Worlds.

There was a tremendous party on board that evening, followed by a ball for the crew and the local fishermen and their families, who seemed somewhat out of place in the great Louis XVI lounge of the *Great Eastern*, which had been preserved intact.

Cyrus West Field slept that night as he had never slept for ten years, ten years of nightmares full of malevolent wire serpents.

It remained now to carry out the second part of the task, namely, the lifting of the 1865 cable. On August 2nd, therefore, the *Great Eastern*, along with the faithful *Medway* and *Albany*, sailed again, until a few days later, at a distance of 620 miles, the ships found themselves once more at the spot which recalled so many disappointments.

The grappling irons equipped with 12,000 feet of solid mooring ropes were immediately thrown overboard. The ship lay to the north of the supposed position of the cable, then steered her course south, hoping that the anchors raking the depths would find the long-sought-after cable. A month went by. Finally, on September 2nd, the iron tentacles were seen firmly clasping a black, viscous cord.

"There was complete silence on deck at that moment, only the voice of Captain Anderson rang out from time to time. This tense calm formed a contrast to the enthusiastic shouts which the previous Sunday had greeted the first appearance of the cable on the surface of the water."

31. "Father Neptune hangs out his washing on the Atlantic Cable." A cartoon from *Punch*, 1858

Immediately sailors swung down on knotted ropes all along the side of the *Great Eastern* to take hold of the cable with auxiliary grappling hooks. Finally it was hauled on board and could be wound on to the winches to be examined at leisure. Everyone wanted to touch it to make sure it was really there, in spite of the covering of dirt that it had accumulated during the thirteen months of its stay in the depths.

It was now necessary to examine its state of preservation and its power of conductivity. The technicians, led by Samuel Canning, locked themselves in the instrument room and listened in for a long time. Then minutes later a man came up on deck. They had been able to make contact with Valentia, which appropriately had sent its congratulations. A great cheer from 500 throats greeted the end of the nightmare, while the flags of all the nations in the world were run up.

The cable was then spliced with the extra length coiled in the hold of the *Great Eastern* and the ships sailed again for Newfoundland where the great news had already been sent by the first cable, which in reality was only the second one.

Finally, on September 8th, 1866, Cyrus West Field[1] was able to

[1] In 1867 Congress awarded its Gold Medal to Cyrus West Field. He later took part in the organisation and financing of the elevated railway in New York. Field was very generous and towards the end of his life his best friends stripped him of his money. When he died at the age of seventy-two he possessed only a few thousand dollars.

announce that the Old and the New Worlds were joined together according to the sacred formula "for better or for worse" in less time than the forty minutes promised by the mischievous Puck to Oberon, the King of the Fairies.[1]

[1] The first telephone cable across the Atlantic was laid in 1956 between Oban in Scotland and Portland in the United States.

VII

THE AMERICAN
TRANSCONTINENTAL RAILWAY

Allons! whoever you are, come, travel with me!
Traveling with me you find what never tires.
The earth never tires,
The earth is rude, silent, incomprehensible at first . . .
Be not discouraged, keep on, there are divine things well envelop'd,
I swear to you there are divine things more beautiful than words
can tell.

Walt Whitman
Leaves of Grass, 1855

I

AFTER THE DELUGE

THE TRANSCONTINENTAL RAILROAD, which links New York to San Francisco, was certainly the best "Western" ever, and it was made not with celluloid, but with picks, spades and dynamite.

In the United States more than in any other country, the railway was the instrument of lightning civilisation and progress. Ever since the early nineteenth century groups of European immigrants, travelling on foot, on horseback or in their heavy covered waggons, carrying tools or rickety furniture, had been making their way towards the wild west, and their only wealth was their own self-confidence.

In order to reach Eldorado, namely, California, the immigrants could take two routes; those that came from Europe could either go round Cape Horn, or cross the Isthmus of Panama and then reach San Francisco by paddle-steamer; but the dangers of the Strait of Magellan and the fevers of Panama eliminated many of them. Only the most courageous saw the Golden Gate of San Francisco open before them.

The same fate also overcame those coming from the East and the Mid-West, who usually left Fort Leavenworth on the Missouri about May or June and reached the Sacramento Valley the following autumn. The immigrants grouped themselves together in long caravans of hundreds of waggons which were drawn by horses, oxen or mules. They helped each other in every way, warding off attacks from Indians and heaving their waggons through the passes of the Rocky Mountains and the Sierra Nevada. Sometimes too there was a shortage of water and the animals had no pasture. When this happened the immigrants abandoned them, and their skeletons lay scattered along the ruthless trail.

For thousands of years men had gradually explored the world, but means of locomotion made no progress at all, and George Washington had no better means of transport than the Pharaohs of Egypt.

The immigrants, the Gold Rush and the railway all came at the same time and provided wonderful opportunities for the young country. Naturally, the United States had not waited for experiments in Europe to be completed before they took an interest in steam engines. They found themselves in a dilemma, however, for since the beginning of the century (1810–1825) vast sums of money had been spent in the Great Lakes area on the building of 5,000 miles of canals which had linked lakes and rivers, and these waterways already provided immense services in the Eastern and Middle-West States.[1]

These canals were restricted to the few States with natural water resources, and where the absence of mountains isolated them from areas previously inaccessible, but these undertakings had used up both public and private funds and it was suddenly found that further conquests needed something more than strong arms and courage. The pioneers of New England hesitated, but not for long.

Every new religion and every Promised Land has its charlatans and visionaries and when it came to railways the United States had the same experience. Extraordinary developments could be expected, therefore, in the New World, where the search for the unknown and contempt for tradition were the rule.

The Baltimore and Ohio Railroad Company was the first American railway company, but when its thirteen miles of wooden rails laid on stone blocks were first opened to the public in 1828 the technicians did not yet know if the carriages would be drawn by steam-engines or horses. Attempts were even made to use the wind to convey passengers, who courageously took their places in a huge wicker basket surmounted by a mast and a sail.

On its maiden voyage this remarkable vessel was shipwrecked in a gale in a muddy pond beside the track. It was decided to go back to horses, which for some time drew the heavy wooden waggons. But in Ohio the cows found the grass between the sleepers very much to their taste and frightened the horses, who refused to go any farther and left the rails.

Eventually, therefore, the technicians decided to use steam, and in 1830 "Tom Thumb," the first locomotive built in the U.S.A., finally came into service. There was even a competition between the locomotive and a horse-drawn waggon running on a path parallel to the track, but when "Tom Thumb" tried to go faster it puffed in vain and its boiler burst.

Another locomotive, "The Best Friend of Charleston," replaced "Tom Thumb" but its driver jammed the safety valve and its boiler gave out in the same way. At this period the carriages were connected

[1] In 1830 there were more than 13,000 boats on the 400-mile canal between Erie and New York.

to each other by chains, with the result that every time the train stopped or started the passengers were thrown smartly down on to the floor. The passengers remedied this defect themselves by placing heavy horizontal rails between the waggons which acted as a brake when the train started.

Many problems were gradually solved in the same way, either by the company or the passengers, who began to get used to these dangers. For a long time, however, buckets of water were placed in the carriages of the Ohio Railroad for putting out fires caused by the red-hot cinders which poured cheerfully out of the enormous funnels on top of the locomotives. These minor incidents were so much a part of life that the following Christian precept was printed on the back of the railway tickets: "The passenger to assist the Conductor on the line of road whenever called upon."

E. & S. RAIL ROAD.

Elizabeth-Port and Bound Brook.

☞ The passenger to assist the Conductor on the line of road whenever called upon. *Man'gr*

32. The reverse side of a railway ticket, about 1851

In order to avoid the cows grazing along the track a kind of sloping barricade was placed in front of the train so that they were not killed but pushed more or less brutally out of the way. These cow-catchers were not always sufficient protection and sometimes a man had to stand at the front of the locomotive and shoot at them with dried peas.

Much later, when the trains crossed the vast prairies of the Middle-West, herds of buffaloes appeared and the cow-catchers were useless. The passengers, who rarely travelled without their rifles, fired at them from the platform of the observation cars, which was good sport and a pleasant way of breaking the monotony of the journey, but not entirely satisfactory for dealing with herds which crossed the line for days on end.

The following incident may seem extraordinary, but it was by no means a mirage from the Middle-West.

"One day before 1870," relates General Dodge, "I went past a big herd of buffaloes which I estimated at fifteen or twenty head per acre and twenty-five miles in extent. Trappers passing that way assured me that the herd had been going through this place for at least five days, which meant that it extended as far as fifty miles. That is to say, assuming the mass to be elliptic in shape, I calculated the total area to be about a thousand square miles, consisting of at least 12,000,000 animals."[1]

A grown buffalo is about six feet tall, nine feet long and weighs nearly 2,000 lb. and it must be admitted that even one at a time would form an unpleasant obstacle for a locomotive.

When trains encountered migrations of this size they had to stop, and although the travellers boiled with impatience they could at least be certain they would not die of hunger.

These minor incidents did not affect progress on the railways. In 1850, in order to encourage railway speculation and increase the value of the West, it was decided to attract all possible immigrants by offering them plots of ground at $1·25 per acre. There were soon dozens of railway companies and at the height of the railway boom in 1885 there were as many as 6,000 companies in the U.S. Nowadays there are only about 600, and 130 of them carry 99 per cent. of the traffic and control 95 per cent. of the lines, which, including branch lines, cover the fantastic distance of 355,000 miles.

The period 1850 to 1860 marked the definite supremacy of the railways over the canals, while even in the Great Lakes region and in the East the railways spread to an amazing extent, dozens of small companies springing up everywhere. While the railways increased in this way from 3,000 to 30,000 miles the waterways were only extended by 400 miles. The romantic paddle-steamers could not be used in winter because the lakes were frozen and in summer the waterways sometimes dried up; after rendering remarkable service during the first part of the century the boats were gradually abandoned for the railways.

At first railway technique was little concerned with theory. The lines were roughly laid over sleepers which were placed very close together, thereby avoiding the need for careful ballasting. Sometimes long detours were made in order to avoid building bridges or tunnels.

[1] Buffaloes have now practically disappeared from the U.S. and the last specimens are carefully protected in reserves.

The stations were placed wherever they happened to suit the technicians[1] and were indicated merely by a notice fixed on a stake or by a rough well which had been dug to provide water supplies for the engines. Then the first train arrived with its living cargo of gold prospectors, immigrants and adventurers who were to wrest the Government territory from its Red Indian occupants.

At first the timetables were completely erratic. Travellers sometimes waited for hours on end in a log cabin beside a long stretch of track waiting for smoke to appear on the horizon. When the train bell was heard through the roar of the steam men rushed on to the track and signalled to the train to stop. The length of the stops was as vague as the waiting time. Sometimes shortage of fuel meant that trees had to be cut down rapidly all round and the strongest passengers were asked to help. When time pressed too much then nobody minded turning the station into fuel. This did not happen often, but it happened all the same.

These long waits at the stations led to bad habits: the passengers would wait until the last moment and then rushed in a crowd towards the compartments, a typical American steeple-chase popularised in many engravings which can be seen among illustrations of railway history.

Train delays were usually caused by the use of single-track lines, since the down train had to wait for the up train to pass before it could go on its way. The telegraph was a help in these cases for it allowed the drivers to fix their own timetable. Thus, on September 22nd, 1851, the engineer Minot, who was travelling in a carriage owned by his company, the Boston and Maine, had to wait half a day for the down train, which showed no signs of coming. He decided to take over by telegraphing from station to station to stop it. Finally he arrived at Port Jervis where the down train was waiting, champing at the bit.

The laying of the tracks led to incidents of many kinds, some comic, some tragic.

One farmer, when he learned that the track was going to pass along the edge of his land, decided to dig a huge hole above the probable level of the line. He then laid down his spade and pickaxe and waited quietly for rain to transform the hole into a pond. Next he wrote to Loder, the President of the Erie Railroad, and told him that near his farm was a nice little pool fed by underwater springs which he offered

[1] Jim Hill, for instance, the famous railway engineer, refused to build a station near a village in Minnesota because he was not on speaking terms with the mayor.

to the company for their permanent use in return for the absurd sum of $2,500. The engineers arrived, examined the miraculous pool and paid cash. A pipeline was laid down to the track but after a few dozen tenders had been filled the little lake dried up completely, for good.

The Redskins, though less elaborate in their devices, were more subtle. One group of engineers planning to cross a somewhat infertile Indian reserve considered they had the right to go through for practically nothing. They therefore pointed out to the Indian Chief that the track would not affect the cultivation of their land.

"That is true," the Chief replied between two puffs on his calumet, "but you find my land good enough for growing trains on it."

This reasoning was well worth the $10,000 that the railway company had to pay.

In the Great Lakes region, where huntsmen and trappers had never heard of railways, the locomotives were taken for monstrous animals. One bold trapper, John Pick, wagered that he would capture the "beast." He set up a kind of huge trap over the line and waited. Fortunately he was caught in time, for otherwise the locomotive would have been trapped like a mere beaver. More touching is the story of Mrs. Horton, probably the first heroine of the American railways. One fine day in the spring of 1854 she noticed that a huge tree had fallen over the track near a bend in the line where no engine driver could see it. When she heard the whistle of the train she leapt on to the track and waved the first red object that came to hand. It happened to be her bloomers. As a means of thanking her Ramsdell, President of the Erie Railroad, granted both her and her husband the right to travel on his line free of charge for life, and with his letter he sent a box which contained, he said, "A certain article of clothing," modestly giving no exact description of it.

The same year saw the rise of Daniel Drew, a former cattleman who had become rich by selling animals which had been given highly salted food, causing them to drink a great amount and grow fat. After trafficking in the Lakes steamers he became involved in the Erie Railroad and introduced two colleagues, Jim Fisk, a former travelling tinker, and Jay Gould, a genuine financier engaged in railway promotion. Having taken over the company by fraudulent means they issued unauthenticated shares and blocked the convertible bonds in such a way that the Erie Railroad shares fell by 50 per cent. The famous Vanderbilt tried to deal with these swindlers and was stripped of several million dollars.

It was decided to arrest Drew, Fisk and Gould, but they all three fled to Jersey City, taking $6,000,000 with them. Once there they retreated to the Taylor Hotel and transformed it into a fort where several hundred armed men protected them against the sheriff, who was powerless and resigned. To keep their hands in Fisk and Gould, making some clever internal speculations, ruined their accomplice Drew.

Gould was eventually arrested for fraudulent misuse of funds. As for Fisk, one morning he was found dead on the staircase of the Broadway Central Hotel in New York; as the result of some romance he had been riddled with bullets.

Since these adventurous times the Erie Railroad, with its network extending from New York to Chicago, has become a highly respectable and powerful company.

Politicians always take an interest in important engineering or constructional work when they think it can help their electioneering propaganda or bring them some private profit. In the United States, therefore, every Congressman wanted the railway track to pass through his territory.

But straight lines depend both on geometry and economic conditions, and the technicians had to have their say. In 1853 the Federal Government, in order to find better itineraries and establish military posts for the protection of travellers where necessary, decided to send various expeditions to explore the completely unknown territories lying between the Mississippi and the Pacific.

Between 1853 and 1856, therefore, American and foreign experts carried out twelve exploratory missions, which were combined military expeditions and topographical commissions, in an effort to find the best way from the 35th to the 47th parallel.

Results proved that these areas, which had previously been regarded as impenetrable, offered few obstacles to large-scale railway development. The worst hold-ups came from the electioneering programme of the Representatives in the South. But as soon as the Civil War broke out these Representatives lost their powerful influence over Congress and the Government decided to build the Transcontinental Railroad, the great undertaking which, after the Civil War, would definitely unite the disunited States.

Between 1855 and 1860, therefore, many plans were made but Congress perpetually postponed their decision as to the best and most rational itinerary, which was to be flanked also by a strategic defence line, since, apart from the danger of Civil War, there might also be foreign aggression caused, for example, by immigrants from China.

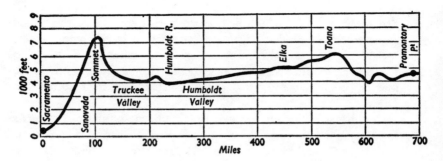

33. Profile of the Central Pacific Railroad

Eventually it was decided to join the two oceans by a straight line, going across the immense peaks of the Rocky Mountains and the Sierra Nevada. This line was to be 1,800 miles long, running from San Francisco in California to Omaha in Nebraska, which was already linked with Chicago, 600 miles away, by the North-Western Company. The meat-packing town itself had been connected to Washington and New York in 1853 by the Baltimore and Ohio Railroad Company.

On July 1st, 1862, President Lincoln signed the Pacific Railroad Act. On the same day Theodore Judah,[1] one of the founders and chief engineer of the Central Pacific Railroad Company, telegraphed to his colleagues:

"We have raised an elephant, now we must see if we can harness it."

Lincoln's Act designated also the two great companies which were to build this giant serpent and its accompanying telegraph line.

One of the companies, the Central Pacific Railroad Company, the C.P.R., was founded in 1861 by Judah, and associated later with the men who were known in the West as the Big Four, Leland Stanford, Collins P. Huntingdon, Mark Hopkins and Charles Crocker. They were already prepared of course for the fact that somewhere, but preferably as far as possible from the Pacific, they would meet the second company, the Union Pacific Railroad (U.P.R.) which was created along with the Pacific Railroad Act. The U.P.R. was directed by Generals Dix (later United States Minister in France), Casement and Dodge, the financiers Thomas C. Durant, the Oakes brothers and Oliver Ames, the great technician Peter Dey and the administrators Dillon and George F. Train.

[1] One of the greatest and most remarkable technicians of the American railways. In 1931 a magnificent monument was erected to him in Sacramento where he died of yellow fever in 1863 without seeing the completion of the line.

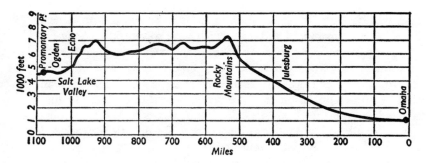

34. Profile of the Union Pacific Railroad

The two companies had Government permission to float a loan of $27,000,000 in the form of bonds redeemable in thirty-six years with an interest of 6 per cent. guaranteed and paid by the Federal Government Treasury. Further, each company had the right to issue secondary bonds for the same sum at the same interest, in debentures on the companies' credit and redeemable in thirty years. It was also understood that the entire operation had to be concluded by July 1st, 1876, or the Government would take over.

Further, the Government subsidised the companies by allowing them from $16,000 to $48,000 per mile of work completed, according to the nature of the ground or the route followed by the track, payable in instalments per forty miles completed, after official inspection.

In addition, of course, Washington gave each company a section of land amounting to 13,000 acres per mile, that is all the land extending to a width of ten miles on both sides of the track. The company could dispose of it as it wished and did not hesitate to do so, for the sales or concessions it made on its territory to the pioneers at the price of $2.50 to $20 an acre[1] compensated them for the money they spent. Naturally, however, the company undertook to buy privately owned land themselves and as we have seen the price such land fetched varied a good deal. Since at this time the privileges of compulsory purchase were not recognised by the State, a check was kept on the companies' activities.

In this way the two companies received a total of 20,000,000 acres of land from the Government, the official valuation of which was $40,000,000, an unreal estimate since they were unable at that time to sell more than half of it. The deserts and mountains were unsaleable

[1] The price depended on whether the land was wooded or not, for at this period timber was much more important than the degree of fertility of the soil.

and, what is more, the State reserved for itself any land with mineral deposits, apart from coal and iron which were to remain the property of the companies.[1] As soon as these arrangements were made the companies were to begin work, the C.P.R. starting west of Sacramento, 120 miles from San Francisco, and the U.P.R. in the east, starting from Omaha on the Missouri. The two lines were to meet somewhere near the Great Salt Lake, but in fact each company found it worthwhile to build a line as long as possible, because for each mile completed they received compensation from the Government, both in kind and in territory. Later on it will be seen that competition between them became fierce and sometimes comic.

The work began at Sacramento on January 8th, 1863, and on the Missouri side on December 2nd of the same year.

Both companies were to encounter two types of problems, both equally trying but totally different from each other. The C.P.R. had to bring its supplies of rails and rolling stock along an enormous loop going from east to west round Cape Horn, and the U.P.R. began in the midst of tactical operations by the armies of the North and South, which had been at war with each other for two years. What is more, these areas were infested with Indians.

We shall begin our fantastic journey with the U.P.R.

II

WIND FROM THE EAST

Omaha, a little village in Nebraska consisting of barely 3,000 inhabitants (today there are 250,000), occupied with raising livestock and agriculture, became in 1863 the railway centre of the United States. In less than a year the place was transformed into a huge mass of workshops and foundries surmounted with plumes of smoke and steam. The rails came from Pennsylvania and the materials for the rolling stock from Chicago.

The wooden sleepers were made from the thousands of poplars growing beside the Missouri and the Platte River. All kinds of trees growing nearby were also used, from the ordinary pine to cedars and sequoias with their valuable resins. The poplar was treated with iron

---

[1] The total number of sections granted by the State and the land bought by all the American railroad companies together eventually amounted to the fantastic figure of 130,000,000 acres.

35. The Transcontinental Railroad

chloride to harden it and prevent it from rotting, whereas the oak and the cedar were used in their natural state alternating with sleepers of soft-wood on a basis worked out by rough calculations. All the timber was brought by sledges or floated down the rivers.

In Sierra Nevada and the Rocky Mountains the tunnels, which varied from 200 to 458 feet in length, were blasted out by dynamite, recently invented by Nobel and prepared on the spot. The building of these tunnels could delay the work considerably,[1] but whenever possible a temporary track was laid round them without waiting for their completion and a junction made at the place where the end of the tunnel was expected to come. Naturally, this had to be carefully calculated.

The bridges looked like stockades in Western-style films; they resembled a heap of logs piled up haphazardly like giant matchsticks. In actual fact the technique of building these "truss" bridges, as they were called, was extremely highly developed and proved the Americans to be skilled carpenters. The medium-sized and culvert bridges were built either of stone or wood. Naturally metal or concrete bridges long ago replaced these temporary structures, and in fact the bridge at Omaha over the Missouri was rebuilt twice, in 1878 and 1930, with two different techniques and under tremendous difficulties.

The laying of the track progressed very rapidly, but as it was a single track there had to be many sidings so that trains could go in both directions. These sidings were usually built in the stations, which were normally situated about fifteen miles apart. In these primitive stations would be piles of locomotive fuel, either wood or coal, for in the mining areas, which had been prospected in advance, surface-mining of coal was quickly carried out at the same time whenever

[1] The height of the track from Omaha to Sacramento reaches 7,200 feet in the Rocky Mountains and the Sierra Nevada (see heights, Fig. 34).

possible. Wells were also dug and water pumped up by steam pumps driven by windmills. In other cases water often had to be brought from a great distance.

When gales and snowstorms made work difficult "snowsheds" were installed along the track so that work could go on, sheltered from the elements.[1]

The telegraph that was installed parallel to the track was a great help, as can be imagined. In the deserts, however, the poles were damaged by buffaloes, for they rubbed against them in the hope of getting rid of their vermin.

In the east all supplies were brought along the railway track itself, which formed its own transport. It brought not only the raw materials but also the food supplies and provisions of all kinds. According to the season the workers lived in tents or waggons, which were more like log cabins raised on platforms and arranged like cabins on a ship, with two or three bunks one on top of the other. It was like a whole travelling town, for there were offices, a bank, restaurants, hotels and saloons. Sometimes there was even a portable Protestant or Catholic church, which also went along the track. But twenty miles behind a gambling saloon in a waggon faithfully followed.

There was also great activity near Omaha, in the factories' workshops and foundries, and by the time the Pacific Railroad was finished in 1869 the U.P.R. already possessed locomotives and rolling stock in proportion to its 1,100 miles of track; 147 locomotives from twenty-five to thirty-five tons, twenty-five first-class coaches, twenty-six second class, nine mail coaches, twelve luggage vans, two coaches for the organisers and technicians, one luxury coach called *The Lincoln*, 1,150 goods vans, 1,500 platforms, three workshop vans and two cashiers' vans to carry the workers' pay, with special armour-plating, as one can imagine.

Naturally the Indian tribes were not very pleased to see the railway track, which deprived them of their land and drove the game a long way from their wigwams. Long before the "iron serpent" came they had laid hands on the convoys of pioneers, the coaches, express couriers and small military detachments. Their resistance was sporadic at first but it soon became general when they realised that the railway track was definitely going to replace the passing waggons.

Most of the railway workers—former soldiers from the Union Army or Confederates, together with countless adventurers, escaped convicts and gun-runners—used to work with a revolver or a rifle

[1] See Fig. 36, p. 193.

beside them. Since General Sherman did not think for a moment that the "savages" could hold up the Great Project he said, cynically:

"A certain number of men dispersed along the track will hand out so much whisky that all the Indians for 300 miles on each side of the track will be killed. . . ."

This was not only the opinion of military men, for the engineer, James Evans, wrote cynically to Durant, Vice-President of the U.P.R.:

"I am of the opinion that the Indians should be exterminated or at least reduced in number in such a way as to render them harmless. To achieve this they must be attacked like savages, using methods which the uninitiated would describe as barbarous. I am convinced that in the long run this method of procedure is *the most charitable and the most human.*"

But bottles of whisky and bullets are not always effective against an energetic race with pastoral traditions, particularly when they are left hungry by the disappearance of the buffaloes which were killed in incredible quantities in order to supply food for the railway workers. Nevertheless General Sherman's terrible prophecy has come true, for comparatively few Indians have survived and they now live mostly in reserves.

The Federal Government had forts built here and there along the track, manned by experienced garrisons, yet they could not always prevent the Indians from carrying out daring raids, attacking the workers, whom they killed and then scalped, or robbing the stores, which they then burned down.

During the winter of 1864–65 General Dodge was forced to undertake a real campaign against the Sioux Indians, which led to violent episodes up to the time the Transcontinental was finished. The destruction of the Custer Detachment in 1876, when the General perished with his 276 men—not a single one escaped—is an incident which the Americans have never forgotten. War against the Indians did not end until 1890 when Chief Sitting Bull was subdued for ever shortly before the decisive battle of Wounded Knee. As can be seen from a report by Senator W. M. Stewart presented to Congress in 1869 the building of the Transcontinental cost 20,000 human lives, without counting the sum of $28,000,000 which was spent on the provision of armed guards.

Some of the shanty towns built along the track have remained, others have completely disappeared. Their varied and picturesque population included immigrants, workers and adventurers. Some of the names of the Californian towns, for example, are reminiscent of the violence and desperation of these adventurous times and recall the kind of men who brought them into being: Brandy Gulch, Hangtown, Piety Hill, Hell's Delight, Puke Ravine, Gouge Eye, Petticoat Slide, Swell-Head Diggings, Poker Flat and others.

Naturally their inhabitants gave shelter to the railway workmen and then to the shopkeepers and artisans who supplied them with food and clothing. Then came a third group of people much less praise-worthy, namely, the parasites, saloon-keepers, professional gamblers and prostitutes, all of whom worked hand in glove to impoverish their clients on pay-days. Often whole towns would fall completely into the hands of gangs armed with Colt rifles, which had just been invented by the Colonel of that name.

From time to time the honest people became exasperated and banded together in efforts to clean up the town. They proceeded to carry out summary executions or to banish the most discordant elements,[1] but they often had to appeal to the Regular Army which operated an equally primitive system of justice. In this way Generals Casement and Dodge were simultaneously called to Julesburg in Nebraska after a pay-day which had been particularly lively. Casement arrived in the morning and Dodge in the evening. Casement went to meet his colleague, shook hands with him, and with his other hand pointed out a small new cemetery which had not existed the day before:

"There lie forty men who died with their boots on, but the fighting's over. May they rest in peace."

The men worked hard, and since there were no distractions whatever in these solitary places the necessary relaxation had to be provided by the saloons, gambling dens, dance-halls and girls. After weeks of work in snowstorms or the dust of the torrid deserts not one of these young men could have been kept on the job without the prospect of these famous orgies.

When their pockets were empty and hunger overcame them they were forced to go back to work, repenting, as the Bible says, in sackcloth and ashes.

But how was the C.P.R. progressing in the meantime on its way to the Pacific?

[1] Some of the excellent short stories by Francis Bret Harte deal with this subject, including *The Outcasts of Poker Flat*, which describes the sufferings of adventurers banished from a town by the ruthless railway law.

III

WIND FROM THE WEST

The Union Pacific had to defend itself mainly against men, but the Central Pacific had to contend in turn with lack of finance, shortage of workers, difficulties in transporting raw material and finally natural obstacles in the shape of deserts and mountains.

Naturally it benefited under the Pacific Railroad Act, enjoying the same advantages as its associated company the U.P.R. It was the lot of the Central Pacific to build the most difficult section of the Transcontinental, going across the deserts on the eastern side of the Sierra Nevada and those of Central Nebraska. The thought of these unattractive stretches of land in fact lost the C.P.R. the financial assistance of cautious shareholders.

The U.P.R. had strong support from the financiers of Wall Street and even from those of the Stock Exchange in London, who obviously were not interested in supporting an associated company which was in fact a competitor, since it also relied on Federal support.

The C.P.R., therefore, could really only count on the capital put up by its directors, and most of such capital was invested in other enterprises. The Big Four, who only became big after their success, were able to raise together no more than the miserable sum of $100,000. When necessary the Californian company could make use of the small subscriptions paid by the towns, of which there were very few, and the rather badly organised districts through which the line was to pass. The result was that a great deal of money was needed to carry out the first forty miles, after which the railway could begin to receive the famous Government subsidies.

The C.P.R. also had to compete with large transport companies working on land and sea, which ever since the beginning of the century, and at great expense, had brought all kinds of goods from the east of the United States.

When the first railways were built in Europe the savings of the mid-nineteenth century middle-class had supplied a gold-mine of investment, but in the American West there was no such possibility, for the immigrants had only their own hands and the gold prospectors were incurably poverty-stricken.

"You won't find a cent for your railways," was the gist of the remark made to the C.P.R. by Lloyd Tevis, the wealthy director of the powerful Wells Fargo Company,[1] whose interests were threatened by the building of the rapid and more economic Transcontinental Railway.

In order to obtain additional capital at any price the C.P.R., along with the official geologists, descended to subterfuge. The company built its line as close as possible to the Sierra Nevada, over ground which did not present many technical problems but where the Government subsidies amounted to $48,000 per mile, the maximum figure allowed. It had, in fact, been laid down that the first track should not include more than 150 miles at this high figure. President Lincoln was otherwise occupied and did not condescend to look too closely at this subtle plan, which came near to fraud. At this period and at such a distance it was a mere schoolboy's trick.

It should be added that the C.P.R. had one advantage over the rival company: it was founded first, and was able to buy certain areas of land at very low prices, which were eventually sold at prices in proportion to the length of the line and the comfort of the coaches, bringing them valuable financial support.

When the first railway tracks were built in Europe they naturally followed the main roads between the towns. In the far West, since there were neither towns nor roads, the track followed a line that was as straight as possible, taking into account a river bed across a plain, a pass or a valley in the mountains, the proximity of a lake which fertilised the surrounding district or a water point in the desert.

In this way they had to deal one after the other with granite, slate, chalk, sand, volcanic lava or remains of glaciers. These variations delighted the geologists but alarmed the engineers, who could find no trace of metals suitable for casting the rails or building locomotives. All the supplies had to be brought from the east.

The east was 3,000 miles away as the crow flies, but in actual fact by sea this meant a distance of 15,000 miles from New York, and via the Strait of Magellan it meant a journey of four months. For some time attempts were made to cross the Isthmus of Panama but this route proved so costly that it had to be renounced. It cost $143 to transport a ton of rails from New York, and then they had to be loaded on flat-bottomed barges which covered a distance of over 100 miles from San Francisco to Sacramento along the river of the same name. The cost of transporting each one of the first locomotives was $2,300 by

[1] A large transport company working with waggons and coaches possessing more or less the monopoly of transport in the West, including the postal services. Hundreds of its stage coaches have been destroyed on cinema and television screens for our entertainment; the famous Colonel Cody, or Buffalo Bill, began life with Wells Fargo.

Cape Horn and $8,000 by Panama. It is understandable why the United States took such a strong interest in the Canal that was begun forty years later by Ferdinand de Lesseps.

The timber problem was solved by the existence of magnificent forests covering the plains and the valleys. The trees often rose to a height of nearly 30 feet but when they stood in the way of the line the roots, which went just as far down into the ground, had to be destroyed by dynamite.

All this work needed a big labour force. The Gold Rush of 1849 had brought thousands of white men to the coast but they were attracted by the precious metal and not very interested in digging out stones, cutting down trees or juggling with rails.

After a vain attempt to attract the Mexican *peons*, Chinese labour was called in, for the Chinese were emigrating from the southern part of the Celestial Empire to the coasts of California to escape endemic famine.

Strobridge,[1] who was in charge of the work, did not want the Chinese at all when he first saw them, pointing out that these little men, whose average weight was just over 120 lb., would be incapable of carrying out such exhausting work. After trying out a group of them he changed his mind and "ordered" 15,000 of them, who arrived from the other side of the Pacific packed in the holds of ships.

The Chinese slave trade was organised like a real industry. Five American companies located in China recruited the unfortunate inhabitants, coaxing them away by attractive pictures of life in Eldorado.

The emigrants were then taken over like cattle, collected in Hong Kong, sent to California at the companies' expense and there the companies were able to recover the cost at a big profit by arranging a long mortgage on the traditional savings of the Chinese. When they reached San Francisco the emigrants were placed in the hands of two other companies which then exploited them. These were Chinese companies, the Wing-Yung and the Fouk-Ting-Tong, who never lost sight of the men during their lifetime and afterwards. It is well known that a devout Chinese regards it as indispensable that his ashes should return to his native land, for otherwise he cannot hope for an eternal blessed life in heaven.

[1] James Harvey Strobridge, known as "Stro," lived with his family during the whole of the enterprise in a coach which followed him along the track. He was energetic and violent, always taking an active part in things and in this way he lost an eye when a charge of dynamite went off too soon.

The Wing-Yung housed and fed the new arrivals until they had found work, and kept part of their salary to cover their costs.

The second company was more of a secret society which controlled the relationships of the Chinese between themselves. It also operated the "Death Fund," which was destined to meet the expenses of sending the ashes of the deceased back to Hong Kong. In the meantime the bodies were buried in the Laurel Hill Cemetery in San Francisco where they waited quietly for their return *en masse* to the land of their ancestors.

This was no concern of the C.P.R., whose appreciation of the Chinese was limited to the materialistic point of view.

"The Chinese," said Strobridge, "work like wizards, they learn quickly, they do not fight, they do not go on strike over a 'yes' or a 'no,' and they are very clean. They quarrel rather noisily amongst themselves but they do so without animosity." The engineer failed to add that they were paid much less than the white workers.[1]

What is more, the coolies were very sober, cooked their own food in family groups and drank enormous quantities of tea, a drink which had the merit of being made with boiled water, and in this way eliminated the risk of sudden epidemics. They worked in gangs under the orders of a boss, which avoided incessant discussions like those which occurred among the white workers—the Anglo-Saxons, Irish and Canadians, all very different from each other but with one characteristic in common, the taste for alcohol. In the west, however, Strobridge showed a strong hand, forbade absolutely the drinking of whisky and organised, when he needed them, commandos who destroyed at one stroke the clandestine saloons and left them completely "dry." This was not entirely legal: the men complained to the courts in Sacramento or the sheriffs in California, who inflicted heavy fines on the C.P.R. and made them pay the costs. Strobridge paid for the damage without raising an eyebrow, for he preferred this to drinking bouts. "Wherever I go," he announced, "there is only one law, the railway law."

There was about one white man to ten Chinese, but the whites supplied the specialist workmen and the foremen. They received a high bonus and also enjoyed the benefit of being able to make enforced savings. Although the Chinese worked hard they were terrified of the Indians, and a gang of whites had to stand guard in case any feathered

[1] The Chinese were paid from $30 to $35 a month, much more than they earned in the towns, but the whites received $3 to $5 a day and the technicians had very good salaries. Everyone received bonuses. Payments were made exclusively in gold coins, the famous "eagles."

head-dress appeared from time to time on the top of a rock or among the bushes. Unlike the U.P.R., the C.P.R. did not have much trouble from Indians for there were very few of them, apart from the Paiutes and the Shoshones, with whom the company made a remarkable and very useful treaty, allowing them free and constant use of the trains. The chiefs had the honour of sitting in the passenger accommodation while the trucks and tenders were thought good enough for their subjects.

The ground, the raw material and the Indians were nothing compared to the fearful winter storms. During the winter of 1866–67 alone there were forty-four of them, causing avalanches which obstructed the track and buried the workers. Twenty Chinese were carried away for ever in one storm and after this the snowsheds were built.

During this same winter of 1867 when foot upon foot of snow piled up and threatened to stop work, Crocker had galleries cut through it in order to lay the sleepers on the bare rock in the Donner Summit

36. A snowshed

Pass. Finally, in order to bring food to the men and supply the raw material for the other side of the Pass, where work was already going on, Crocker had forty waggons carrying supplies and twenty-five miles of rail brought by sledges over the Summit.

In order to transport the three locomotives necessary for continuing work Crocker assembled gigantic platforms of logs. He fixed the machines on to them and with the help of mules, oxen and even his men, he made them follow the same road as the supplies and the rails.

The bridges were built by the same techniques as in the east and the arched bridge at Secret Town, which was 100 feet high and 1,050 feet long, was considered for a long time as the masterpiece among all the wooden bridges on the Transcontinental Railroad.

The first stroke of the pickaxe was carried out with great ceremony at Sacramento on January 8th, 1863, by Leland Stanford, chairman of the company, and this day of celebration and speech-giving has been immortalised in a great fresco which can still be seen at the Southern Pacific Railway Station in Sacramento. Stanford was the type of businessman frequently found in the United States at this period. He was a farmer's son who was able to study law and became a lawyer. He was vegetating in Wisconsin when the town was burnt down, and he lost his library and his clientele. He then went to California, grew rich during the exploitation of the mines and finally became one of the Big Four. Later he was elected Senator and finally Governor of California, which he ruled almost like a king. He was always on the lookout for business and not always very scrupulous—it was said that his seat in Congress cost him $100,000—and he became the target of the Opposition newspapers, who wrote his name like this: £eland $tanford.[1]

In November, 1863, the first locomotive of the C.P.R. arrived, called naturally, *Governor Stanford*; it came from the east round Cape Horn but it was not attached to a passenger train between Sacramento and Roseville until February, 1864. It had taken more than a year to lay down those twenty miles, but from then onwards work went ahead quickly.

Since labour was cheap and transport, consisting of horses and waggons, was available on the spot, it was found more practical to build a road parallel to the track so that all the raw material which arrived by sea at San Francisco could be brought up and deposited. At the same time stations and workshops were built in advance and channels

[1] His life came to an honourable close, and he founded the University of Pala Alto in California, endowing it with $4,000,000.

were cut in the deserts, often bringing the water from a great distance—from the Truckee River for instance, which was nearly forty miles away.

Work was carried out as much as 100 miles ahead of the track and coordinated by means of a hastily installed telegraph system. One gang dug the holes, another made the poles, a third put them in place, while a waggon brought up the rolls of copper wire, unwinding it as work progressed.

Thanks to this system the line was put together like a gigantic puzzle for which the pieces, consisting of tunnels, bridges and stations, seemed to appear in a haphazard way; but in fact Strobridge, Crocker and their collaborators calculated everything carefully. Using this method progress was rapid, especially when the gangs of men were kept on the job with splendid extra bonuses.

Seventeen thousand men were working on both sides of the Sierra Nevada while thirty-three ships went round Cape Horn or Panama unceasingly, bringing metal of all kinds, and countless steam-operated sawmills in the valleys turned out miles of sleepers and frame work along with mountains of logs to supply heating.

The workmen from both companies challenged each other through the newspapers, whose columns published news of victories like war communiqués. In this way the average length of track laid each day rose from one to three miles. Then in March, 1869, excitement grew as the day approached when the junction would be made, and the record of nine and a half miles in one day was reached. Durant, of the U.P.R., challenged Crocker to do better. Crocker accepted the bet of $10,000 then carefully chose his day, fixing it as close as possible to the day of the final junction and making sure he had everything on his side. Lastly he chose a solid experienced gang of eight tall Irishmen. He then invited all the journalists from the west along with observers from the U.P.R. When the sun went down behind the mountain on April 28th, 1869, the sons of St. Patrick had laid ten miles of track in one day, namely 3,500 rails weighing altogether 1,000 tons.[1]

On the other side the men of the U.P.R. were also juggling with sleepers and rails. It should be remembered that the Pacific Railroad Act had laid down that the two companies would meet each other "where they could," although it was thought that the place would be somewhere near the Great Salt Lake area, a flourishing fertile district which it would be in the interest of both companies to serve. The more

[1] This exploit was commemorated by an inscription which can still be seen at the place (Challenge Point).

miles were laid, the more sections of land could be sold at a good price to the pioneers.[1]

Then the following absurd incident occurred. Early in 1869 both companies were overcome with frenzy and, apparently unaware of each other's work, they went forward so rapidly that instead of meeting each other, the two tracks overlapped and proceeded in parallel lines for more than 200 miles, and the Government had of course to pay out subsidies to both sides. And, as a result each company felt obliged to blow up the rival track with dynamite while gangs of Chinese and whites threw the building materials at each other's heads and fought for their own company out of pure railway patriotism.

These fights between gangs from different companies occurred frequently in the United States during the railway fever. The two following incidents are famous in the annals of the "Santa Fe" Railroad.

The men of the Santa Fe, in order to prevent the men of the Rio Grande Railroad from laying their track, were ordered to fire on them and disrupt the work without killing them. Good marksmen were engaged (and since the war was just over there was no shortage of them) and positioned on top of the Racoon Pass, a very narrow defile in the Racoon Mountains. The veterans aimed at the building tools and shattered them, at the hats, blowing them right off the workers' heads, and at the camp cooking pots, which they turned into colanders. Later on occurred the much more serious incident of the Royal Gorge, where one man was killed, and a train full of soldiers, along with a cavalry detachment, had to be sent to silence the Colts and Winchesters. By an irony of fate these memorable railway fights took place near the Sangre de Cristo Mountains and Purgatory River.

In the meantime Washington was somewhat annoyed by these extra lengths of track which the two companies had presented to the country with a bill for $1,000,000. The Federal Government decided that the joke had gone on too long and fixed the junction of the two lines at Promontory, a deserted valley to the east of the Great Salt Lake, and it was to be carried out, to use the exact words of the Act of Congress, full of involuntary humour, "so that the rails are linked together in a manner forming a continuous line!"

On May 10th, 1869, therefore, more than seven years before the date anticipated for the completion, the two heroic companies of the railway age were united in great pomp with four magnificent rivets made of precious metal.

For the event a real town was built along the track after the junction

[1] As it happened, the Mormons, who founded Salt Lake City.

had been effected, and as a special exception Strobridge permitted the building of saloons, gaming-rooms, dance halls and even brothels.

At noon two representatives of the companies, Strobridge and Reed for the U.P.R., wearing frock-coats and top hats, finally put in place the last sleeper, made of extremely valuable wood, polished Californian laurel, and bearing a silver plate with the names of the principals, directors and technicians of both companies.

Then the rails were placed on the sleepers, and the great moment came for the two figureheads of the companies, Stanford and Durant. They were presented with the famous spikes made of gold, silver and iron, given by the States through which the trains would soon run.

General Dodge pointed to the last two rails and said, "Now at last the work of Christopher Columbus is complete. This is the road which leads to the Indies."

Finally, Stanford and Durant, using silver hammers, drove in the valuable spikes and everyone present bared their heads. A clergyman said a prayer while the telegraph operators transmitted the sound of the hammering in Morse to San Francisco, New York and Washington. All over America bells were rung, cannon were fired and bonfires were lit as the "great message" arrived.

Two locomotives, one from the C.P.R. and the other from the U.P.R., moved slowly towards each other until their cow-catchers touched; then a bottle of French champagne was broken between them, while in the town quantities of whisky were consumed in an atmosphere of excitement. A similar excitement ran through the whole country, which was finally united by the good news. A poet of the Far West, Joaquin Miller, went so far as to write that day, "There is more poetry in the railway that crosses the Continent than in all the history of the Trojan War."

Soon afterwards the town of Promontory completely disappeared and only desert remained. Nothing is left now except an obelisk fifteen feet high at the mercy of the sandstorms which are gradually obliterating the touching inscription "The last spike completing the first Transcontinental Railroad was driven at this spot on May 10th, 1869."[1]

[1] The valuable sleeper and the gold and silver spikes soon disappeared, the former slashed by souvenir hunters and the others merely because they were not very durable. At the beginning of the twentieth century it was still possible to distinguish between the two different types of telegraph poles at Promontory Point, for the C.P.R. used square poles and the U.P.R. round ones.

IV

THE PROMISED LAND

While the workers were struggling against the weather or risking their lives fighting Indians, a fine scandal was brewing in Washington. Soon after the junction of the two lines it was discovered that many members of Congress had been "honoured" in order to ratify the Pacific Railroad Act. They had been honoured not with wads of banknotes, naturally, but with satisfactory numbers of shares in the "Crédit Mobilier" which distributed the governmental subsidies. In the course of the enquiry it was found that from 1867 onwards, before the Pacific Railroad had transported a single passenger, the "Crédit Mobilier" had distributed a dividend of 100 per cent., which even at this period of wild speculation and successive gold rushes came as a shock to honest people.

But it should be added that these dividends were stock dividends; that is to say, dividends paid in the form of supplementary shares in the company, a practice which was common at this period in the U.S.A. and worked as follows: the company retained during a few financial years the total amount of profit realised and available for distribution. It then presented the shareholders with shares or scrip shares. In fact it was a forced new loan. In this way one can understand how Vanderbilt, with the "Crédit Immobilier," was able from 1868 to 1869 to pay out imaginary dividends which even exceeded the amount of the original shares.

The scandal led to the appointment of a parliamentary commission. Its findings were published after enquiries had proceeded for some years and involved even James Garfield, a Senator and a man of great political power, although he was easily influenced. Despite this, Garfield was later to become President of the United States and— whether by fate or coincidence—was assassinated in 1881 in a station in Baltimore.

When in 1894 the C.P.R. and the U.P.R. were due to reimburse the Federal loans approved in 1862, the active competition from more recent companies and the policy of reduced charges which the older companies had been forced to introduce *force majeure* in order to exist, had already used up all their reserves, and ruin stared them in the face. All the other railway companies were more or less in the same situation and Wall Street had a hint of the terrible depression that eventually came in 1929. There were cases of sensational failure and remarkable profits at the same time, and the building of the Panama Canal was creating a similar situation. But the scandal in America came to a head after the work had been finished and did not affect the consolidation and perfection of the Pacific Railroad in any way. This was by no means the case as far as the Panama Canal was concerned.

The railways in Europe were originally designed for the transport of freight, and people had been content for centuries to travel by coach. Mankind took second place as a user of the railway and comfortable metal coaches with corridors were hardly known on the Continent until early this century. In America, on the other hand, passengers were treated as important freight. After all, there was no need for goods to be brought to a place where, as the journalist said, "the hand of man has never set foot." The merchandise was already there and there was no shortage of it in the new America. As a result comfort on the railways became the main concern of all the American companies, who developed great rivalry and considered the comfort of a coach to be just as important as the technical perfection of a locomotive.

The new Pacific Railroad, therefore, was very quickly fitted out with all possible comfort; even in the third-class accommodation heating was supplied by water from the engine instead of by the dangerous stoves which had been installed in the coaches of the eastern company. At night temporary bunks could be set up quickly and the passengers were able to lie down, using their own mattresses and blankets, which often formed their only possessions. When ladies were travelling, smoking was forbidden in the compartments, but there were platforms at each end, just as there are today. Many coaches were equipped with spacious cloakrooms where ladies and gentlemen went in turn at prearranged times. There were even tiny kitchens with wood fires where hot meals could be cooked. In 1853 Vanderbilt equipped coaches with permanent couchettes, but it was Pullman whose name was to be linked with sleeping cars.

George Mortimer Pullman was a former builder who in his youth had slept for a long time on a layer of bricks and knew how hard they could be. His first great exploit was to repair the Tremont hotel in Chicago, which was sinking into the soft ground beneath it. In a few hours, using 200 workers and 500 jacks, he brought the building back into place inch by inch and then braced it up without any interruption to the life of the hotel and without breaking a single window pane or teapot.

This was the start of his fortune, which he consolidated later by arranging for "beds on rails" to travel without jerks, which was still easier than propping up a large building. His first sleeping-car was built in 1858 and was quite complete from the very first, but care had to be taken to ensure that the passengers took their boots off before lying down. Curtains screened each bunk, light was supplied by candles and there was a stove at each end of the car.

Then in 1863 he invented seats which could be unfolded at night and transformed into comfortable divans. All these coaches were the property of Pullman and although the railway company guaranteed their transport at the expense of the former it was Pullman who made the passengers pay for their use.

His first luxury coach was the *Pioneer*, which cost $20,000, and inside it there was not one inch of metal to be seen, for it was all concealed by expensively carved wooden panels.

When President Lincoln died his widow asked for his huge coffin to be transported from Washington to Springfield in the *Pioneer*. This journey was memorable for other reasons, for the coach was so wide that parapets of bridges had to be demolished and station platforms made narrower so that the *Pioneer* could proceed. Thousands of sorrowing Americans paid their respects in silence as the remains of their great President passed by.

After this success Pullman built dozens of *Pioneers*, which were soon in circulation all over America; the former builder was completely ruthless and unhesitatingly disposed of all his competitors, using any method that occurred to him. In 1880, since his company employed 20,000 people, he caused the town which bears his name to be built near Chicago.

In 1869 he built a hotel-car, a combination of a sleeping-car and a dining-car staffed by butlers and stewards, along with hairdressers and secretaries. The cost of travelling in it was exorbitant but the food was the finest in the U.S.A. and as the journey proceeded the menu was enriched by the best local specialities including "buffalo hump" and venison.

When his coaches began to be infested by professional gamblers who stripped idle travellers of all their money, Pullman had little cards printed with the following warning, which was repeated on his tickets: "It is dangerous to play cards with persons unknown to you."

Whenever a member of the staff saw someone about to succumb to this temptation he discreetly slipped one of these cards into his waistcoat pocket. If he did not understand Pullman gave him up.

It was "forbidden to die" in a Pullman couch. If ever a death occurred the dead body was discreetly removed at the next station and buried at Pullman's expense, provided there was an undertaker in the town. If there was not, the body was coldly deposited in the waiting room.

Pullman was also the first to add sheets to his couchettes and not very long ago one could still read in the Pullman cars in America, and on the tickets too: "Travellers are requested to remove their boots before retiring," but he did not go so far as to tell them that there was no need to place a revolver under their pillows before going to sleep.

The first complete transcontinental trip did not take place until 1870 when all the bridges and tunnels were finally in order and the lines laid between Sacramento and San Francisco, Omaha and Chicago.

It was a memorable official trip in which 120 people took part, the men, women and children of the best Boston society. During two weeks 50,000 people visited the famous train, which brought in easy money. George Pullman and four of his hotel cars took part in the trip. A small printing press was even installed and published every day *The Transcontinental*, probably the first newspaper printed on a train. It was distributed right and left as the train proceeded, even to the illiterate Indians, who, as they watched the train go by, realised sadly that the age of buffaloes was past.

The train consisted of eight cars, for in addition to the hotel cars there was a restaurant car, a sleeping car preceded by an ice waggon, a smoking compartment, a hairdressing saloon, a library and two organs.

The convoy stopped at Chicago in the midst of considerable enthusiasm. At Salt Lake City, the Mormon capital, President Brigham Young and one of his apostles were invited on board, but not their families. (The venerable President, who was 62 at this period, had sixteen wives and forty-nine children.) Finally the train reached San Francisco, where water from the Atlantic was mixed with that of the Pacific.

On the way back the train was stopped by a swarm of locusts which descended on the track, the only incident in the trip. The Bostonians, who are regarded as the most snobbish people in the United States, had at last something else to talk about instead of the gossip of Tremont Street or Concord Place. They had shaken hands with Mormons, gold prospectors, cowboys, ranchers, farmers, carpenters, trappers and Indians; they had crossed the deserts of Utah, the plains of the Great Salt Lake, the canyons of the Rocky Mountains, the snows of the Sierra Nevada and dipped their fingers in the azure waters of the Pacific. They had at last gazed on a sequoia that was bigger than the Bunker Hill Monument.[1]

Lastly, they had seen the descendants of the founders of the Union and, thanks to the railway, something which no American had ever seen before:

"The finally United States of America."

[1] A famous Boston monument commemorating the victory of Bunker Hill over the English (June 17th, 1775).

VIII

THE LONDON UNDERGROUND

"The train rocked alarmingly. It was so packed with people that getting in or out was a regular scrimmage. We entirely endorse the railway company's advertisement in that it is the 'warmest line in London.'"

Punch, 1890

I

PEARSON'S CRAZY PLAN

LONDON ABOUT THE middle of the last century was still a mediaeval town, but it was the capital of an Empire at the height of its power under one of its most remarkable Sovereigns; it was the centre of the largest railway network, the greatest port and the most densely populated city on earth.

Supremacy in so many fields had brought so much activity to the banks of the Thames that the capital city was over-crowded. In spite of their remarkable conservatism, the British, and especially Londoners, had to admit that traffic was becoming a problem.

It was estimated in about 1850 that every day some 750,000 citizens coming on foot, on horseback or in every kind of public conveyance with noisy, iron-bound wheels, went in or out of London. The traffic included omnibuses, cabs and coaches, without counting the waggons transporting fish to Billingsgate, fruit and vegetables to Covent Garden and meat to Smithfield.

In addition coal waggons came from Cardiff, heavy carts brought steel and iron from Leeds or Sheffield, and huge bales of cotton goods arrived from Manchester.

Until the sixteenth century there had been many convenient water courses which were used especially for merchandise arriving at the Port of London. In addition to the Thames there were other small rivers such as the Walbrook in the City, the Fleet in Blackfriars, the Wandle in Wandsworth and the Effra in Vauxhall.

During the Elizabethan period remarkable efforts were made to improve the roads throughout England and they were used by the coaches, a name given to these first public conveyances because they were manufactured at Kocs in Hungary. They had four wheels, were drawn by four horses and rarely travelled farther than thirty miles from London and the big cities.

One of the most famous transport organisers was Hobson, who hired out horses in Cambridge; his method was to force his clients to take the mount that stood "as close to the stable door as possible." His forceful insistence on this point has been preserved in the well-known expression "Hobson's choice," implying take it or leave it, and expressing a very British attitude.

About 1625 two novelties in passenger transport were introduced: sedan chairs and hackney coaches, which were small coaches seating two people The latter were hired either by the hour or by the distance in the Strand near what is today King's College. There were fifty hackney coaches in 1637 and about a thousand of them in 1771; early in the nineteenth century they became hansom cabs, which looked strange because their coachmen were perched high up at the back. Sedan chairs, however, remained in use until about 1825.

After 1650 the smaller coaches were gradually replaced by stage coaches which came into more or less general use during the eighteenth century. These were of two types: those which covered the "long" stage between London and the large towns in the provinces, even including Scotland (1675 to 1840), and those covering the "short" stages between London and the smaller towns nearby. Then at the end of the eighteenth century the short stage coaches began to run between the City and Paddington, now part of London but in those days only a village. The journey lasted over an hour for a distance of three and a half miles. There were, however, long stops on the way, for the driver sometimes went to pick up passengers at their homes or else told them long stories as they drove along, or would even, if other inspiration failed, play the violin.

These, then, constituted the first forms of public transport in London, but a true service of a more rapid and regular nature was introduced by George Shillibeer, who, on July 4th, 1829, began to operate omnibus carriages with eighteen seats drawn by three horses. His name was painted on the box and for the moderate sum of one shilling and sixpence passengers were taken from Paddington to the Bank of England. The carriages made thirty journeys every day, which for this period was a good service. Nowadays the Bank is served every day by 7,050 large red double-decker buses operated by London Transport.

Finally, in 1831, appeared the first steam-driven buses operating between Whitechapel and Stratford in Essex. They lasted until 1840, when the Turnpike Acts introduced extensive tolls for going in and out of London. These Acts were passed to benefit the first railways which brought passengers into the capital.

This did not mean that the horse-drawn omnibuses ceased to run; in 1832 the State Carriage Act authorised Shillibeer to pick up or deposit his clients anywhere along his route instead of stopping at predetermined stations at specific times. But it was the Compagnie des Omnibus de Paris which in 1858 founded the London General Omnibus Company Ltd. (L.G.O.C.L.), the first important omnibus service worthy of its name and of the capital city. At first the "General," as it was then called, acquired between 600 and 800 companies which had grown up everywhere after Shillibeer's innovation. There had been complete chaos concerning routes and fares, which had made the traffic problem very much worse. The "General" became therefore the first coordinated transport group in London and for a long time it was an active competitor to the Metropolitan.

They were to exist side by side, with varying fortunes, until 1933, when all transport in London was coordinated. It was finally nationalised in 1947 and brought under the sole direction of the London Transport Executive.

All these new and ingenious means of transport continued to increase but they did not improve the circulation of the traffic in any way, and the railways were bringing a floating population of transitory visitors to London, which itself was getting larger and larger. Because of the timetables these visitors had to be dispersed as quickly as possible. In London there were already half a dozen railway termini situated in the most populous thoroughfares. They formed a railway nucleus, but there was no automatic means of organising the floods of humanity which crossed the town from north to south and from east to west. The ideal solution, obviously, would have been to build railways between these main-line stations, but for the time being this was absolutely out of the question.

There was talk of building an overhead railway, as was done later in New York, but this one was to run on a huge glass platform above the streets on the outskirts of London. Steam-driven trains were to run round and round in a gigantic circle setting down travellers in auxiliary stations attached to the railway termini. This "crystal way" was the idea of a certain Dr. Cummings and gained some support, but the Press and public opinion were not greatly impressed by the idea.

However, in 1861, an American engineer, Francis Train, tried to work out a route with horse-drawn tramcars which had seats for twenty and standing room for twelve. The rails, however, came up beyond the level of the road and caused accidents which led to the withdrawal of his licence.

Then someone thought of a railway running under the streets and buildings of London. This man of genius was not, as one might have expected, an engineer, an architect or even a municipal councillor, but a simple obscure solicitor named George Pearson.

It should be added that Londoners had got into the habit of going under the Thames from Rotherhithe to Wapping through the famous tunnel constructed by the engineer Brunel, who had also built the no less celebrated ship the *Great Eastern*. Although a famous journalist wrote that "The famous Blackwall Tunnel is the admiration of all civilised Europe," it had had little more than a curiosity value, for Londoners preferred to cross the bridges over the Thames, from where they had a good view of the Port of London.

Nevertheless, the technical success of Brunel's work made Pearson's plan easier. Gradually the most serious and influential people in London came to consider the solicitor's crazy plan as the only means of relieving the congestion in the centre of the city once and for all.

Pearson's plan was based partly on the idea of Dr. Cummings; the intention was to link the railway termini by a tunnel, so that travellers were not forced to cross the town or to get out at intermediate stations. This plan provided the scheme for the Circle Line which still exists as part of the London Underground railway.

It is interesting to note that when the Paris "Métro" was built forty years later it did not adopt this typical English arrangement. The "Métro" lines followed the banks of the Seine and were based on the intersection of straight lines, a system adopted more to deal with "the suburban spread" than to improve links between the railway stations.

In actual fact Pearson's plan was more than modest, but along its three-mile route, which was roughly the same as that of Shillibeer, four out of its five stations, between Baker Street and Farringdon Street, linked important railway termini. Edgware Road Station served the Great Western Railway, Baker Street the Great Central Railway, King's Cross the Midland and the Great Northern railways, and Farringdon Street the London, Chatham and Dover Railway.

Pearson considered that this transport system should be used not only for conveying passengers but also for transporting heavy goods traffic between stations, using the same gauge as the railways. From the financial point of view, therefore, Pearson had to obtain support from the Corporation of the City of London for passenger transport, and for goods transport from the powerful railway companies.

While the fanatic solicitor attempted to influence these respectable bodies and obtain large-scale subsidies from them, local reaction was very strong and very varied in character. At first the opinion expressed in the aristocratic and conservative London clubs was that Pearson was a dangerous anarchist who wanted to destroy ancient buildings such as Westminster Abbey, St. Paul's Cathedral and even the Houses of

Parliament, causing great offence to the religious and political authorities. The Press joined in and did not fail to pour fuel on the flames. The most legitimate fears were expressed by housewives, who were convinced that their homes would collapse on top of them as a result of vibration from the trains. They were afraid that at the sacred tea-time hour they would suddenly find themselves sitting astride the boiler of a railway engine.

Electricity was not yet used in industry and the trains could only be driven by steam. This was not the least important of the objections to the Pearson plan; how, in fact, would one eliminate the steam and smoke, which would fill the tunnel with fumes and suffocate the intrepid travellers? It will be seen later how this serious inconvenience was overcome more or less successfully, at least at the beginning.

What is more, travelling at the risk of one's life was of minor concern for traditional travellers like the British; but respectability was shocked by this descent into the "sewer train," as it was called by *Punch*, which published a cartoon representing one of those vast basement kitchens to be found in London. In the foreground was an engine driver from the future underground railway pushing his hairy coal-black head through the floor and saying to the maid-servants, who were terrified by this apparition from the infernal regions: "Excuse me! Have you got a shovelful of coal, please? I think my boiler's going to go out!"

Public opinion was further alarmed by several of the open-air meetings held at Hyde Park Corner. At one of them Dr. Cummings, who had imagined the Crystal Way, announced very seriously that the building of the underground railway would certainly bring about the end of the world.

"So," he would conclude with reasonable logic, "why not build an overhead railway instead? Surely it would be better to meet the devil on earth rather than dig directly down to hell?"

And, in fact, it would be necessary to go down through the infernal regions of London, through a maze of sewers, water-pipes and gas-pipes. The engineers and architects had no technical experience of any kind and, what is more, they could not disrupt the active life of the city too much.

Pearson suggested that the "cut-and-cover" method should be used; that is to say, a wide trench would be dug out in small sections to the depth of the rock-bed, lined at the sides and overhead with a thick wall of bricks; the tunnel would then be roofed over and covered in again to restore the road to its previous appearance.

II

"THE MET"

Finally, in 1853, Parliament passed a Bill in favour of the underground railway and in 1854 the North Metropolitan Company was set up, with private capital and an additional subsidy of £45,000, which was wrung out of the Corporation of the City of London and the Great Western Railway.

Although the greater part of the future Metropolitan Railway followed the main roads of the city, it was sometimes necessary to effect expensive expropriations and straighten the lines, whereupon both the municipal authorities and the individuals concerned proved themselves somewhat grasping. Certain private individuals initiated legal proceedings and some of these cases were not settled until after the line had been completed. It was even necessary to re-site old churches which had stood for centuries in the mists of London and wrangle with certain parish authorities to whom heavy prices had to be paid. As a result one director of the Metropolitan Company made this remark to them:

"We hope, gentlemen, that you will pray very hard on our behalf, for we have certainly deserved it."

Finally, in 1861, that is six years after the setting up of the company, the first excavations began.

It is only three and a half miles from Paddington to Farringdon, but the building of the first section of the London "Met," known as the Fleet Valley Trunk Line, because it followed more or less the former bed of the River Fleet, was a complex undertaking. Work was begun on the surface and the road had to be dug out in small sections to avoid a complete stoppage of the traffic in one of London's busiest streets; then demolition work had to begin, as when, for example, the old cattle market at Farringdon had to be taken down and rebuilt at Islington, but once this vast space was empty a large railway terminus was built there, beneath which the G.W.R. later established a goods depot for taking merchandise to the other stations of London. Fortunately the route taken included very few ramps, but it had to pick its way carefully through countless pipings and the foundations of a certain number of public buildings which could not be knocked down or re-sited. Fortunately too it was placed fifty feet above the Thames and there was no danger of infiltration from the river. Infiltration did take place later, however, when the Metropolitan was extended towards the south. There was a serious accident also in 1861 when the line was taken alongside the Fleet.

This river gave its name to the famous street in London where the newspapers are published; in Elizabethan times it was a pleasant watercourse where Londoners used to go fishing, but early in the nineteenth century it had been made into a trunk sewer emptying into the Thames. The result was that the inevitable happened: either through old age or carelessness, the pipe burst and in no time at all the trench prepared for the future Metropolitan was filled with ten feet of filthy water.

London complained, but at this moment the Press was on Pearson's side. One amusing incident took place and the tale is still told in Fleet Street: a journalist on night duty came out of his club a little the worse for wear and heard that the buildings in this important street were about to collapse. He went back to his paper as quickly as he could to give them this sensational news:

"I've always said that the tunnel was too near Fleet Street. Our office is going to fall down any minute!"

"No matter," replied the editor, "the paper's been printed."

This flooding was the only outstanding incident during the work on the Met. However, very careful precautions had to be taken at first in order to brace the side walls of the tunnels so that neighbouring buildings would not fall down if the ground subsided from time to time. Wooden props were used for this. Further, pipes which had been laid practically at ground level had to be partly reconstituted, and with all possible speed. The work progressed very slowly because it was only possible to undertake small sections at a time and this piecemeal method held up progress considerably. As soon as a portion of the tunnel was finished the roof was filled in so that the street which had been dug out above it could be replaced and new buildings could be set up at places which had not been affected.

Stations were built at the same time and between them ventilation "blow-holes" were made through the road, protected by grids, for dispersing the steam and smoke. In 1930 it was still possible to see grids of this type in Paris, sometimes included in small buildings on the Sceaux-Luxembourg line.

However, when the tunnel went through open ground or a series of gaps between isolated buildings it was not roofed in. The walls were reinforced by brick buttresses, further strengthened by massive horizontal beams of cast iron which supplied additional safety. In this way the longest covered-in section of the railway only measured fifty-five chains, and the rest was open.

The haphazard route followed by the line between buildings or across pleasure grounds sometimes gave offence from the aesthetic point of view, even if it did not affect public health. One of the four-storeyed Victorian houses in Leinster Square, Bayswater, is absolutely identical with those on either side and it has the same balconies and pillars, the same stone steps and even a letter-box in the front door. In actual fact, however, the house is only about five feet deep and is no more than a façade resting against a supporting wall. It is, however, numbered 23-24, an address which is well known to certain practical jokers in London who ask for coal, milk and various goods to be delivered there. It used to be a joke, too, to send out invitation cards for various ceremonies or parties from this address, and people would arrange to meet their friends there. This curious dummy house was built there at the expense of the Metropolitan Railway, at the request of the inhabitants of the square, to conceal the entrance to the tunnel which went through it. This relic of the old heroic days was fortunately untouched by bombs during the last war.

All these technical accidents or unforeseen expenses affected the price of laying the line. The cost of one linear yard varied from £39 to £108, which brought the company into worse financial difficulties a few months before the completion of the enterprise, and relations with the organisations concerned became more and more strained.

37. An entrance to a Metropolitan Railway station about 1870

The City Corporation reproached them for the time taken to carry out the work, and since the tunnel had absorbed almost the entire capital available the G.W.R. was obliged to supply rolling stock and locomotives, which had not been provided for in the contract.

It was also necessary to lay an additional third rail, allowing the use of two different gauges, and although this was not a major inconvenience it increased costs still further.

Then, when the rolling stock had been placed on the rails, it was noticed that the doors could not be opened without touching the walls of the tunnels. At first the Board of Trade forbade their use, but gave permission in the end provided that a notice warned passengers of possible accidents.

Finally, on January 9th, 1863, three years and six months after work had begun, the Prime Minister, Mr. Gladstone, accompanied by his wife and the entire Cabinet of Her Majesty Queen Victoria, made a short tour of inspection in goods vans kindly lent by the contractors. The next day the official inauguration took place by a run from Bishop's Road to Farringdon, after which an immense banquet was held in the hall of the latter station, profusely decorated with green plants and flags.

The same day, from nine o'clock in the morning, the public had rushed to the turnstiles, and many of the working class and the aristocracy crowded into the rough and ready carriages. Each time the train returned from Baker Street the City Brass Band played loudly, but it could hardly be heard for the excitement of the crowd and the terrified cries of ladies trying to keep their crinolines in order, while their escorts cheered loudly. On January 10th, 1863, 30,000 Londoners made their first trip on the first underground railway in the world.

Its success continued, and during the first year 9½ million passengers rode enthusiastically on the "sewer train." There were three classes of carriages: those of the first class were luxurious, fitted with carpets and mirrors, the second class were less comfortable and spacious with wooden benches, while in the third class space was even more restricted.

Smoking was absolutely forbidden. If any employee found a gentleman smoking a cigar or a pipe they respectfully pointed out to him that he was breaking the regulations. As a rule the smoker gave up his cigar, which was always accepted with pleasure.

Lighting was supplied by oil lamps, but they were not sufficiently powerful, so, in order to read their newspapers comfortably, the Londoners brought candles with them and stuck them on the sides of the carriages. Later on gas was used, carried in rubber bags fixed on the roofs of the carriages, until eventually the more solid metallic cylinders were adopted. At first, heating was supplied by hot-water bottles which could be hired at the stations, but economy-minded travellers provided themselves with blankets.

The stations were announced inside the carriages by signs which were changed by a guard each time the train started, or by a rod worked by a lever placed on the line, but this did not always function correctly.

The signalling system was extremely elementary. Niches had been built at suitable spots along the walls of the tunnels and in each niche stood a man who, either by raising his hand or by displaying panels of wood painted in the usual colours, relayed information about incidents along the track or maintained the correct intervals between the trains.

But the most curious protection system was used later along the Baker Street–Swiss Cottage line and lasted until 1883. This was a single-track line continuing the Farringdon line with a by-pass at St. John's Wood, where the up- and down-trains were forced to meet each other. At this period automatic signalling had not been invented and the technique used was somewhat complicated but extremely picturesque. Two "token men," one wearing a blue cap and the other a red, accompanied the driver of each train, and their presence meant that the line was clear; when the two trains met at St. John's Wood the two pilots had to change from one to the other to show the driver that his line was clear. This change of train had to be carried out with skill and precision and it earned the admiration of the passengers. The younger people of London regarded the "tokens" as heroes, and not a few, on seeing their acrobatics, decided that one day they too would wear one of those famous caps.

The smoke, steam and soot caused great inconvenience and were extremely harmful to public health. The tunnels and stations soon became as black as the inside of factory chimneys and the travellers' clothing suffered as a result, to the great satisfaction of the London dyers and cleaners. The engineers, drivers and guards came out of the "Met" with smoke and steam pouring out of their clothes. It was so difficult for them to keep their faces clean that they asked permission to wear beards and moustaches, which was granted, although at first it had been forbidden by the regulations:

"Every worker is required to come on duty clean in person and clothes, shaved, and with the shoes blacked. They are also required to keep their hair cut. Not any instance of intoxication, whistling or levity on duty will be overlooked; besides being dismissed the offender will be liable to punishment. Fines will be imposed for talking, shouting, hooting or making any unpleasant noise, or unseemly actions, whether by hand, mouth or otherwise.

"It is urgently requested that every person on Sundays and other Holy days, when he is not required on duty, will attend a place of worship, as it will be the means of promotion when vacancies occur.

"The company's officers and servants are not to allow any person to stand in any of the carriages, or waggons, but compel them to sit upon the seats or floors: should they refuse to comply, they must be removed and given into the charge of the company's police."

All railway staff were forbidden to wear red clothes of any kind since this colour was used as a signal to stop or a danger warning.

Many funny stories about the railway circulated round London.

Shortly after the inauguration by Mr. Gladstone, Miles Fenton, later Sir Miles Fenton, director-general of the "Met," received the following note from the president of White's, the London club:

"In order to save further heavy wagering within the precincts of the club, the manager would be grateful if you would inform him of what became of the earth removed from the tunnels."

"Tell your president," Fenton replied to the messenger, "to go to Chelsea and see for himself."

And there it was. However, when the line was lengthened at later stages the earth from the tunnels was loaded on barges, taken down the Thames and emptied along the banks of the estuary.

We have seen that relationships between the Metropolitan and the Great Western Railway were not of the most cordial, even before the "Met" was opened. They deteriorated further during the months that followed, and in August, 1863, the G.W.R. gave the Metropolitan seven days in which to return its rolling stock and locomotives.

Fortunately the Great Northern Railway supplied its engines and carriages, but they were narrow-gauge, like everything they used. The "Met" could use them because its three-rail track could take both gauges, but the new carriages were less comfortable than the ones they replaced and the locomotives emitted much more smoke than those of the G.W.R.

In order to offset this major inconvenience various systems were adopted. The ventilation was greatly increased, including the famous grid-covered "blow-holes" on the pavements, and they continued to pour out steam, to the great terror of passers-by and especially of horses. Certain places were spoilt by the smoke, like the Temple

Gardens, where the fine old lawns were affected. Horizontal shafts were also arranged along the tunnel conveying the smoke and steam into places where they would cause less trouble.

Lastly, the locomotives were fitted with a device which allowed the driver to send some of the steam and smoke into the water-tanks where condensation took place. As a result of the rise in temperature produced in this way, the condensation reached saturation point and the engine lost steam, leading to a reduction in speed and irregularity in running times. As a result the drivers preferred not to use this device too often.

But the "Met" remained popular in spite of its dangers, which were not all imaginary for, during its first three years, three deaths took place. Inquests were held, and the Coroner stated that these unfortunate deaths were due to natural causes "accelerated, it is true, by the suffocating atmosphere of the underground railway." Later, scientific investigation revealed that there was the same proportion of oxygen in the tunnels as outside them and that the greatest danger was caused by the rubbing of the wooden brakes against the wheels every time the train slowed down and stopped, giving off a highly poisonous carbohydrogen.

But the Metropolitan had one great advantage for the Londoners. It was warm—and as well as travelling comparatively faster than above ground, they had not to struggle through the mud in winter. In particular they could escape from the famous London fogs which often paralysed traffic completely and led to fatal accidents.

The Metropolitan had achieved its aim in preventing road traffic congestion to a great extent. During its early years, at least, it was also a successful commercial enterprise with the result that the city capitalists, thinking of their own interests, soon contemplated extending it.

In 1864 a new company was formed, called the Metropolitan Railway. It was distinct from the first company but collaborated with it all the same, in order to complete the circuit of the London main-line stations, along with many intermediary stops.

Twenty years later, in 1884, the double circle of lines serving the districts north of the Thames was completed. Then other companies established branch lines which already went as far as the important London suburbs.

The trains belonging to the first two companies went round these two circles in opposite directions. They covered the distance of ten miles in seventy minutes, and when electrification took place later this time was reduced to fifty minutes. Express trains were tried out, carrying only first- and second-class passengers, but the experiment was not continued.

Naturally the London railway stations used the underground trains for goods transport, and there was even a branch connecting these stations with the General Post Office. This goods transport lasted at least until 1926, when it was finally abandoned.

One of the great pioneers of the underground railway was Sir Edward Watkin, president of the Metropolitan Railway from 1872 to 1894. He had even conceived the most grandiose railway plan in the world, which was to transform the Metropolitan into a vast permanent way linking the north and south of England, from Manchester to Dover; next he envisaged the extension of this artery into Europe by a tunnel beneath the Channel; and it is clear that if this had been done Paris would have had its "Métro" before 1900. Watkin's intrepidity and ambition were such that if he had succeeded he would have extended his project considerably, taking the Orient Express to India, the Caucasus or Constantinople.

But by the grace of God England was an island subject to winds and tides, and the negotiations between the governments broke down, although in 1876 two companies, one French and the other British, carried out experimental work on both sides of the Channel. In 1882, British public opinion revealed itself to be so fiercely insular that the Board of Trade stopped the work at Dover, for they believed the Channel Tunnel might lead to a threat of invasion.

In spite of the success of the Metropolitan it did not bring good dividends to its shareholders, because in the streets above it horse-bus companies had increased enormously; they were certainly less rapid but they were cheaper than the underground. The company fought back with the same weapons and, on August 6th, 1866, the Metropolitan brought into service its own horse-bus company. It was somewhat paradoxical to see an underground railway company forced to increase the surface congestion, which it was in duty bound to relieve, only three years after it had been brought into service.

It should be added that at the end of the last century the remarkable increase in the population was enough to make all kinds of transport undertakings thrive. In the twenty-two years during which Watkin was chairman of the Metropolitan, he increased the annual number of passengers from 44 million in 1872 to 88 million in 1894; the number carried in 1954 by the Underground alone was 650 million.

But the use of electricity in industry was already competing with steam power, and it was no longer possible to use the "cut-and-cover" method for future extensions. By 1900 or so the underground passages were full of new compressed air ducts, electric cables, telephone and telegraph wires. The next move was to dig down deeper and the underground railway was replaced by the famous London "Tube."

III

"THE TUBE"

In fact the first tube goes back to 1862, when the first tunnel was made. During that year the old Lambeth Bridge was built and Peter Barlow, the chief engineer, noticed that the iron cylinders, forming the piers for the bridge, could be driven into the river bed with relative ease.

He immediately thought that it would be just as possible to lay horizontal cylinders in the clay soil of London. Brunel's first tunnel beneath the Thames had been built of brickwork and proved a difficult, costly enterprise, although it did not greatly ease traffic problems between the two banks of the Thames, as has already been mentioned. In 1867 Barlow published a pamphlet dealing with the traffic problem, which he proposed to ease by building an underground railway running in a "tube" under the Thames, operated by a cable.

Work began in 1869 on both sides of the river simultaneously, and vertical shafts were sunk, measuring sixty-five and fifty-five feet respectively. Then, using a circular metal shield designed by the engineer, the "Tube" was bored out under the Thames. Barlow's machine consisted of six symmetrical pieces of curved sheet-iron firmly joined together with a central opening through which the tunnel was dug out while the soil was thrown back.

By means of a somewhat complex mechanism of levers and hand-operated jacks it was possible to go about five feet forward in twenty-four hours, by successive forward movements of about twenty inches each. By this method a small preliminary gallery was excavated in front of the shield along which it could move. Next, a space was made behind it large enough to take one of the 800 cast iron rings which were to form the outer lining of the tunnel, joined together by cement. It is obvious that this technique was more economical and rapid than the brickwork used by Brunel.

Another advantage of this method was the possibility of protecting the finished part of the tunnel against any accidents. If any warning was received it was only necessary to close the opening in the shield to prevent any infiltration of soil or water. This method was somewhat different from that adopted later for building the Paris "Métro." In London each "tube" only carries one line, while the tunnels in Paris take two lines.

It was found in the end that Barlow's cable railway had little success because it was slow in operation and gave poor results. Londoners abandoned it just as casually as pedestrians had given up using Brunel's first tunnel.

Although the results were not particularly effective, Barlow's method nevertheless represented an important innovation and a valuable example of tunnelling technique. But twenty years were still to pass before the first travellers could take their places in a real electrically operated tube train and go through a tunnel under the river.

A more advanced shield was then used, developed by James Henry Greathead, one of Barlow's collaborators. It had a diameter of thirteen and a half feet and was driven by hydraulic jacks while the iron rings were joined together with cement under pressure.

Later still, in 1906, Price's rotary excavator was used for the first time; this was a further development of Greathead's shield, and included a rotor with a triangular blade which, as it turned, dug out the soil like some gigantic drill and threw it back into the interior. Naturally, when some solid or rocky mass was encountered recourse was had to the human hand or to explosives. This excavator was very effective for carrying out the work quickly, as, for example, when it was used to join two lines together during a few precious hours at night-time when trains were not running.

In contrast to surface-working which was carried out by labourers, "tube" working turned the men into moles; the work was arranged as a rule in the following manner.

The lines were planned in a way that would take them under buildings as little as possible, for the vibrations would have shaken the foundations, and the tunnels were taken as deep as possible in order to avoid the many sets of pipes; this was not difficult to arrange, however, for the sub-soil of London consists for the most part of a thick layer of clay going down in some places as deep as 500 feet. It is for this reason that visitors to London find the tube very far below ground, and certain stations, such as Hampstead, are built 200 feet below street level.

As soon as the route had been decided on, vertical shafts were dug, first at the beginning and the end of the line, at places where stations were planned, and then at certain strategic points for bringing up material and for the removal of rubbish. These shafts formed relay points between which the tunnelling shields were placed, sometimes over three miles apart. The calculation of the levels, which was too long a process to describe here, was so accurate that the surveyors and technicians succeeded in making the two parts of the tunnel coincide exactly.

The shields were so easy to handle that by skilful manoeuvring of their outer edges they could be made to turn slightly at the curves or go up and down to make artificial slopes. These ramps were arranged at the arrival and departure points for the future stations, because they helped the trains to slow up and start. This system saves the company a great deal of electric current and wear and tear on brakes, for there are 277 stations in Greater London and at one of the busiest, Charing Cross for example, trains stop 643 times per day.

Two parallel tube lines are seldom laid simultaneously; the second is begun only after a certain length of the first has been completed. Unlike the Paris "Métro," where all lines are double-track, the lines in London do not necessarily run parallel to each other and sometimes one is laid over the other.

The building of the first "electric subway" by the City and South London Railway Co. marked the beginning of two new eras, the age of the tube and the age of electricity. The tube ran from Stockwell to King William Street, nowadays called Bank; it had been expressly laid down by an Act of Parliament passed in 1884 that steam must not be used because the line was entirely underground and it was impossible for smoke and steam to escape. It had been anticipated that only the American-invented cable traction would be used, but fortunately it was not necessary in the end, for during the building of the line silent electric motors were invented and there were no tiresome connecting-rods to cause vibrations dangerous to buildings.

The double tube-line was begun in 1886 under the direction of Greathead. It was laid at a depth of ninety feet and was completed in 1890.

The Prince of Wales, the future Edward VII, had the honour therefore on November 4th, 1890, of inaugurating the first electrically operated tube railway in the world. Accompanied by his elder son, Albert, Duke of Clarence, and leading scientists and engineers, the Prince went down to King William Street Station in a richly up-holstered lift. On the platform, in the presence of the Lord Mayor, the Aldermen and the Sheriff of the City of London, he was given a golden key, and with it he operated an illuminated switch which lit up the royal party as well as supplying current to the rails. The train then left for Stockwell on the south bank of the Thames, where a traditional banquet was served in honour of electricity, the tube and the Victorian age generally.

The line was opened to the public the same day, and since a heavy fall of snow occurred during the next fortnight the streets became impassable and 165,000 Londoners used the railway for the first time, to their great satisfaction.

In 1891 the line carried 5,365,000 passengers for the reasonable standard charge of 2d., with the result that the public christened this railway "the twopenny tube," a name which clung to it for a long time.

Punch called it the *Sardine Box Railway*, a fairly good description of the strange carriages into which the passengers were packed. Each train consisted of three windowless cars, in which thirty-two passengers sat facing each other on benches that were padded right up to the roof. The cars were equipped with sliding doors, but the designers had not thought it worthwhile to fit windows in the walls, assuming perhaps, and understandably so, that the monotonous landscape of the tube rendered anything of the kind superfluous.

So the passengers were imprisoned in their padded cells and could not read the names of the stations. The company helped them by employing men both inside the trains and on the stations to announce the names, but their Cockney accents made these announcements so unintelligible that windows soon had to be added to the cars so that the passengers could see for themselves where they were.

The passengers, indeed, had no diversions on their underground journey. They could not even enjoy gazing at the posters we see today, for advertising was strictly forbidden inside the cars. All they could do was to meditate on the many severe warnings issued by the company, such as "Passengers are forbidden to walk on the roof of the cars; anyone doing so is liable to a fine of forty shillings." I understand, however, that there was never any need to deal seriously with an offence of this kind.

Naturally these electric trains were much faster than their predecessors. The older passengers liked to recall the strange incidents that used to occur in the old days of steam. One day, at Edgware Road Station, for instance, a guard had a bone to pick with three gentlemen who were smoking large cigars; but while he was respectfully indicating that this was forbidden, the train started for Praed Street, leaving the dutiful guard on the platform. He had to rejoin the train whatever happened. He ran up the stairs to the street and went on running until he reached the next station, where he caught up with the train and resumed his post.

With the coming of the tube the public used lifts which took them directly from the pavements to the platforms. These were installed in pairs at each station, in case there should be any stoppage which would upset the working of the line. They were naturally supervised carefully by staff who were so experienced that they could say to the day, and even to the hour, when a cable was going to break. The same skill was developed in France by the lift-operators on the Eiffel Tower.

Escalators were introduced in 1911 and had many advantages over the lifts. They did the work of four lifts at once and operated with much greater regularity. The public also disliked waiting for the lifts, and when large numbers of passengers reached the pavements or the platforms together congestion resulted. The escalators played their part therefore in easing traffic problems both in the streets and the underground. Accidents are rare, for anyone can stop the moving staircase merely by pressing a switch, but there is a fine of £5 for its improper use.

IV

"THE UNDERGROUND"

In about 1901 the four companies, the pioneer Metropolitan, the District, the City and South London and the Central London, all went through a crisis, for they were engaged in such fierce competition that their very existence was in danger. They were carrying out a heavy development programme and they had a large administrative staff which reduced the dividends to shareholders to nothing. Lastly they were all obliged to modernise their networks and their rolling stock by changing over to electrical operation.

It was an American, Charles Tyson Yerkes, a famous electric train expert, who achieved a technical revolution by coordinating in London the first pool of underground transport, the Underground Electric Railway Company of London, soon known to everyone simply as the Underground.

This cooperation was not achieved without arguments and discussions, for both steam and electricity had their supporters. In 1900 therefore a race took place between a steam train and an electric train on parallel tracks between Earls Court and Kensington High Street. The electric train defeated the other at the post and triumphantly proved its many advantages. From that time the age of steam was over.

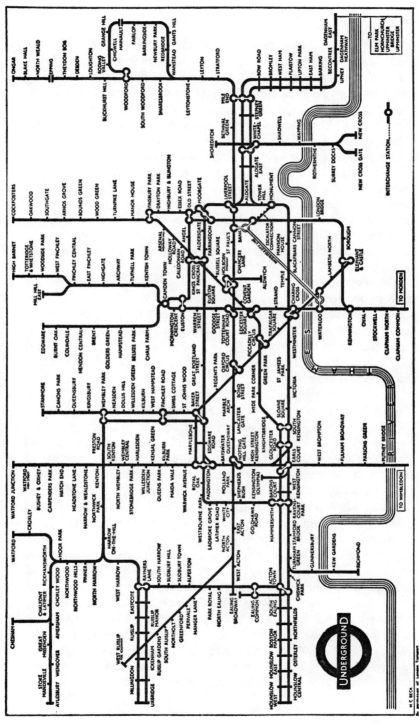

38. Map of the London Underground system

Yerkes next had recourse to intimidation, and succeeded in winning over many small underground companies which had multiplied in the wake of big ones (the "Circus," the "Strand," etc.), persuading them to adopt his ideas, as the Underground had done. Yerkes died in 1905 and his name should be added to those of Pearson, Watkin, Barlow and Greathead in the roll of the great pioneers of London's Underground.

The complete electrification of the tube was successfully terminated on September 24th, 1905. The same year all its users were delighted by the end of a tradition—the Underground ran all day on Sunday, whereas previously it had not run while church services were in progress. The abolition of strange customs of this kind was a sign of progress. Thanks to the Underground, mighty London with its eight million inhabitants scattered over 700 square miles can breathe more easily.

On several occasions the underground network has undergone a major coordination programme. In 1905 a Royal Commission laid down that "the tramcars and the underground railway taking urban and suburban traffic should be amalgamated in a broad system in accordance with the protection of the public interest under the control of the Ministry of Transport," an interesting suggestion which was repeated in 1920 and 1923.

Finally, in 1933, the London Passenger Transport Act set up the London Transport Board, which effectively coordinated all aspects of traffic, including the railways, in the London area; 171 transport companies of all kinds, ten underground companies, 144 bus and charabanc companies, seventeen tramcar and trolley bus companies were in this way included in one single organisation.

The London Transport Executive is continually at work studying or building new routes, and its highly qualified technicians often act as consultants or engineers for subways in great capital cities, such as Moscow, Stockholm, Copenhagen and Istanbul.

I never take the long escalators on London's Underground without thinking of those terrible nights of the last war and the underground passages which sheltered so many Londoners.

Millions of British civilians slept there on rough and ready beds, surrounded by their most valuable possessions, which they took up with them in the morning to the surface, although smoke from the night's fires still hung over the town; and many of these people have told me that the deep safety of the tube saved their lives and allowed them to keep their courage and their belief in victory.

IX

THE TAY AND FORTH BRIDGES

Man proposes,
God disposes . . .

THE TAY BRIDGE DISASTER

Seen from Queensferry on a spring morning the Forth Bridge, with its three humps, standing half-lost in the mist and sea looks like the famous Loch Ness Monster immobilised by some magic spell. As the ferryboat comes closer, the bridge looks more like a prehistoric animal than ever, and with its three piers and two viaducts it resembles a dinosaur. Eventually the tubes and girders become clearer and the ferryboat passengers can see the railway track from which a plume of smoke rises from time to time. The whole structure has a dull, indefinable colour in strange contrast to the brilliant tartans in the Edinburgh shop windows.

This was my first sight of the famous Forth Bridge, which has a span including approach works of 8,000 feet. The earlier Tay Bridge measured 10,760 feet, and for thirty years these were the two biggest bridges in the world. In spite of the huge suspension bridges in the U.S.A., the Forth Bridge remains one of the masterpieces of over-water bridge-building.[1]

Standing beneath the north pier, exactly beneath the bridge-deck which takes the railway lines, I trained my camera on the details of the superstructure. As I turned the lens in every direction I could see through the viewfinder a kind of X-ray panorama of this metal framework which extended upwards and outwards in astonishing perspectives of infinite elegance.

Through the whirring of the ciné-camera the scene resembled some schoolboy's geography book, for an express train crossed the bridge almost in silence, an aeroplane disappeared into the mists on its way to Edinburgh and out at sea a cargo-boat entered the estuary, with white foam in its wake.

About 1870 the British railway system was well in advance of those on the Continent, although Britain carried out no large-scale operations such as the Simplon Tunnel, for instance. It was easy to reach the north of Scotland along the west coast, but on the east the deep

[1] See the list of the twelve biggest bridges in the world (1956) in Appendix II.

estuaries of the Tay and the Forth meant that the lines had to make detours which entailed heavy expenditure of time and money. Ferry-boats across the firths shortened the route for road traffic, and the idea of a railway link between Edinburgh and Dundee, a distance of thirty-three and a half miles, by the building of two vast bridges, became more and more indispensable. They would shorten the journey by sixty-two miles and two hours.

The building of a bridge more than one and a half miles long over the River Tay was considered first, as far back as 1866, not without strong opposition from the public and even from the railway companies, who were alarmed by the scope of such an undertaking, which had never been attempted before.

In 1870, however, designs and plans by Sir Thomas Bouch were approved by the Government and there were no more complaints from the public. The work began in 1872 and was finished in 1877, taking exactly twice as long and costing twice as much as had been originally estimated. The first estimate of the cost had been £130,000.

The Tay Bridge consisted of eighty-five spans built of metal girders with a maximum span of 250 feet, supported by cast-iron piers resting on brickwork foundations on a cement bed, and the whole structure carried a single-track railway line at a height of eighty feet above high-water mark. From a technical point of view it was no different, considerations of size apart, from any metal bridge anywhere in the British Isles.

Preparations were being made to carry out a second bridge of a similar kind over the Firth of Forth when, on December 28th, 1879, the Tay Bridge was swept away as a passenger train was going over it, and not a single survivor was ever found. The train vanished into the night like one of the famous Scottish ghosts and it was impossible at once to discover the exact cause of the disaster.

This is the dry, unvarnished report by Mr. Walker, director of the North British Railway Company, which was immediately given to the Government and the Press:

"According to reports we have received on the terrible accident which has occurred at the Tay Bridge, it appears that several spans of the bridge, along with the last train coming from Edinburgh yesterday evening, December 28th, about half-past seven, were swept into the river. I deeply regret to have to inform you that there were nearly three hundred passengers on the train, in addition to the members of the company's staff who were on duty.

"When the news of the accident was received in Dundee the tragedy appeared so terrible that nobody could believe it, and this feeling soon gave way to one of deep dismay.

"The train had left Edinburgh on Sunday at 4.15 p.m., consisting of four third-class carriages, one second-class and one first-class, one luggage van and the engine—eight vehicles in all.

"It had left Burntisland on time and had remained on time all through Fifeshire, taking on passengers at each of the principal stations. At St. Forth it was exactly five minutes late. It was signalled from there to the signalman at the south end of the bridge who passed the signal on to his colleague at the north end, and from there it was signalled to Dundee. At this moment an extremely strong wind was blowing, a real hurricane, and barely one or two minutes after the signal had been telegraphed from one end of the bridge to the other, the bridge suddenly collapsed. At first it was thought that the train might have lost time, and attempts were made to ascertain this by getting in touch with the south bank of the Tay. But in the end the staff had to accept the evidence and assume that the train had fallen into the river.

"The steamer which sailed at 11 p.m. had the greatest difficulty in reaching the scene of the disaster and arrived just as the moon was beginning to set behind the dense clouds.

"Those on board could nevertheless see that everything had given way over a distance of 3,280 feet. Not even the stump of an iron bar remained. There was a yawning gap and only a few fragments of girders could be seen hanging over each side. Through the darkness the passengers on the boat thought they could distinguish human figures on one or other of the two river banks; but the river had yielded nothing, and what had been mistaken for survivors were remains of cables fixed to the abutment piers of the bridge.

"There is no obvious explanation as to why thirteen massive spans could have been swept away so completely, leaving no trace. The most plausible explanation seems to be that they collapsed as a result of lateral pressure exerted by the wind at the moment when the weight of the train exerted pressure from above, causing simultaneous counter-stress. At this point some weaker section must have given way and the heavy weight of the train must have accelerated the total collapse. It is surprising that the sound of such a collapse was not heard in the town, but this was probably due to the violence of the wind. In fact nothing remains of the bridge except the stone foundations and part of the brick abutment piers with the stumps of the iron uprights."

A careful enquiry which was carried out later, lasting several months, proved that the vertical iron girders, many of which were flawed, had not been able to withstand the force of such an exceptionally high wind, and also that the trains crossing the viaduct had gradually acquired speeds more rapid than had been anticipated in the original calculations.

A few years after the catastrophe a new viaduct was built, and the cast-iron pillars were replaced by iron ones, while some of the spans from the previous bridge were used. They were placed on the new viaduct by means of a floating pontoon equipped with hydraulic jacks. The spans were raised at high tide and lowered on to each pier at low tide. The stone pillars were entirely rebuilt for the bridge deck was widened to take a second railway line.

II

A TECHNICAL REVOLUTION

In 1872 Sir Thomas Bouch had submitted plans to Parliament for a bridge over the Forth based on that over the Tay, but after the tragedy the project was naturally shelved.

Some revolutionary technique had to be devised in order to satisfy public opinion, for feeling still ran high. Without the Tay Bridge disaster we should not have had the Forth Bridge, a masterpiece of structural metal work on horizontal lines, built at about the same time as Paris produced a similar masterpiece on vertical lines in the Eiffel Tower.

With the name of the great French engineer should be associated therefore the names of his English colleagues, Sir John Fowler and Benjamin Baker, who on the other side of the Channel presided with the same skill over the building of this splendid viaduct.

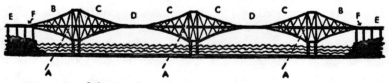

39. Diagram of the Forth Bridge:

A. Column with bridge deck
B. Side cantilevers
C. Central cantilevers
D. Central spans

E. Approach viaducts
F. Anchoring of the side cantilevers
   to the abutment piers

Between Fifeshire to the north of the Firth of Forth and Linlithgow to the south was a promontory about 3,000 feet long, and the small island of Inchgarvie which extended it to a distance of 1,500 feet from the north bank. On each side of this rock the sea and the river met in two channels measuring 1,200 feet across, with a depth of 200 feet.

This was the problem: how, with only these three points of support, was it possible to link two sections of railway line 150 feet above sea-level, allowing the necessary clearance for sailing ships passing beneath, which at that time still carried 130 feet of sail?

The Forth Bridge was planned on the cantilever principle. At each of the three points of support was a kind of pivot carrying beams of equal length, stabilised by their own weight and anchored at each end.

Each arm of the lever consists of two cantilevers, to give them their technical name, joined together by a row of four columns, each 344 feet high; the lower part of the cantilever is subject to compressive stress by means of tubular members and the upper part to tensile stress by means of girders.

On the Forth Bridge these three cantilever units were to be connected by two central spans with upright latticed beams, which were much lower and their weight was evenly distributed between them.

The outer spans or side cantilevers were both anchored to the abutment piers of the approach viaducts to prevent the central cantilevers, which balanced them, from being lowered by the pressure exerted in the middle of the central spans. The approach viaducts at each end were much simpler in construction, built with upright girders, resting on brickwork piers which were mostly erected on land.

Once the two viaducts and the three cantilevers were in position the usual kind of bridge deck carrying a double-track railway line was to be placed in position. Unfortunately the addition of a road was not

40. Illustration of the cantilever principle: two projecting arms reach towards each other, the gap between their ends (i.e. the men's hands) being bridged by an independent, suspended span. The total weight is balanced by the outer arms which reach to-wards the shore (in the case of a bridge) and are anchored down

contemplated, but obviously it was not in the railway companies' interest to consider road transport: competition between rail and road does not date from today.

III

THE FORTH BRIDGE TRIUMPH

The plans for the bridge were approved by the Board of Trade, the House of Commons and the railway companies concerned (the Great Northern, the Midland, North-Eastern and North British) who formed a pool (The Forth Bridge Railway Company) to finance the undertaking. The cost was first estimated at £1,500,000 but it eventually rose to £3,500,000, which was found without the slightest difficulty.

The steel, granite and cement needed for the work, as well as powerful raising equipment, were collected on both sides of the river. Assembly units, repair and maintenance shops, stores and dumps were also set up and a stretch of ground 2,000 feet long was levelled off with a downward slope so that the materials and equipment could be brought to the site quickly and efficiently.

Temporary cottages for the workmen were built in the villages of Dalmeny, Queensferry and Kirkcaldy. Large canteens, dormitories, recreation rooms and concert halls were available for the unmarried men. All the workers were compulsorily insured and in the case of illness or accident received twelve shillings per week.

In spite of the risks and problems involved in handling dangerous materials at heights of over 2,000 feet, accidents were relatively rare. When the newspapers expressed alarm on one occasion a correspondent in London did not hesitate to reply in the following sensible terms:

"There are no more accidents . . . than in an ordinary ship-building yard . . . but as there is only one Forth Bridge, and as everything that takes place on it seems to get reported in every paper in the country, people get quite erroneous ideas about the fatalities that occur."

Infinite precautions were taken to avoid accidents, and steel safety nets were hung at the places where there was a risk of being struck on the head by a bolt or a hammer, as well as below the tubes and girders where an accidental movement could lead to a fall into the sea or on to the ground.

After the contractors had studied the Fowler–Baker plans carefully they found themselves faced by a four-fold task: laying the foundations for the piers, which were of brickwork and metal, erecting the cantilevers, fixing the central spans in position, and then synchronising the work on both sides of the river, as well as on both sides of the island of Inchgarvie, where the large central pier was to be placed. All the materials, machines and tools naturally had to be brought by boats or barges drawn by tugs.

The method used for assembling these vast quantities of metal was completely different from that used by Eiffel in Paris for the construction of the famous Tower. Every section for the Tower reached the site in a completely finished state, with exact dimensions and holes drilled in advance so that they could be assembled just as they were; the pieces used for the Forth Bridge were delivered with rough dimensions, the holes for the bolts or rivets were drilled on the spot and the metal sections modified as necessary.

The foundations of the viaduct on the north bank (in Fife) presented no particular difficulty, for they were placed more or less at low-water level. Those on the Edinburgh side on the south were built with the help of movable dams, temporary square dykes made of wood and cement and measuring thirty to forty feet high.

The three vertical axes of the cantilevers were each supported in the sea-bed by a group of four round piers with a base diameter of about seventy feet. The axes of the north and south cantilevers formed a quadrilateral of 130 feet by 154 feet and those of the Inchgarvie cantilever 130 feet by 268 feet.

Each of the four consisted of a circular granite casing over stone bonded with cement. Their capping was in granite also, fitted with forty-eight-feet-long steel bolts which held in position a metal flange carrying the lower tubular member of each cantilever arm.

The piers were not all of the same height because the profile of the estuary described two different curves which met on the surface at Inchgarvie. Those standing in deep water—the maximum depth was about 200 feet—were built with the help of caissons, huge cylinders made from plates of steel bolted together and looking like gasometers. They were made on land and taken down an incline to the river bank where a tug took them to the right position.

These caissons, which were designed with extreme skill and care, were like perfected diving bells, factory-produced. They included shafts for ventilation and for the deposit and disposal of materials handled by cranes placed at the summit. Cylindrical trucks at their base moved them into position on a minute railway line.

In the lower chamber, which was in direct contact with the sea-bed, the men could work in complete safety by the light of arc lamps. The mud and pebbly clay were dug out with picks or with the help of a hydraulic cutter; then the cement workers laid the foundations which had been prepared by a cement-mixer installed on the upper platform. Lastly, inside the caisson, the granite casing was built and rose gradually above the water level.

The last caisson was placed in position on May 26th, 1884, without any difficulty, in the presence of Lord and Lady Aberdeen. Although it weighed 400 tons it was given a ballast of cement in order to resist the force of the water; all the caissons had to be provided with floating protective breakwaters which prevented them from coming into contact with the many ships which continued to sail up and down the estuary.

When each masonry pier reached the required height of about twenty feet above high-water mark the thick steel flange which was to take the column of metal was bolted to the summit. It consisted of a cylinder of riveted sheet-iron with a diameter of 15 feet 6 inches manufactured in sections of varying length.

The total height of each of these steel columns amounted to 345 feet. It is interesting to note at this point that the total height of the Forth Bridge above high-water mark—about 370 feet—is more or less equivalent to the second storey of the Eiffel Tower, the spire of the Cathedral of Chartres, the Dome of the Invalides, the Cathedral of Milan and St. Paul's Cathedral in London.

Apart from light bracing at the base of the lower cantilever arches, the Forth Bridge (unlike the first storey of the Eiffel Tower) was built without scaffolding and with perfect synchronisation; the cantilevers were built at the same speed and each one of them extended farther out into space until they met the branch being built out from the other side.

The sections of the tubular members were put in position by cranes moving on provisional horizontal girders. They were then joined together by hydraulic riveters installed in circular cages eighteen feet high; they encased the tubes and travelled with them as they gradually rose higher. About half-way up these tubes the interior floor which was to take the railway lines was laid simultaneously as the cantilevers continued to extend, thereby keeping the requisite balance.

When they were completed the cantilevers looked like two huge bird-beaks facing each other in the middle of the estuary; all that was necessary was to link them together by the central spans, which also consisted of metallic tubes and girders.

This operation presented distinct difficulties, and three solutions were contemplated:

1. Sliding half of the span on to each of the cantilevers to make them meet in the middle.

2. Building the entire span in the workshops, bringing it on barges between the arms of the cantilevers and raising it by cables until it was level with their ends. This technique was used in 1916 when the cantilever bridge at Quebec was built, but the cables broke and the entire span, measuring 640 feet, fell into the St. Lawrence River and was only recovered with great difficulty.

3. Raising the span to an overhanging position at each end of the cantilever, still preserving the synchronisation so that the balance would not be upset.

This last solution was the one adopted, an additional technical achievement of the Forth Bridge engineers. Cranes came forward into the middle of the river, cautiously slinging into position tons of tubing and girders which finally achieved the continuous junction of the span.

On that day all the tugs blew their sirens as hard as they could, generously using up the steam that they no longer needed.

On January 22nd, 1890, that is seven years and two months after work had begun, trials took place without incident. Two trains of 1,000 tons each, double the weight that the bridge was called upon to carry (at that time), crossed the two railway lines side by side without causing greater stress than had been anticipated. On March 4th, His Royal Highness the Prince of Wales, the future King Edward VII, solemnly drove in a golden rivet bearing his name, the last of the 6,500,000 which had been used altogether.

Since that date the history of the Forth Bridge has been uneventful, as I was told on the spot and also at Edinburgh Station when I left again for London. However, when I opened my newspaper I learnt that the Tay Bridge was to have a parallel bridge for road traffic and if the funds were available the Forth Bridge would have one also.

X

THE EIFFEL TOWER

"It is the i of Paris firing its dot like a glorious cannon towards the beauty of interstellar space. Sometimes I have anguished nightmares: I can hear the Eiffel Tower falling down. Its dinosaur's tail ends at Brest or Toulon. And along with my forty million colleagues I am buried in broken lamps and shreds of sky. In the morning the proud giraffe has grown a hundred yards taller."

Léon-Paul Fargue

I

AN IDEA IN THE AIR

About 1885 the officials who were organising the Great Exhibition of 1889, which was to commemorate the centenary of the French Revolution, wondered what outstanding architectural attraction they could offer to the gaping crowds—something that would go well with the greatest popular movement of all times.

It was a tradition that every universal exhibition should present some "star turn." In 1878 it was the Trocadero. The well-known building had been built on the former hill of Passy, and took its name from a small town in Spain where the French had won a not very splendid victory in 1823; the architecture of the Trocadero caused a good deal of discussion, but the building disappeared in 1936, and gave way to the more attractive Palais de Chaillot of today.

In 1885, in order to commemorate the centenary of their independence, the Americans had built in Washington a famous obelisk of which they were very proud, for it rose to a height of 557 feet, and at that time it was the highest building in the world. This made it fairly clear to the Old World that their "star turn" should be a tall building too, and everyone naturally thought of some immensely high tower.

Nothing could be more bourgeois in nature than the nineteenth century, which had not yet found a style of its own, although it was only fifteen years from its close. The Industrial Revolution had begun with the railways, and there was no better symbol for it than iron, the most common, universal and useful metal in the whole world—before uranium was discovered.

The idea of a tower made of metal appealed greatly to the organisers of the Exhibition. It was not a new idea, because the British had already thought of it. In 1833 Trevithick, one of the first railway pioneers, had suggested that, in order to commemorate the passing of the Reform Bill, a tower of cast iron should be erected in London. It was to rise to a height of 1,000 feet, with a diameter at the base of 100 feet, narrowing to ten feet at the top. The tower was to consist of 1,500 sheets of cast iron, each ten feet long, bolted together by lead seams, and the whole building would rest on a stone base 460 feet high. It would be possible to go up the tower in a lift worked by compressed air. Unfortunately, Trevithick died before King William IV had approved his plans, and the great monument raised in memory of the victims of the Fire of London in 1666 had no rival to fear.

In 1874, when the Philadelphia Exhibition was held, the Americans had put forward this same idea of a metal tower rising to a height of 1,000 feet. On this occasion, however, they proposed an iron cylinder with a diameter of thirty feet, fixed to the ground by braces secured to a circular surround eighty feet in diameter. It looked like a factory chimney, or the mast of some giant cargo boat, and although it could form a monumental symbol of this great industrial and maritime nation, it made no new contribution to art or technique.

In addition to the material used, the focal point of the French Exhibition had to fulfil other conditions: it had to be economic and support itself by attracting great numbers of visitors; it had also to be temporary, for there could be no question of keeping it after the Exhibition had closed.

But designers of brick and stone buildings did not give up the struggle against their metallic competitor, especially Bourdais and Sébillot, who suggested building a gigantic masonry tower. Because of its very nature, their project was naturally turned down by the Exhibition organisers, who had been definitely intrigued by the idea of a metal tower ever since 1886.

"This manifestation," they wrote, in the style of an Agricultural Show programme, "which is to celebrate the birth of modern France, should be a kind of apotheosis of metal and the machine, which symbolise the triumph of reason over obscurantism."

It was then that Gustave Eiffel,[1] genius of structural metalwork and bold bridge-builder who had earned the admiration of the entire world, put forward his plans for the famous Tower, which were approved on May 26th, 1886, by an irrevocable decision of the Organising Committee. He laid down as a principle that the Eiffel Tower should not be built for the Exhibition, but that the Exhibition should be built round it; and finally, "that the Tower should be an original masterpiece of the metal industry, and that the Eiffel Tower alone seemed to answer this need to the full."

In establishing his adventurous and highly novel plan Eiffel set out at the same time to attack the erroneous and inadequate ideas of those who were still in favour of stone:

[1] Gustave Eiffel was the great-great grandson of Jean-René Bönichausen who emigrated from the Rhineland to France in the early eighteenth century.

"In theory," he said, "it is very difficult to plan a stonework tower, and in practice it would present considerable dangers and drawbacks, the least of which is its high cost, which is entirely out of proportion to the aim to be achieved . . . further, Antiquity, the Middle Ages, and the Renaissance, took the use of stone to the farthest extremes, and it seems hardly possible to develop these materials further, especially since the art of building has not made very much progress from this point of view for a long time."

Once the idea of the Tower was accepted, 107 plans were examined, with the intention of fixing the site of the Tower on the Champ-de-Mars, within the boundary of the Exhibition, which was forced to keep to these limits. The most absurd of the plans were turned down, and the more convincing ones retained: Raulin's tower became a monumental entrance tower to the Exhibition, while Nachon-Cassien placed his astride the Seine over a bridge which was to link the Esplanade des Invalides to the gardens of the Trocadero. This idea was very attractive but it became obvious at once that it would be impossible to lay foundations near the river bed solid enough to support a building weighing 7,000 tons. What is more, the Exhibition programme laid down that the Tower was to be on the Champ-de-Mars, as already stated. In the end Eiffel's project was the only one approved; he placed his Tower not far from the Seine on a line drawn from the Trocadero to the École Militaire, but it was not to serve as a monumental entrance.

II

MONSIEUR EIFFEL'S TOWER

In adopting the height of 1,000 feet, which had already preoccupied two continents, Eiffel had not chosen an arbitrary figure, for in this way he fixed the dimensions of a square base with sides measuring 328 feet, describing elegant curves which would support the first storey of the Tower, and enclose within well-calculated proportions the views of the Trocadero and the École Militaire.

From the architectural point of view the Tower was in fact a pyramid, not with straight ridges like those of Egypt, but with hyperbolic curves, which were carefully planned to withstand wind stress, a problem which does not arise in the case of a vertical building in stone. In this, Eiffel came curiously close to certain natural curves which

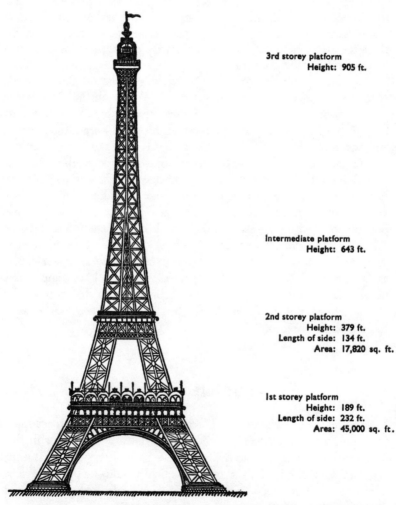

3rd storey platform
Height: 905 ft.

Intermediate platform
Height: 643 ft.

2nd storey platform
Height: 379 ft.
Length of side: 134 ft.
Area: 17,820 sq. ft.

1st storey platform
Height: 189 ft.
Length of side: 232 ft.
Area: 45,000 sq. ft.

41. Dimensions of the Eiffel Tower (according to the *Société d'Exploitation de la Tour Eiffel*)

develop of their own accord to withstand the wind, such as the concave outline of certain large conifers.

Various people were associated with Eiffel from the very start—the engineers Emile Nouguier and Maurice Koechlin, from his own company, as well as Stephen Sauvestre, the architect of the Tower, which, as a public building, raised problems of architectonics.

It could not possibly rise to its full height of 1,000 feet without intermediate storeys, which were useful both from the constructional and commercial points of view. A crowd of as many as 10,000 visitors had to be accommodated all at once, and they could be spread over the different storeys.

Restaurants, shops and kiosks of various types were planned for the first and second storeys, for they brought in more money to an exhibition than the mere entrance charge. The first storey, at a height of 189 feet, was envisaged as a high promenade with four restaurants in the centre, which could accommodate as many as a thousand people. The outside length was 1,000 feet, with a width of 8 feet 6 inches, and 2,000 visitors could stand there at once to admire the view. On the second storey, at 379 feet, there was to be a post and telegraph office, a bakery and a printing press. The intermediate platform (at 643 feet) between the second and third storeys was only a stopping place for changing lifts, as it still is today. These lifts, as we shall see, are by no means the least interesting feature of the Tower. The third storey, at 905 feet, was an observation platform where visitors could at last savour the pure pleasures of height, like the climber who is the first to reach the peak. At the very top of the building were various superstructures not open to the public, reserved for the staff, for scientific observation, for colleagues of the designers, or for guests who were to be received with special honours.

The Tower was regarded as a "phenomenon" as temporary as the Exhibition itself, but it was to be used also for scientific tests and experiments, which were regarded as important at this time. These would include astronomical observation, for the air was very pure; experiments in plant chemistry; meteorological statistics; checks on the behaviour of falling bodies, and experiments with optical telegraphy by the War Office and the Admiralty. In the evenings the Tower would form a huge beacon illuminating the Exhibition and the capital.

When all these arrangements had been worked out, less than three years before the opening of the Fair, a final agreement was signed between Eiffel, Lockroy, the Minister of Commerce, and the Prefect

Poubelle (whose name is still used in France to describe the metal dustbin which he more or less invented). Among other things it was agreed as follows:

"Monsieur Gustave Eiffel shall remain subject to supervision by the Exhibition engineers and the Special Commission set up on May 12th; he shall receive a subsidy of 1,500,000 francs paid in three instalments, the last of which will fall due on the day the work is completed."

Throughout the Exhibition he was authorised to develop the Tower from the commercial point of view, by the opening of restaurants, cafés and other similar establishments, subject to the two conditions that the charge for going up the Tower between 11 a.m. and 6 p.m. should be restricted on ordinary days to five francs for the top and two francs for the first storey; and on Sundays and holidays to two francs for the top and fifty centimes for the first storey; also the licences granted to cafés and restaurants, etc., were to be approved by the Minister.

"The continuance of his enjoyment of the Tower is guaranteed for twenty years from January 1st, 1890. After this date the enjoyment of the Tower will return to the City of Paris, which will take over the ownership of the building from the State, after the Exhibition."[1]

The City of Paris also signed an agreement with Eiffel on January 8th, 1887, and the terms were more or less the same as those of the agreement existing today between the city and the private company which operates the Tower.

Eiffel could now begin work, for he had a free hand and no worries. But the following month Monsieur Alphand, director of works for the Exhibition, and all the Paris newspapers, received a famous petition.

III

AESTHETIC PRINCIPLES AT STAKE

"Sir,

"We, the undersigned, writers, painters, sculptors, architects, lovers of the beauty of Paris, which so far has remained intact, write to express our indignant protest, in the name of taste, and the threat to the art and history of France, against the erection in the heart of our

[1] In 1910, the City of Paris granted its development rights to a private company, and this contract was renewed in 1950, the City of Paris retaining an interest in the receipts and profits. Naturally all maintenance and repair expenses are borne by the Government. In 1951 the former shareholders of the Tower received a dividend of 1,100 francs for each share held.

capital of the useless and monstrous Eiffel Tower, which public malice, so often expressive of common sense and fairness, has already christened the 'Tower of Babel.'

". . . Does the City of Paris intend to be associated any longer with the baroque and commercial ideas of a machine-builder, which can only lead to irreparable ugliness and disgrace? For there is no doubt that the Eiffel Tower, which even America, commercial-minded as it is, would refuse to have, is the disgrace of Paris. Everyone feels it, everyone says so, everyone is deeply distressed, and we can only echo feebly the legitimate alarm that is universally felt. Lastly, when foreigners come to see our Exhibition, they will cry in astonishment, 'Did the French build this horrible thing to give us an impression of the taste of which they are so proud?' Their laughter will be justified, for Paris with its sublime Gothic buildings, the Paris of Jean Goujon, Germain Pilon, Puget, Rude and Barye, will have become the Paris of Monsieur Eiffel.

"In order to realise the implications of what we say, it is only necessary to imagine for one moment this absurd building towering over Paris from a dizzy height like a gigantic black factory chimney, its barbarous mass dwarfing and humiliating Notre Dame, the Sainte Chapelle, the Tour Saint-Jacques, the Louvre, the Dome of the Invalides, the Arc de Triomphe, and all our buildings, which will disappear beneath this astounding conception. And for twenty years this revolting column of bolted iron will hang like an ever-widening blot of ink over our entire city, which is still alive with the genius of so many centuries.

". . . And if our cry of alarm is not heard, if our reasons are not listened to, if Paris obstinately insists on bringing dishonour to Paris, at least we will all of us have uttered an honourable protest.

"Signed: E. Meissonier, Charles Gounod, Charles Garnier, Victorien Sardou, Edouard Pailleron, H. Gérôme, Louis Bonnat, Alexandre Dumas (fils), François Coppée, Leconte de Lisle, Sully-Prudhomme, Guy de Maupassant, J-K. Huysmans, etc."

There were three hundred other names, more or less well known, in addition to these famous ones; most of them are forgotten now-adays, and the Eiffel Tower still stands today like an inscription which, without malice, has retained only their memory.

The dispute over the Tower attained epic proportions in Paris and throughout France. In spite of the Boulanger crisis, however, it was excluded from the encounters between the General's friends and enemies. Ironical *chansonniers* and poets composed satires and doggerel verse about the Tower, and even the Judiciary entered the field, suggesting to owners of land bordering on the Champ-de-Mars that they should take legal action against the City of Paris "for infraction of aesthetics." Naturally the cases were dismissed.

Alphand's reply to the famous petition is not known; he passed it to Lockroy who, remembering that he was the son-in-law of Victor Hugo (he had married Charles Hugo's widow), seized his pen, and in fine form wrote as follows:

"The newspapers are publishing a so-called protest addressed to you by French artists and writers. They are protesting about the Eiffel Tower. The sweeping phrases, the beauty of the metaphors, the subtle and precise Attic style lead one to believe, without even looking at the signatures, that this protest is the result of a collaboration between the most famous writers and poets of our time.

". . . Do not be carried away by the splendid presentation, and let us look at the facts. The protest comes at the wrong time; you should point out to the signatories that the building of the Eiffel Tower was decided a year ago and that work on the site has been going on for a month. They could have protested at the right time; they did not do so, and their honourable indignation made the mistake of breaking out too late.

"What I would like you to do is to receive the protest and keep it; such fine and noble prose signed by names known all over the world will certainly attract crowds and probably cause astonishment."

The Minister limited himself to this talented expression of irony and gave no real reply. It was Eiffel himself who granted the famous interview to *Le Temps*. He defended not so much the Tower itself, but like an excellent counsel he pleaded for the principles of true art as opposed to those of academic art upheld by the petitioners.

"What motives," said Eiffel, "lead the artists to think it is a useless monstrosity? I believe myself that the Tower will have a beauty of its own; just because we are engineers do people think that we are not concerned with beauty in our designs, and that when we put up solid and lasting buildings we do not try to achieve elegance of style? Do the true conditions of strength not always coincide with the secrets of harmony? The first aesthetic principle in architecture is that the main lines of a building should be determined by its perfect suitability for the purpose for which it is intended. Now what is the most important thing I had to consider in my Tower? Resistance to the wind. I maintain that the curves of the four main lines of the building, as obtained by calculation, rising from an enormous and unusual shape at the base and narrowing towards the summit, will give a great impression of strength and beauty....

"... Further, colossal structures have an attraction and fascination of their own, to which the theories of art in the normal sense can hardly be applied. Can it be maintained, for example, that it is through their aesthetic value that the Pyramids have made such a deep impression on men's imagination? Are they anything more, after all, than artificial hummocks? And yet what spectator remains cold in their presence ... and what is the reason for our admiration except the immensity of the labour involved and the grandeur of the result? The Tower will be the highest building ever yet raised by man; will it not therefore be grandiose in its own way? And if something is admirable in Egypt why should it be hideous and absurd in Paris?

"... It is, moreover, an extremely false theory, although the view is widespread even among artists, to believe that a high building overwhelms surrounding structures. If you look at the Opéra you will see that the surrounding houses dwarf it just as much as it dwarfs them. On the contrary, the houses certainly seem to be as high as they really are, that is about fifty feet, and one has to make a mental effort to convince oneself that the Arc de Triomphe is three times as high.... As a result it is a complete illusion to believe that the Tower can prejudice in any way other outstanding buildings in Paris. These are mere words."

Fifty years later, Paul Valéry, author of *Eupalinos ou l'architecte*, and therefore more or less above suspicion, summed up the engineer's plea:

"Architects of our great periods always conceived their buildings *visibly* as a complete whole, and not in two mental phases or in two series of operations, one relating to form and the other to matter. If I may be allowed the expression: *they thought in materials*."

IV

A THOUSAND FEET OF ADVENTURE

Long before the first foundation stone was laid, popular imagination had taken the famous outline of the Tower and with the help of fantasy had embellished it with decorative superstructures and other buildings; incongruous wings and a globe on the summit—all of which destroyed the simplicity of its design as much as the manifesto from the critics.

Every great invention and enterprise has had the same fate: the nineteenth century bequeathed us balloons of the most astounding shapes, and the Panama Canal bears little relationship to the first plans drawn up by Ferdinand de Lesseps.

Eiffel achieved the same apotheosis of design in his Tower with vertical metal girders as he had earlier attained with horizontal girders in his bridges. What is remarkable about his work is the perfection with which his plans were drawn up and the precise way in which they were carried out.

The Tower was built in exactly twenty-six months, from January 28th, 1887, to March 31st, 1889, and rose towards the sky over Paris like a giant rose-tree tended by some Cyclopean gardener. Parisians went to see it in family groups on Sundays just as they might visit some suburban garden, and the Press kept up with its development by reporting every incident of its adolescence. On the contrary, one of the signatories to the petition, and not one of the least famous, Guy de Maupassant, remained unshakeable. While it was being built he lived where he could not see it: "I have left Paris," he wrote, "because in the end the Eiffel Tower became too boring. . . ."

After a careful study of the geological stratification of the Champ-de-Mars, Eiffel realised that although the building of the two stone foundations to the south and east would not be very difficult, the two others on the side nearest the Seine presented a somewhat knotty problem, because of the alluvial tracts of land. But it was not more complicated than building piers for bridges on river banks, and he had dealt with cases of this sort many times. The foundations were to be laid sixteen feet below the level of the Seine, and it was not possible to carry out surface excavation, for water infiltration would have held up the work continually.

He used metallic compressed air caissons which had already been used in building harbours and piers for bridges. They consisted of a kind of diving bell divided into two parts and the upper part was weighted by concrete which caused them to sink down into the soft soil.[1]

The water which infiltrated was maintained at a certain level by the injection of compressed air through two vertical shafts. These shafts also provided a means of access for the workmen who, in the lower part of the caisson, dug out the soil with spades and pick-axes, working by the light of powerful electric lamps. Naturally, the waste material

[1] There were four of these caissons to each pile, measuring fifty feet in length by twenty feet wide.

was removed by dredging apparatus operated by chains, also placed in the shafts.

After the foundations for each pile had been laid in this way they were surmounted by a heavy mass of stone carrying bolts twenty-six feet long, fixing in place the shoes which were to take the base of the principal rafters. When this was done, Eiffel called together a delegation of architects and engineers. He pointed out to them that these foundations could take a pressure of over one ton per square centimetre, whereas the total weight of the Tower only exerted a pressure of about sixty-six pounds, that is to say, the weight of a millstone wall thirty feet high. This coefficient of security (forty times as great as was necessary) reassured the public. They could go up into the Tower without any danger.

Another remarkable thing about the basement is that the ground between the four masses of stonework which each support one of the ridges of each pile is hollow. It houses all the machinery for driving the lifts to the second storey, the pumps which work the pistons for the lifts to the third storey, the pumps taking drinking-water supplies to the restaurants and ice-cream sellers, along with a minute generating plant which provides the Tower with an independent electricity supply.

I have seen this labyrinth of cables, wheels, dynamos and pumps, and found my descent into the Cyclops' cave below the Tower just as impressive as going up to the top.

A close look at the framework of the Tower reveals it to be a kind of gigantic Meccano model, composed not of metal strips but of

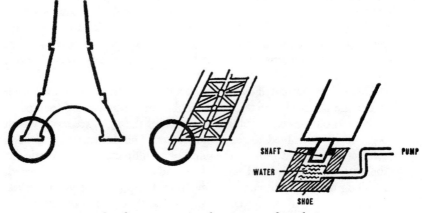

42. Hydraulic system in the Tower foundations

extremely resilient light iron angles, assembled by means of sheet steel brackets. It is this that gives the Tower its airy appearance, so that we never feel cut off from either heaven or earth, its spider-web structure in which the threads interlace in a perfect geometric design.

This extraordinary lightness has led people to discuss curious statistical comparisons: Charles Edouard Guillaume says in *Le Premier Quart de Siècle de la Tour Eiffel*, that "7,000 tons of iron were used to build the Eiffel Tower. Although this figure sounds vast it is relatively very small.

"Imagine a tower of the same design reduced to one-thousandth of its size. Every dimension of length, width and volume must then be reduced in proportion. The tower would measure one foot high, but with the other reductions necessary it would only weigh seven grams, or as much as a sheet of writing paper.

"Let us suppose now all the iron in the Tower made into a flat sheet extending to the outside edge of the area occupied by the base of the Tower, which measures 400 feet square. This sheet would only be 2½ inches thick; or if we imagine it in the form of a cube, the sides would not be more than thirty-three feet long, that is, the equivalent of a small three-storey house.

"Let us describe a circle on the square occupied by the base of the Tower, and regard it as the base of a cylinder 1,000 feet in height . . . its volume would be more than 233,000,000 cubic feet, and the air that it contained would weigh more than the iron used in the Tower.

"This gives some idea of the miraculous lightness of the Eiffel Tower; it is light because all the material in it has been used under the most rational conditions that could be determined by calculation."

These calculations had been made in the Eiffel Company's offices at Levallois-Perret, where the entire Tower was divided into twenty-seven panels, each with their own working diagrams, and the complete collection of plans amounted to no less than 5,000 sheets measuring one yard square each.

Devised and executed over two years by forty draughtsmen working under the personal direction of Koechlin, the diagrams represented to scale, without omitting a single one, each of the 15,000 sections which were to be assembled to form the Tower. The dimensions had been calculated by logarithms, to the tenth of a millimetre, and in particular the hole for each rivet, of which two and a half million were needed, entailing drilling a distance equivalent to a depth of forty-four miles.

The British and Americans were not less skilled than the French in structural metalwork, but their methods were very different. In 1887 the colossal Forth Bridge was being built in Scotland. Its unique cantilever construction has not yet been surpassed; but this system was very different from that used for the single-span or arch bridge of which Eiffel was at that time the undisputed champion.

On the Forth Bridge site the assembly diagrams were received at the same time as the elements of the major parts, and it was the responsibility of the assemblers to make the best use of the materials brought to the site. It was often necessary to bolster them with cranes or jacks or to recut and drill with the help of forges or machine tools.

On the contrary the Eiffel Tower site worked closely with the technical department; the working diagrams went to the factory at Levallois-Perret where the parts were scrupulously manufactured. They reached the Champ-de-Mars on platforms or trucks drawn by sturdy draught-horses. Each angle and bracket was carefully numbered and stored at the site until it was needed. All fitted together with clockwork precision.

However, when the floor for the first storey was laid, everything had to be adjusted by a few inches before the tops of the columns were at the same level. This was inevitable—neither Euclid nor Einstein could have done better.

Eiffel then adopted an ingenious procedure. In the cast-iron shoes resting on the foundations, which were to take the feet of the base columns acting as pistons, he had provided for a cavity to be filled with water by a pump. The pressure of the fluid was sufficient to adjust the columns by the few inches necessary.

Naturally, when the Tower was firmly in position on its four enormous pillars, measuring fifty-three feet along each side, a metal collar was placed round the piston to fix it definitely in place. It is this skilful method of assembly that still leads many of our contemporaries to claim that the Tower rests on hydraulic jacks "in order to correct any tendency to lean over." The director of the Tower, Monsieur Vannesson, who is in charge of its commercial development, told me with a smile how many visitors still repeat this absurd statement and asked me to correct it by giving this explanation.

Another constructional difficulty was that of achieving equilibrium in the overhang of the columns which rose towards the first storey at a tangential angle of 52°. This was dealt with by building three pyramids of wood, somewhat similar to the derricks used in oil-wells—which rose to a height of ninety-two feet half-way up to the first platform. When this level was reached four more square wooden pylons were built in the centre of each side of the Tower. The four large

252

beams connecting the pillars at a height of 142 feet were then placed on top of them.

The first storey was finished on March 26th, 1888, and before the four large arches had been placed in position below the principal beams, a contemporary, J. B. Dumont, gave his impressions of the scene with such restraint that there is nothing further to add.

"I was standing," he wrote, "at a height of about 200 feet, among a maze of ironwork painted with red lead, drilled with holes and arranged in criss-cross fashion as far as the eye could see; above a confused greyish mass of timber, and looking very small in such a grandiose setting, 250 workmen came and went in a perfectly orderly fashion, carrying long beams on their shoulders, climbing up and down through the latticed ironwork with surprising agility. The rapid hammer-blows of the riveters could be heard, and they worked with fire that burnt with the clear trembling flame of will-o'-the-wisps. The workmen, as though imbued with the importance of their task, were active and silent, while only the foremen raised their voices to issue orders.

"The four cranes—one for each pillar—which brought up the pieces for this vast metallic framework one by one, stood out against the sky with their great arms, at the four corners of this lofty site. A special team of workers operated these powerful machines.

"There were twenty riveting shops, each one consisting of four men and a portable forge. A young workman called a 'cabin boy' was entrusted with the bellows for the forge and he brought the white-hot rivet to a workman who was called the 'holder-up'; he drove the rivet into the hole, holding it by the head which was already shaped.

"The 'riveter' hammered it at the other end to flatten it and start making the other head; the fourth worker, called the 'striker,' finished it by striking it as hard as he could with a sledge-hammer.

"During the short winter days, when night fell, the twenty forges blazed in the high wind, casting a sinister glow of light over this tangle of girders, until it acquired a fantastic aspect. The men worked as late as possible and moved about like shadows between these dark red smoky fires."[1]

The entire staff employed on the Tower—varying from 200 to 250 men—were employees of Eiffel's company, a special team that the chief had selected from his workshops of Garabit or Le Portugal. They were mostly former carpenters who were attracted by the new techniques with iron, or simply by higher pay than that offered any-

[1] J. B. Dumont: *Les Grands Travaux du Siècle.*

where else in France. The flying scaffolding was carried out by former sailors, who rigged the pulleys and blocks as easily as if they were working in the vast top of some gigantic sailing-ship.

To save time Eiffel set up a huge canteen on the first storey where for one franc five centimes each man could have a meal consisting of two meat dishes, two vegetable dishes, two desserts, half a litre of wine, coffee and brandy. The men had to eat well, for this work allowed nobody to weaken, and Eiffel paid a subsidy of fifty centimes per man per meal. They were forbidden to go down, for sometimes if they had too good a meal they did not come back again. The work was carried out by gangs, each trained as a unit, and the absence of one man would have upset the rhythm of work and delayed the completion of the Exhibition centrepiece, which would not do, for the opening date was definitely fixed.

The men worked ten hours a day, the "beaters" and "holders-up" were paid fifty to fifty-five centimes an hour, the riveters and assemblers, sixty centimes. As the building progressed they were paid more, up to eighty-five centimes. During the terrible winter of 1888 the Exhibition sites were deserted because of the severe frost, but work on the Tower continued. During the winter of 1889, however, there was a three-day strike, not because of the increased risk of working at higher levels—for the risk was the same at 800 feet as at eighty feet—but in order to obtain a minute pay rise, sheepskins and hot wine. Eiffel gave only the pay rise.

Working conditions in 1889, when national insurance and paid holidays were unknown, were much harder than they are today. The men working on the Tower received wages hardly any higher than those paid on ordinary sites, but they did not regard this work as different from or more dangerous than any other; they were never upset by the height, and moved about in the Tower without thinking of the ground.

Eiffel and his supervisor, Compagnon, a carpenter who had risen from the ranks, did not spare themselves in keeping a careful watch on the safety and firmness of the scaffolding. As a result their men worked with perfect regularity and assurance. The Eiffel Tower claimed only one victim, a riveter's assistant called Dussardin, who accidently fell from the first storey.

To achieve perfect coordination of the building work telephonic communication had been established between the various parts of the Tower; offices on the ground and the platform issued orders everywhere. Eiffel, his foremen and supervisors went continually up and down the total of 1,789 steps on the lookout for idle workmen, and went round at night to make sure that the watchmen, when they fell asleep, did not allow the forges that heated the rivets from daybreak to go out.

The great engineer knew most of the workmen by name; he talked to them, clapping them in a friendly fashion on the back, enquiring affectionately after their families and sharing their small worries as if they had been his own children. Whenever some important stage in building the Tower was reached there was a family celebration; Eiffel had a cask of white wine sent up, and standing, glass in hand, in the midst of his men, he improvised a little speech which caused both spirits, and the Tower, to rise. When the third storey was reached all his workers had a bonus of five louis, and two hundred of them had their names carved on the Tower.

In 1890 Eiffel invited them to a famous banquet which took place on the first storey, where each one of them was seated between a technician and some celebrity invited specially for the occasion.

Those who had worked on the Tower from beginning to end went to present the President of France, Sadi Carnot, with an Eiffel Tower in silver. The President gave each of them a handsome medallion in the same metal, and made a delightful speech at the Elysée, in which he reminded them that he was a builder too, for he was a former student of the École Polytechnique.

Another ingenious aspect of the Tower was the procedure for assembling the girders. This was achieved easily by means of cranes bolted on to the four columns. With arms forty-five feet long they exerted a force equal to three tons and raised the pieces from the ground with iron chains weighing a ton each. They brought them to the foot of the site, and then when they could reach no further they were unbolted and taken up higher.

When the first storey was reached it acted as an intermediate depot. Then a steam-operated crane was installed which distributed the metal to the four corners of the Tower by small waggons on wheels.

When the girders for the two upper storeys had to be put in place, it was found, just as with the assembly of the principal rafters, that there was a difference of six millimetres between the placing of the columns. The hydraulic jacks on the shoes were then brought into action again. This small device was also used when it was found at the end of a hot day in summer that the columns exposed to the sun showed a variation of three millimetres over those on the opposite side.

These minor incidents of technical importance were eagerly awaited by detractors of the Tower. They gazed through telescopes to gauge its equilibrium, and never failed to communicate to the facetious and jubilant Press the result of their ill-advised criticism. This was how the unspeakable paper *Le Matin* came to publish seriously on January 28th, 1888, the following headline: "The Tower is Sinking," with the comment, "If it has really begun to sink, any further building should stop, and the sections already built should be demolished as quickly as possible."

Eiffel was unmoved by the growls from the Press and continued imperturbably with his Tower. The three storeys were finished one after the other at the prearranged times: the second on December 26th, 1888, and the third on March 31st, 1889. On that day it was Eiffel himself who placed on top of the Tower the flag that is always hoisted on every new building, even a modest suburban bungalow.

The unfurling of the Tricolour did not signify, however, that the Tower was completely finished. It was now necessary to install the lifts, a delicate technical operation reserved for Adolphe Salles, Eiffel's son-in-law. Naturally they were operated by a hydraulic device, for electrically operated machinery was still in its infancy.

They were not to be operated like lifts in blocks of flats, by vast piston-rods penetrating below ground. It was decided to use three very different systems for reaching each of the three storeys. For the first storey an endless chain was established with two lifts which went up and down like the buckets on an excavator. To reach the second storey a piston thirty-six feet long was used, operating two large pulleys placed on a bogey[1] forming huge winches which when operated in low gear could raise the lift.

Visitors left this lift on the second floor, and entered a third lift with a central piston. It was impossible to lengthen it to 525 feet, for it would have immediately sunk into the ground; so it was made of two parts each weighing eight tons and each 262 feet 6 inches long. They balanced each other, and each made half the journey by raising and lowering two cabins, which naturally made it necessary for the visitors to change cabins at the intermediate platform, which was built for this purpose.[2]

It was then necessary to paint the vast structure, which was already daubed with red lead, and it took 300 tons of reddish-green paint to do so. It is carefully renewed every seven years.

[1] The same system is used today for the continuous ascent of the two lower storeys, but the equipment is now housed in the basement of the Tower.
[2] See Fig. 43.

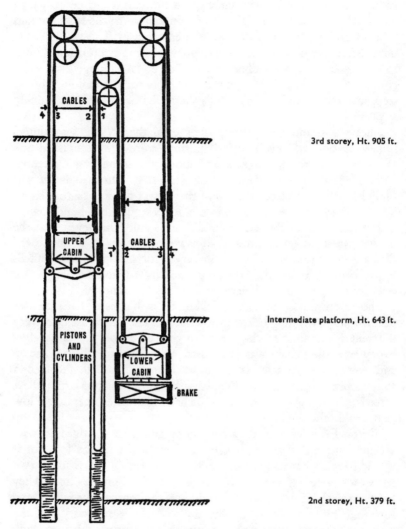

In the diagram:

CABLES
4 3 2 1

3rd storey, Ht. 905 ft.

UPPER CABIN

CABLES
1 2 3 4

Intermediate platform, Ht. 643 ft.

PISTONS AND CYLINDERS

LOWER CABIN

BRAKE

2nd storey, Ht. 379 ft.

43. Diagram of the lift between the second and third platforms

In the offices of the Tower I have held in my hand the sample metal plate giving the exact colour which does not clash with the sky of Paris over the green of the Champ-de-Mars. Finally, since everything was completely ready, the Exhibition was opened on the date pre-arranged, July 15th, 1889.

V

APOTHEOSIS

Eiffel would have preferred the unfurling of the flag, which measured 24 feet 8 inches by 14 feet 9 inches, to have taken place quietly in the presence of his workers alone. But he had to withstand the onslaught of the 400 journalists, various officials and members of Parliament who on that day cheerfully mounted the 1,789 steps to the summit—a symbolic figure if ever there was one, but it had not been chosen on purpose. This upward procession left the ground at 1.30 p.m., and reached the top at 2.35 p.m., which was an honourable feat. When the Tricolour flapped in the first gust of wind twenty-one cannon shots announced this astonishing news to the world.

On April 28th of the following year the first electrical transmission took place, and finally, on Exhibition D-day, Sadi Carnot, standing as rigid in his frock-coat as the Tower in its iron garb, opened the Exhibition with the ritual speech.

During the six months of the Great Fair, 1,968,287 visitors went over the "eighth wonder of the world," and the first person to buy a ticket to go up was a Spaniard by the name of Don Carlos, which was highly symbolical. When the Exhibition closed its gates, the Tower alone had earned for Eiffel and its shareholders 6,459,581 francs and 20 centimes of entrance money, which in addition to the 1,500,000 franc subsidy allocated by the Government amounted to a total which easily surpassed the 7,799,401 francs it had cost.

The ordinary people adopted the Eiffel Tower with touching fervour, and wanted to have it in their own homes, like the Madonna they brought back from pilgrimages. But they wanted it gilded, and millions of miniature copies, transformed into thermometers or watch-stands, can still be seen everywhere, standing proudly on many chimney-pieces between two family portraits.

Then the cult turned into a fetish: people ate from plates on which the Eiffel Tower replaced the blue landscapes of Delft, and on the famous French Camembert cheese the giraffe of the Champ-de-Mars now replaced the Normandy cows. Then when the meal was over, after swallowing a liqueur from an Eiffel Tower made of glass, everyone sang a popular song with words by Victor Meusy which referred to pictures of the Tower on cane handles, salt and pepper pots, candles, dishes and mirrors.

Just like the ordinary people, kings and outstanding contemporary personalities made their pilgrimage too, probably in a spirit of humility. They included the Prince of Wales (the future King Edward VII), his son, the future George V, the King of the Hellenes, President Krüger, Sarah Bernhardt, and a dozen negro kings who all signed an amazing Golden Book which has been carefully preserved by the Eiffel family.

Some people also made touching and honourable amends. Gounod, who had signed the manifesto of the 300, one day came to the Tower in secret. By chance Eiffel met him there and invited him to a banquet that he was giving in honour of the great Edison. When the last course was reached the composer of *Faust* sat down at the piano while the director of the Musée Grévin modelled a portrait in wax of the famous American.

And so a famous trinity of Science, Industry and Art were brought together in Paris by the equally famous Tower.

When the Tower had received universal acclaim Eiffel, as he had promised before it was built, gave his work over to pure science, and made it into a laboratory; then, with the future General Ferrié, the radio pioneer, it became the first wireless aerial in the world.

And then occurred an extraordinary event, as unlikely as a miracle. One September evening in 1914, during the first dark hours of the First World War, the receiver on the Tower intercepted a German radio message from General von Kluck's headquarters. This highly opportune piece of information allowed General Gallieni, Governor of Paris, to mobilise the heroic taxis which played their part in the victory of the Marne.

That is how, fourteen centuries after Saint Geneviève, the blessed Eiffel Tower in her turn saved Paris.

XI

THE PANAMA CANAL

"Wednesday, February 21st, 1827: *At table with Goethe. He spoke a great deal, and with admiration, about Alexander von Humboldt, whose work on Cuba and Colombia he had begun to read, and whose views on the plan to cut through the Isthmus of Panama seemed to interest him greatly.* . . .

"*It is certain, however, that if a cut can be made of a type whereby ships of any tonnage can go from the Gulf of Mexico to the Pacific Ocean, the consequences to the whole world, civilised and uncivilised, will be incalculable.*

"*I should, however, be very surprised if the United States were to let such an undertaking slip through their fingers.*"

J. P. Eckermann.
Conversations with Goethe, Vol. III

I

DREAMS AND CONFUSION

THE IDEA OF linking the Atlantic and Pacific Oceans through the Isthmus of Panama is as old as the New World. On his fourth and last voyage in 1502 Christopher Columbus heard the natives speaking of "a narrow strip of land beyond which lay a great sea." He thought, and rightly, that this must be a strait which would lead him to China and India. He attempted to cross it, but without success, almost on the site of the town which bears his name today.

It was only in 1513 that the conquistador Nuñez de Balboa crossed the Isthmus of Darien and discovered the Pacific. The date was September 25th, almost four hundred years exactly before the day when the two oceans finally met within the Isthmus of Panama on October 10th, 1913.

Less than seven years after Balboa's expedition Saavedra conceived the idea of cutting a canal, a plan which was taken up again by Fernando Cortez in 1525. The conquistador of Mexico visualised it much farther to the north, at the base of this territory, exactly between the Bay of Campeche and the Bay of Tehuantepec.

It should not be forgotten that the isthmus measures more than 1,430 miles as the crow flies, the same distance as a shore-line uniting Gibraltar to the Orkneys or Suez.

In 1550 another Spaniard, Pedro Galvao, published a work suggesting four plans for a canal between the two oceans: Uraba-San-Miguel, Nicaragua, Tehuantepec and, naturally, Panama.

The Emperor Charles V seems to have taken an interest in this work, but his successor Philip II preferred to demand ever-larger quantities of gold from his conquests rather than allow the royal fortune to be swallowed up in an attempt which, as Goethe foretold, would have incalculable consequences for the whole world, civilised and un-civilised. The sovereign of the Spanish Empire therefore proclaimed with great subtlety that it would be tempting Providence to unite two seas that it had separated, and "anyone who attempted to build this canal would be put to death."

The royal threat does not seem to have been made in vain, for during research on early ideas concerning the great canal I found, literally, more than a hundred attempted projects or tentative plans, all of which came to nothing.

During the sixteenth and seventeenth centuries, however, the Spaniards, who none the less wanted to reach the Pacific without disobeying Philip II's command, built a road across the Isthmus which they pompously entitled "Via reale," the "Royal Road." It was in fact no more than a track and it was jealously concealed from everyone. It linked the mouth of the capricious Chagres, the river that ran through the isthmus, with the Rio Grande at Panama.

Every year a convoy of ships left Peru and landed at Panama, while a second convoy left Cadiz in Spain and dropped anchor at Colon. Merchandise sent by the Vice-King of the Inca Empire, consisting of spices, fabrics, feathers from rare birds, and gold and silver bars, then crossed the isthmus on the backs of mules or on flat-bottomed boats and were later sent to Spain.

This skilful move avoided crossing the Magellan Straits, which was a difficult passage, and shortened the route considerably, allowing the ships to sail in convoy and avoid the risks of a disastrous encounter with pirates or filibusters who infested the oceans. This was the origin of the first route across Panama, and in 1855 the railway followed it fairly closely.

Although the secret was well kept, Sir Henry Morgan, the famous British buccaneer, learnt of its existence and in 1670 he came from the Atlantic, followed the "Via reale," crossed the isthmus in a few days, took Panama by surprise, set fire to the town and wiped it out completely; then, laden with the rich Spanish booty, retraced his steps and finally dropped anchor in Jamaica which was British and impregnable.

In 1780 Charles III of Spain ordered a technical mission to explore Panama, but the French Revolution soon gave him other worries. In 1804 the German traveller Alexander von Humboldt expressed himself in support of a canal in Darien but opposed to any cut through Panama. This plan interested Goethe, as we have seen, for as a German he was already aware of the existence of geopolitics.

In 1825, however, Bolivar, the liberator of Colombia, granted a concession for building a Panama canal to a Frenchman, Baron Thierry. Unfortunately, the French lacked capital and the concession passed to an Anglo-Swedish group who in their turn drew up a plan. This came to nothing, however.

Next the Netherlands came on the scene, in the person of their well-educated, wealthy and learned King William III; he had the original idea of piercing the isthmus through Guatemala, with which he signed a treaty. But the Revolution of 1830, leading to the separation of Belgium and Holland, brought this project to a close.

In 1843 a French company sent Napoleon Garella, the engineer, who made a complete study for both a canal and a railway, but only the latter was approved. The capital was not found, however, and finally the concession obtained from the Colombian Government was cancelled, and the French company lost their rights; they passed then to a group of American financiers who began to build the railway in 1850.

During this time Prince Louis-Napoleon Bonaparte was moping in the fortress of Ham, after his conviction following the military plots of Boulogne and Strasbourg. In order to pass the time the future Emperor studied a plan for a canal passing through Nicaragua. In this way, by a curious coincidence, he unconsciously took up again a plan outlined by Nelson, who had defeated his uncle at the battle of Trafalgar. Although he obtained the agreement of Nicaragua, Louis Bonaparte was unable to persuade the French Government to give him back his liberty. Then came the 1848 Revolution in France, and the prince became President of the Republic, which meant that he was occupied with other affairs.

If Louis-Napoleon had gone to Nicaragua the Second Empire in France would certainly never have existed. As Emperor, however, he gave extremely valuable protection to Ferdinand de Lesseps when he began the negotiations which led to the Suez Canal.

In the meantime, from 1850 to 1855 the Americans were building the Panama railway, following roughly the course of the Rio Chagres through a maze of torrents, hills and marshes. This was the route taken by the men who came from the east of the United States and the Old World for the California gold rush, and some of the materials for the transcontinental railway passed this way en route for San Francisco.

The town of Colon was also called Aspinwall, from the name of the director of the Panamanian Railway Company. His problems were magnified by local legends: it was said that a Chinese labourer was buried beneath each sleeper and that 154 station-masters had died at one station within a few years! There was a fearfully high mortality rate, due to swamp fever, *vomito negro*, and lack of hygiene, but the administrative report of the company disposed of these exaggerations, which recur again in a curious way when the causes of the bankruptcy of the French Panama Canal Company came to be discussed.

The American railway company was privately financed, for President Monroe, in accordance with the doctrine which bears his name, had declared in 1823 that "the American continents, by the free and independent condition which they have assumed and maintained, are henceforth not to be considered as subjects suitable for future colonisation by any European powers. . . . We owe it, therefore, to candour, and to the amicable relations existing between the United States and those powers, to declare that we should consider any attempt on their part to extend their system to any portion of this hemisphere as dangerous to our peace and safety."

In 1849 therefore the United States signed a treaty with Nicaragua reserving the right to build an interoceanic canal on its territory. This treaty was of great importance later when the Americans took over the completion of the canal in 1902.

But the British now showed their teeth and even sent a fleet of warships to Nicaragua; the United States were obliged to negotiate with them and in 1850 signed the famous Bulwer–Clayton Treaty, of which the substance was as follows:

1. Neither of the two contracting countries would have exclusive control over the Nicaragua canal, nor would they have any right to build fortifications there.
2. Both countries would keep watch over the security and neutrality of the canal and would invite other nations to do likewise.

This "distrustful treaty," to use André Siegfried's description, was later to retard rather than stimulate the establishment of sea communication between the two oceans.

The United States had promised neutrality in the Nicaraguan project and took very little active part in it; on learning in 1869 that the Suez Canal had been opened, however, they quickly signed a treaty with Colombia for the building of "an American canal, with American gold, on American soil." Then, without delay, a small army of engineers was sent to Panama to survey the isthmus. After three years the mission declared that the Nicaragua route was definitely the better one. The United States could ask nothing better; but then they were caught up in the reorganisation which followed the Civil War, the building of their vast railway network, the fighting against the Indians, and expansion in the West, all of which absorbed enormous quantities of capital, so they tended to forget these treaties, which still allowed them to play watchdog, and prevent any European country from carrying out work in this area.

The Republic of Colombia was extremely anxious for the canal to be built, however, for she rightly saw it as an immense source of revenue, since ships would now call there instead of going the fantastic distance round Cape Horn. Since America did not seem inclined to get down to things, the chance went to France.

II

FERDINAND DE LESSEPS,
THE "ISTHMUS-PIERCER"

Naturally this "appeal" from Colombia to France was only metaphoric in nature. It was dictated neither by resentment, nor by despair, nor even by national affinities, and events did not take place in a simple straightforward manner. First of all the British and the Americans did not fail to put diplomatic spokes in the wheels; negotiations began and lasted until the Convention of 1878.

The British were still in a state of confusion and sent various missions to different parts of the isthmus from Tehuantepec to Darien. In the meantime, the first important Congress of Geographical Science took place in Antwerp in 1871. Unlike many such meetings, which are merely pleasant social gatherings, this Congress had very precise aims, including the planning of future developments in shipping, commerce and industry, for at the end of the nineteenth century it had become essential to find new fields of operation.

After the Congress had fêted Lesseps, who had built the Suez Canal and made the long journey round the Cape of Good Hope unnecessary, the question of the Panama Canal was naturally raised, for in its turn it would replace the passage round Tierra del Fuego and shorten many journeys by as much as a third.

The next session of the Congress took place in Paris in 1875. It was only fair that Monsieur de Lesseps should be invited, for he had already expressed some very decided views on the route and building of the projected canal. But the Congress wisely adjourned any decision until the whole question had been examined thoroughly from all points of view by a French Committee appointed to study the question. Naturally de Lesseps was acclaimed as president.

This Committee formed a company which was to finance the exploration and study the isthmus. The company later sold its rights to the French Panama Company, the last administrative body exercising financial, industrial and technical control over the laying of the canal.

It is strange to note that the leader of the party entrusted with the exploration and layout of the future canal was a great-nephew of Napoleon. This was Lucien-Napoleon Bonaparte-Wyse, grandson of Lucien, the Emperor's brother, whose mother Laetitia had married the American Thomas Wyse.

Bonaparte-Wyse was an officer in the French Navy, and he left for Panama accompanied by eminent colleagues and experts, just as his great-uncle had left for the conquest of Egypt. He carried out an exact survey of the isthmus, and the work was so arduous that many of his companions died. He drew up an initial plan including locks and tunnels, but he did not succeed in pleasing Lesseps, who was a convinced and dictatorial partisan of a sea-level canal, using the same technique that he had used for Suez. Wyse then left for Panama again, and took up his calculations and plans once more; he then completed his journey by an outstanding diplomatic exploit, reaching Bogotá, capital of Colombia and seat of the Government, after a memorable and dangerous ride of 500 miles over the top of the Cordillera mountains, lasting twelve days.

There, on May 28th, 1878, after discussions which were as exhausting as his journey, Wyse signed with General Salgar a definitive treaty which granted him the exclusive concession of the canal through Panama. It was subject to one important stipulation; the exclusive rights would run for ninety-nine years from the date of opening of the canal, which must be finished twelve years after the formation of the company which was to build and develop it; lastly, state-owned land extending to a certain distance on both sides of the canal was granted. The Government of Colombia for its part was to receive royalties on the raw materials produced by the development of the canal, etc., provided that the French company could buy back from the Americans the Colon-Panama railway, which, while useful for the technical operations of building the canal, would lose any future commercial value. These clauses were to constitute the "Panama Canal charter" until the canal was completed.

Bonaparte-Wyse, with the backing of such a guarantee, and flushed with success in the technical, diplomatic and commercial fields, returned to France, taking with him a basic plan for the organisation of a sound enterprise, which was to be founded in 1878 by the "International Interoceanic Canal Study Congress."

The Congress reassembled therefore, this time at the Hall of

Geography in the Boulevard Saint-Germain. It consisted of ninety-eight members coming from twenty-three different countries: France, Britain, America, Italy, Spain, Mexico, Colombia, Holland, etc., including the venerable mandarin Li-Shu-Shang, who represented China, a country with very little power at that time.

Fifty projects had been placed before the members. One of the strangest was a plan for placing ships in dry dock on a huge platform on rollers which would be pulled along rails by a chain of locomotives. A similar system was used by the Greek sailors in the first century B.C., who sent their ships across the isthmus of Corinth on wooden sledges to escape the contrary winds from Cape Maleus.

Fifteen projects were selected for serious discussion. In the end two of them were chosen: the Nicaragua route with locks, and the Panama route with a sea-level canal (the second Wyse project). The future was to settle, by means of dramatic episodes, the unfortunate conflict which was about to begin.

The second of the two plans was adopted, thanks to the energetic, even passionate promptings of Lesseps. The cost of the canal, although it was estimated at 1,200 million francs, was definitely higher than for a canal with locks, estimated at 570 million francs, but the Congress thought that the latter system caused loss of time to shipping, and finally it was decided that the transit tariffs would bring in enough money to justify the expense. The future was to reveal all the weaknesses of the plan adopted.

The creator of Suez was by now in his seventy-fifth year. He enjoyed undisputed prestige and in his greatness he rose above parties, finance, and even technique. He was praised by the chauvinistic because Suez annoyed the British; he was held in high esteem by the important and middle-class capitalists who owned shares in Suez, and Victor Hugo wrote poetry in his honour: "Astonish the world with might, that is not the might of war."

And yet it was a war in which the elderly Lesseps was engaging, a struggle which was to be greater than that of Suez and in which he was not to be always victorious. But flattery from Panama was very pleasant after praise from Egypt.

Lesseps did not regard Panama as a task but as a challenge to be transformed into an apotheosis. He challenged nature, the entire world, and most of all the New World.

"The Americans," he said at the closing session of the Congress, "were taken aback when they saw the triumph of a method which had escaped them, especially after examining the question for so long.

Things of this sort happen every day; one must make the best of it."

So Lesseps won the day and the motion was carried by twenty-eight votes to eight with twelve abstentions, the latter being considered as polite opposition. Those against the project, who included Gustave Eiffel, were greeted with derision.

When the Congress had voted, Lesseps announced officially in the following terms that he would undertake the Panama Canal: "Now that we are to separate, I must confess that I have been extremely perplexed. A fortnight ago I did not think that I would be obliged to take the lead in a new enterprise. My best friends tried to dissuade me from it, saying that after Suez I should take a rest. But if you ask a general who has won one battle whether he wants to win another, he cannot refuse."

This was the reasoning of a military man, not of a technician, and it was to lead Lesseps into misadventures.

Things began rather badly for he had great difficulty in finding the first 10 million francs necessary for buying over the Colombian concession to Bonaparte-Wyse. In August 1879 Lesseps, relying on his name alone, tried to float the first loan, which was a total failure and he had to reimburse the few who subscribed. He then worked on public opinion by lecture tours in France, the United States, Britain, Belgium and Holland, by the publication of the Bulletin of the Inter-oceanic Canal, by paying for Press publicity and by the formation of a share syndicate. Then in December 1880 he floated another loan. This time subscribers rushed to buy and brought in 300 million francs. Without waiting for the legal constitution of the *Compagnie Universelle du Canal Interocéanique de Panama* (January 31st, 1881), Lesseps sailed for the isthmus to set up an organisation and administrative machine which it must be admitted were as complicated as the enterprise itself. He took with him his family and an international technical commission.

On January 1st, 1880, Lesseps gave the first symbolic pickaxe blow, which was respectfully repeated by the leading personalities who surrounded him; then the Bishop of Panama gave the ritual blessing to the new undertaking. Finally, Mademoiselle Ferdinande de Lesseps lit the fuse which was to explode the first mine in the Culebra. This is a Spanish word, meaning a serpent: it proved difficult to swallow.

III

THE CULEBRA

The layout of the canal between the Atlantic and the Pacific fell into three distinct parts:

1. From Colon to Gamboa it crossed the winding Rio Chagres and its tributaries for a length of twenty-seven miles. This river was highly temperamental. It was liable to sudden flooding which multiplied its flow a hundred times in a few hours. Its course nevertheless dictated the layout of the canal. But when the plan for a sea-level canal had been changed into a canal with locks it presented various problems which were finally solved by the Americans.

2. From Gamboa to the end of the Culebra there was a mountainous ridge, a branch of the Cordillera, seven miles long. A huge dam five-eighths of a mile wide was to be built on Gamboa which would hold the water coming down from the hills.

But the Culebra, rising to a height of 400 feet, formed the watershed between the Pacific and the Atlantic. Before the canal could be taken through it was necessary to blow up or dig out 130,000,000 cubic yards of rocks and earth, that is almost half of the total quantity excavated for the canal itself; this proved to be the stumbling block of the operation.

3. From Paraiso to the Pacific the route followed the valley of the Rio Grande for twelve miles; this could be dug out with dredgers and presented no particular difficulties, especially in comparison with the previous sections.

Lastly, at both extremities of the isthmus, at Colon and Panama, landing stages and large-scale port facilities had to be built, with channels taking the canal into the oceans. Further, it was intended to build at Panama a tidal harbour (a three-chambered lock) to make the adjustment between the differences in level between the Atlantic (two feet) and the Pacific (twenty feet).

Before the work itself was begun headquarters were set up at Panama and Colon—residential districts, stores and workshops. Then materials and workshops were established along the route, linked together by the American railway line and a telegraph line. Whole villages of huts were built, with canteens and infirmaries, including a general hospital with 400 beds at Ancona and a sanatorium on the Island of Taboga in the Gulf of Panama.

The year 1882 was devoted to this preliminary work and building. In 1883 actual operations were put in hand. Under the overriding authority of the director twenty contractors, including French, British, North American, Dutch, Italian, Swiss and Colombian firms, went to work along the entire route, attacking the ground with mines, dredgers and spades.

Contrary to what has often been written the equipment was excellent, of the most modern type, and in good supply. The engineers knew what they were about and their work was perfectly carried out. This can be stated without any chauvinism and the Americans, who were to benefit later from the important work that had been done, recognised the fact quite frankly.

In 1910 the London newspaper the *Standard* published an interview between its correspondent and the American engineers, ending with the following words: "... (they) spoke, not from generosity, but from the professional point of view, of the excellence of the work done by the French engineers. According to most of the officers responsible for the major work on the canal there has never been anything except well-deserved praise for the foresight, skill and technical prowess shown by the French."

In 1886 M. G. de Molinari published a book on Panama, and this is his brief list of equipment received at the isthmus by January 1st, 1886: forty dredgers, ten hopper-barges, 103 ordinary barges, twenty-nine tugs, 171 locomotives, 129 travelling-cranes and semi-fixed machines, 500 pumps; eighty-two excavators, 4,600 waggons, 6,700 tip-trucks, 109 miles of railway line, 1 foot 7·68 gauge; the permanent buildings included three large workshops measuring 12,000 square feet, two supplementary shops and even a foundry capable of producing pieces weighing fifteen tons.

The recruitment of the workers, at least at the beginning, was extremely easy. They were mostly negroes, descendants of slaves from Jamaica and quite accustomed to the climate. In 1886, however, out of the 40,000 workers on the books, it was hardly possible to count on the attendance each day of more than a third of the total strength. There was also a subsidiary staff of whites, adventurers who were attracted by high salaries but could not stand up to the work for long; oddly enough they included the great painter Gauguin, who toiled with a spade for a few months in 1886.

The workmen were controlled by a supervisory staff of 700 Europeans, mainly French, who unfortunately had to be frequently replaced. But from the beginning there were four great problems which conducted the entire undertaking to a first, and then a second state of bankruptcy. They were as follows:

1. The lack of coordination between the contractors and the general management, which was hampered by inefficient administration.

2. The "geological" inadequacy which could not deal with the famous Culebra Cut, and finally caused Lesseps to consider the building of locks.

3. Illness and epidemics which lowered morale among the men.

4. The lack of capital which led to financial collapse and the "scandal."

The administrative failure is clearly described by Philippe Bunau-Varilla, who cannot be reproached for any kind of partiality. He was a young civil engineer trained at the École Polytechnique and was twenty-four when he took over the management of the work in 1888. He was really responsible for the completion of the canal, revealing himself as a diplomatist as well as a technician, and his name should be closely associated with that of Lesseps, of whom he said in his book on the Panama Canal, published in Paris in 1906:

"Lesseps was not an engineer and did not like engineers. He preferred what are called 'practical' men. He never understood that such people have no sure understanding beyond the extent of their personal experience. They do not know moreover that the advice they give in other fields is extremely dangerous. Their limited intellectual background prevents them from conceiving and assessing hitherto unknown factors which bring with them new problems.

"At Suez Monsieur de Lesseps had arbitrated on differences of opinion between technicians, often with common sense and intuition, but frequently with dangerous courage which as a rule turned out well but could have turned out badly. He thought he could use the same method at Panama."

This is why Lesseps turned to the same Belgian contractors who had worked with him at Suez, Couvreux and Hersent. But they were given inaccurate calculations of the volume of earth to be cleared, and unforeseen climatic and technical factors worked against them. This was the first failure from a general point of view, and there was no overriding technical authority. Less than a year after work had begun they gave up. Their contract had to be terminated but they received an indemnity of more than a million francs.

At the end of 1882 Lesseps found himself obliged to reorganise the general arrangement of the work. He entrusted it to eminent technicians one after the other, but most of them died a few months after they reached the isthmus. The work was then departmentalised within the framework of the Interoceanic Committee.

The Culebra was the stone of Sisyphus. This rocky mass had to be lowered by 328 feet to the average level between the two oceans before the sea-level canal could go through it. In 1886, that is to say four years after work on the cut had begun, the level had only been reduced by eleven feet at the highest part. The rock was very compact and it was difficult to keep the excavated portion in place. It remained stable during the dry season on both sides of the trench, but the first rain caused the sticky mass to slide down towards the railway lines which were used to remove the equipment, and swept away sleepers, rails and tip-waggons. In 1886 the Anglo-Dutch company which had followed the Belgian went bankrupt and withdrew, although like their predecessors they received a handsome indemnity.

Bunau-Varilla, who was director-general of operations, then resigned in order to devote himself personally to the Culebra problem, which appeared insoluble. He adopted a new clearance system, which gave excellent results. Unfortunately the cost of excavation rose from 6 francs 95 to 150 francs per cubic metre, but the level of the cut was reduced by thirty feet in two years. The height of 220 feet above sea level had been reached when work stopped in 1889, and it was at this height that the Americans took over the work in 1907.

When Bunau-Varilla saw that he could not lower the pass to sea-level he contemplated persuading Lesseps, though with no great hope of success, to reconsider the idea of a canal with locks, for in this case it would only be necessary to lower the ground by a further 100 feet. In this way, using new and powerful technical equipment the Culebra would be reduced to a height of eighty-five feet. When the Americans took over the work later they realised that out of the 150,000,000 cubic yards of earth handled by the French, half of it was caused entirely by landslides, which they themselves could only avoid with difficulty.

It was no longer possible to consider a sea-level canal and Lesseps had to accept the idea of locks, although much against his will. He had to be treated like a child; the solution was put to him as a temporary one only, on the understanding that the sea-canal could probably be built later, for he had said that "he would never agree to this as a permanent substitute."

The original route of the canal was not changed; it would only be necessary to deepen the channel where the locks were planned. It was

Eiffel who, in 1886, supplied the entire needs of the company as general contractor and in this capacity he was responsible for building the huge lock-chamber gates. At the end of 1888 the state of the excavation work, apart of course from the Culebra, was advanced enough to allow the iron frameworks to be put in place and the concrete lateral walls to be built.

During the Congress of 1879 Eiffel had been one of the strongest opponents of the sea-level canal, and the future was to show that he was absolutely right.

In 1887 Eiffel was completely absorbed with his Tower, which was then under construction, but in an extremely unselfish way the great ironwork engineer agreed to lead the enterprise and signed a contract with the company by which he undertook to finish the work on the canal in thirty months, in return for the sum of 137 million francs.

A further 12 million francs had to be paid to the contractors whose contract was being cancelled and the company undertook to supply and deliver all the necessary equipment.

The new canal was to have ten locks of unprecedented height, measuring twenty-five to thirty-six feet, which allowed the ships to be raised or lowered to a total height of 160 feet above low water, the difference between the Atlantic and the Pacific; each lock measured 600 feet in length and sixty feet in width.

It was estimated that the locked canal could allow the passage of ten ships in twenty-four hours, and assuming the ships to be of 2,000 tons on the average, the capacity of the canal would be about 20,000 tons per day. It was thought that a ship would take about an hour to pass through a lock and about eighteen hours maximum to go through the canal. It was calculated that the total amount of water held in the locks would amount to 612,000 cubic yards, kept in reaches along the canal. These estimates were greatly modified by the Americans, but as a rule the changes related only to questions of proportion or technical details which had been improved by twenty years of industrial progress.

Part of the huge sliding lock-gates which had been built at Nantes were ready to be despatched to Panama in November 1888, that is to say less than a year after the new contract had come into operation, when in December Lesseps, who had aged by ten years in three months, ordered them not to be sent.

All these gigantic problems delayed the work considerably. The workshops, which had been open for seven years, should have closed in 1889. Unfortunately by the start of the seventh year it seemed as though only the initial experimental period was coming to an end and three more years of labour were necessary. In the meantime terrible financial and political events were brewing in France which inevitably brought the enterprise to a standstill.

IV

ROME AND SUBURRA[1]

Before describing the parliamentary and financial corruption in France itself, mention must be made of the moral corruption and sickness which raged in Panama in addition to the technical and administrative muddle.

The company has been reproached for its lavish expenditure, costly buildings, "palaces" for the directors, fabulous salaries, banquets, and for the magnificent receptions which Lesseps gave in Panama. But later these expenses were purposely increased as part of the Panama liquidation scheme.

Admittedly Lesseps' visits resembled those of some nabob travelling round his estates. That of 1886 was comparable to the triumph of a Roman general after his victory and the "Gran Frances" was received in greater style than the President of the Union of Colombia.[2] There was an immense banquet in Panama which ended during the afternoon with a procession of eight decorated floats, the last of which represented "The town of Panama, with the people of Panama working to complete the canal," with two magnificent paintings each side reproducing "the canal in process of execution and the canal completed."

Naturally the company paid the bills, which were anything but allegorical. But the next day Lesseps visited the hospital, for illness was taking a heavy toll.

The isthmus of Panama had a near-equatorial climate with luxuriant vegetation which Lesseps described as "delightful." It was of virgin forest in which the lianas formed an inextricable tangle, interspersed with stagnant pools known as *quebradas*, giving off disease-ridden exhalations, and where Noah's ark seemed to have left all the worst animals—hungry jaguars and caimans, deadly serpents, giant spiders,

[1] Streets and living quarters on the Esquiline Hills, where in Ancient Roman times the working people lived.

[2] Colombia was at that time a federation of States which included Panama.

huge scorpions, without counting the vermin, which consisted mostly of ferocious ants.

"One day," wrote Bunau-Varilla, "I saw on the canal bank a continuous black streak which I had not noticed before. When I looked more closely I realised that all the leaves were literally disappearing beneath a layer of enormous tarantula spiders; they were as big as horse chestnuts complete with their rinds."

Rain which falls for half the year caused a perpetual, depressing humidity. Yellow fever and malaria were endemic and became worse when excavation was carried out in the marshy areas round the Chagres and its tributaries. Although Bunau-Varilla tried to minimise the seriousness of its effects one can only quote from the horrible details he gives:

"And yet death continually stalked around me. Never did yellow fever take such a terrible toll of human life. A few cable lengths from my house, at Colon, ships lay at anchor, but their entire crews were dead. I can still remember twelve sailors in British uniform waiting in a queue outside the doctor's door for admission tickets to hospital. A week later they were all dead.

". . . On many occasions I made a tour of inspection on ships laden with men arriving from Europe. Many of those who had embarked cheerfully felt their hearts sink when they reached the low-lying, warm and misty shores of the death-bringing isthmus. The expression of some of these revealed clearly that they were afraid. I often noted their names to see how they behaved. Almost without exception they died within three months, if they had not left again."

The making of coffins had become a flourishing business in the isthmus. The local papers of the time published notices like this one which was not meant to be funny in any way:[1]

NOTICE

I have the honour to inform the inhabitants of this town that I am always in a position to supply coffins of all sizes. Price from 6 to 100 piastres.

Dingler, director of works, arrived in 1883 and his family followed him; five months later his daughter, her fiancé, and his son were dead, and his grief-stricken wife died soon after her return to France. The new directors Blanchet and Boyer succumbed in their turn.

[1] R. Courau, *Ferdinand de Lesseps*. Paris, 1932.

Depression and nerve-wracking discussions only aided and abetted the yellow fever. After a quarrel the contractor Lillaz took to his bed and as he lay dying, in a state of delirium, vowed that Boyer would be dead in a week's time.

In October 1886, out of thirty engineers who had reached Panama, thirteen died during the following month. In 1885 and '86 twenty-seven graduates from the École Centrale arrived from France, but by 1887 only sixteen of them remained; in one year, at the hospital of Ancon, twenty-one of the admirable Sisters of St. Vincent de Paul died out of the twenty-four who formed their community.

The exact number of deaths will never be known. Like the financial waste within the company it was grossly exaggerated. But even today, in the well-kept cemetery of Ancon near the hospital, there stand thousands of crosses, reminiscent of old battlefields.

The workmen, especially the whites, were continually decimated by illness. They had to be attracted to the isthmus by increasingly higher wages which reached as much as ten times those paid in Europe. It is a well-known fact that the cost of living rises when wages rise, and the same applied in Panama. At first, however, it was wisely decided to allow free trading, which in addition to the exemption from customs duties permitted by the Colombian Government, stimulated the competition between the tradesmen, who were mostly German or Chinese, and appeared to stabilise prices of basic commodities. But generally commercialisation crept in, and the traders took advantage of the low morale caused by the climate and illness.

Soon there were adventurers in quantity, and gambling and debauchery were rife in the towns and workshops. Roulette in Panama and Colon, dice in the billets, brothels installed more or less everywhere, with "boat-loads of girls from Europe and the islands," all increased the financial chaos and administrative corruption.

The poison spread through the administration also; equipment was bought at random, the contractors were paid for work which had not been done, as well as for non-existent clearance work and imaginary pay-days. Finally, when the small contractors gave up, the company paid them heavy indemnities; for Colombian law, which operated throughout Panama, "regarded contractors as tenants whose expulsion had to be paid for."

The company had no time for discussion, or for long and expensive lawsuits which would have held up work. The company had to pay increasingly, both for work to be done and for work to be stopped. This corruption and waste were not unknown in France, however, and Bunau-Varilla tells a somewhat scathing anecdote. When he appeared later on before the Commission of Enquiry set up by the French Government, he explained that it was impossible to avoid paying these scandalous penalties. A member of the Commission asked him the following question:

"Well, sir, would it not have been possible to obtain a satisfactory and rapid judgement from the Colombian judges for a much smaller sum?"

French parliamentary corruption judged Colombia by itself.

Local politics also played their part. According to well-established traditions in Central America, revolutionaries and governments often came to blows and seized power from each other in turn according to a carefully established pattern. These practices did not interfere with the company very much, although the burning of Colon in 1885 threatened its buildings and depots. But right in the midst of the rising the leaders of the two parties gave a most courteous assurance to the directors that the "Great Undertaking" would be respected as far as possible.

On the whole the company did not suffer too much, but the local workmen left the building sites, laying down spades for guns, no doubt in order to keep their hand in . . . for politics are important. And in France, too, politicians made demands on the people.

v

BANKRUPTCY AND SCANDAL

On January 21st, 1881, the first General Meeting of the *Compagnie Universelle du Panama* took place. This time Ferdinand de Lesseps was far from optimistic. "A sum of 600 million francs will be necessary if the Panama Canal is to be opened to large-scale shipping within seven or at the most eight years. . . ."

Lesseps had underestimated the cost by at least fifty per cent. This was the main cause of the financial collapse, for the shortage of money followed the difficulties described in the preceding chapter.

It is outside the scope of this book to describe how the crash occurred, and the scandal that followed, but these events should be mentioned for they affected the technical and administrative history of the canal.

After having awarded themselves comfortable salaries and set up costly offices in Paris, Lesseps and his colleagues found themselves faced by the sharks of the Bourse and the Press, who gradually absorbed more than 10 per cent. of the total of the successive loans. The raising of the loans took place between September 1882 and June 1888, taking almost 1,500,000,000 francs from French investors, a colossal sum for this period. Incredible methods were used, varying from dishonest promises to unheard-of log-rolling, while quasi-governmental complicity was acquired by bribing many members of Parliament, including at least one minister.

In spite of everything, the six share-issues did not bring in anything like enough support for an undertaking which absorbed millions of millions. The company had adopted too lightly a plan of campaign which in the first place had not been studied carefully enough and led, after technical setbacks, to modifications and even expedients which were unworthy of such a great enterprise. "In 1887," confessed Lesseps, "the company had to start all over again; this is essential in public works. . . . We went to the mountain for it could not come to us."

By statutory means the capital could have been doubled during the work, but the enterprise was short of money from the start. Work should have begun with a capital of 1,000,000,000 francs at least, and not with a succession of small loans which made subscribers distrustful, hostile, and finally completely deaf to the last appeals, especially when Lesseps announced to each general meeting that the inauguration date had had to be put off for one more year. "As for the parliamentary scandal," wrote Loewel in *Le Canal de Panama*, 1913, "it was unfortunately only a very significant example of the way in which certain financial concerns doomed to failure tried to obtain official support. . . . This scandal was only a desperate move on the part of the company to save a situation that was already lost: it did not precede the failure, but followed it, and was the consequence, not the cause. The Panama scandal was already over when it became public."

Before they could even begin work, the company was forced to pay a very heavy price for certain rights, for which only normal sums had been set aside. In the first place 10 million francs had to be paid to Bonaparte-Wyse (he asked for 15 million) to obtain the concession that he had bought from the Colombian Government for a mere 60,000 francs. He might have been expected to take some part in the enterprise. He certainly possessed the necessary merit, but the uncompromising Lesseps would not come to terms with him.

Then, according to the agreement with Colombia, the Panama railway had to be purchased, which entailed buying almost all the shares. In 1881 they were worth eighty dollars each at the most, but instead of proceeding to buy them discreetly, without allowing the speculators time to make a profit, the company marked time and the New York stockbrokers leapt in. The shares went up to 250 dollars and Lesseps had to buy them for the prohibitive, all-in price of 100 million francs, thereby using up the initial capital which was already too small. Expenditure following the first share-issue had already been exceeded by 20 million francs, and the company had to borrow again almost before the first spade had been used in Panama.

One thing led to another and by the end of 1888, as we have seen, the company had already got through the 1,500,000,000 francs and only 163 millions remained. In order to avoid the failure that was inevitable, it was necessary to ask Parliament to pass a law authorising the prorogation of the payments which fell due. The Chamber of Deputies refused to discuss the project and the company had to suspend payments. On February 4th, 1889, the Tribunal Civil de la Seine, the competent court, dissolved the company and appointed a liquidator.[1]

Then first Lesseps himself, his son Charles and various other directors of the company were charged with corruption. There were several dramatic moments, such as when the president of the appeal court asked Charles de Lesseps if the money that he set aside to bribe Baihaut, the Minister of Public Works, was *given with felonious intent*. Charles de Lesseps had to admit, "No, it was like the purse or the watch you give up when someone threatens you with a knife in a dark lane."

The president (innocently): "You could have called the police. . . ."

Charles de Lesseps: "But what do you do if it is the policeman himself who is holding you to ransom?"

In spite of the brilliant speeches for the defence by Barboux and Waldeck-Rousseau, Ferdinand and Charles de Lesseps were both sentenced on February 5th, 1893, to five years' imprisonment and fines of 3,000 francs. Gustave Eiffel was sentenced to two years' imprisonment, a fine of 20,000 francs and the repayment of 3 million francs.

The sentence on Ferdinand de Lesseps was not carried out because of his advanced age, and as far as Eiffel was concerned the Cour de Cassation quashed his without having it heard by another court. But it is impossible not to mention the many suicides among small investors

[1] Many books have been written about the Panama scandal and the resulting court actions. These are the most interesting of them:

A. Dansette, *Les Affaires de Panama*. Paris, 1934.
B. Weill, *Panama*. Paris, 1934.
A. Zevaes, *Le Scandale de Panama*. Paris, 1931.
There is also a German historical novel: C. E. Ganter, *Panama—Kanal*. Hamburg, 1953.

whose confidence had led them to lose all they possessed in the bottom-less pit of the Panama Company.

As for the members of parliament who had been bribed, they were all acquitted, which naturally led to their triumphant re-election at the next general election.[1]

The publicist Thiebaud summed up the affair thus:

"The Panama Company collapsed because there is no Government in France, there is only a collection of responsible subordinates. It can safely be said that if there had been a Government, a Government that was merely honest and sensible, ships would have been sailing through the French ship canal in Panama since 1891 or '92."

Nevertheless some Frenchmen did not give up hope of seeing the canal finished, even by other hands. In 1889, when the monument to Ferdinand de Lesseps was unveiled at Port Said, the Prince of Arenberg said bitterly:

"In a few years' time the Panama Canal will probably be finished . . . perhaps by those who were most strongly opposed to it, who will then say that it was a worthwhile operation and not a mere dream. The naval and merchant fleet of the young nation which will soon influence the destiny of the world, will perhaps soon sail through this canal, and it will become the most effective element of its strength and power."

The future was to prove His Highness an excellent prophet.

VI

AMERICA TAKES OVER

After the collapse of the company, the liquidators were faced with a new tragic situation: the time limit set for the completion of the canal by the Colombian government had almost expired. With great difficulty they were able to obtain various extensions until 1904.

Also, in order to preserve the small amount of capital that remained, as well as the equipment which was beginning to go rusty or sink into the muddy swamps, the provisional directors of the old company tried to set up a second one under the name of the *Commission Nouvelle du Canal Transocéanique de Panama*. It was incorporated in 1894, with a capital of 60 million francs, along with what remained from the

[1] With the exception of the Minister Baihaut, who was sentenced to five years' imprisonment, loss of civil rights, and a fine of 750,000 francs; in addition, he had to pay compensation of 375,000 francs. He died in 1934, when he was director of the Suez Canal Company (according to A. Dansette).

defunct company, and sent a new Commission of Enquiry out to Panama. When it returned its members stated that the equipment was still serviceable and that 650 million francs would be needed to finish the canal within the time stipulated by Colombia. Naturally, the company would continue the system of locks and sluices instead of excavating an artificial bed in that of the Rio Chagres.

But the mention of Panama sounded like a knell in the ears of the shareholders who had been fleeced of 1,500,000,000 francs, and the attempt to float a new loan was a total fiasco.

Eiffel was again asked to help on the technical side, but refused categorically to take any part in the undertaking, saying, "I shall not act as contractor for the new company for I shall again be accused of making money out of it!"

What is more, Ferdinand de Lesseps ended his life in moral and physical deafness, in a state of semi-coma and prostration which brought him rapidly to his death on November 17th, 1894. The *deus ex machina* of the new canal was Bunau-Varilla, who was an energetic, intelligent man, and also a skilful diplomat.

While the new company was looking for the capital it was unlikely to find, Bunau-Varilla went to Russia and succeeded in interesting the all-powerful Count Witte, the Tsar Alexander III's Minister of Finance.

"I explained to Monsieur de Witte," he wrote, "how work on the Panama Canal, which was virtually finished, had been stopped by a clumsy financial move . . . I justified the intervention of Russia by the following considerations:

"1. The growing alliance between the two countries (Franco-Russian enthusiasm was then at its height) would find in their common effort the material expression of their common aspirations.

"2. By the completion of the Panama Canal Russia would see the complement of the Transsiberian Canal, which at that time had just been started. The Suez Canal, I said, which mingles the waters of the Atlantic and the Pacific, is the complement of the transcontinental railways which link the two oceans on the American continent. In the same way the Panama Canal links the two oceans and is the complement of the Russian Transcontinental railway which links them on the Asiatic continent."

Count Witte gave no reply but authorised his engineer to discuss his Franco-Russian projects with the French Government, in the person of Casimir-Périer, who was then President of the Council, and on the point of being elected President of the Republic.

"In this case," said Casimir-Périer, who agreed in principle, "we will go half-shares with Russia, and if the United States want a share, we shall offer them one."

This was a strange and subtle kind of arithmetic but it was not devoid of common sense.

In the meantime the Government fell, Carnot was assassinated, Casimir-Périer made only one appearance at the Elysée before he was forced to resign and leave political life, while Nicholas II succeeded his father on the throne of Russia. The Franco–Russian balloon was deflated.

All these events, this "terrible fatality," as Bunau-Varilla aptly called it, did not discourage him, and he now turned to the United States, with which he was more successful.

At this moment the States were at war with Spain, and were soon to capture Cuba, their last American colony; in this way, after their annexation of Louisiana and New Mexico, they consolidated a formidable hegemony. In order to reach Cuba they had to take their fleet from the Pacific through the Magellan Straits, and American public opinion began to see at last that although a canal through the Isthmus of Panama might not be a very flourishing commercial enterprise it was extremely important from the strategic point of view, especially if it were an American canal.

In April 1898, therefore, Congress appointed a technical commission and sent it to Panama to study, once more, the possibility of cutting a canal through Nicaragua, while diplomatic conversations were opened with the Nicaraguan authorities. In 1899 the commission submitted a favourable report. The necessary legislation for the canal was voted by the House of Representatives and ratified by the Senate in 1902. It was the end of Panama ... but then the remarkable and intrepid Bunau-Varilla appeared on the scene.

Nature also intervened; the eruption of Mount Peleus and a tidal wave had just destroyed the town of St. Pierre in Martinique, leading to an earthquake; then the volcano Monotombo erupted on the shores of Lake Nicaragua.

Bunau-Varilla thought immediately that American public opinion should be alarmed, and pointed out that an earthquake in Nicaragua might destroy locks in a few seconds and put the canal out of action for an indefinite length of time. The Americans are realistic and when they decide to understand they understand quickly.

Nicaragua had always denied the existence of these dangerous volcanoes. In 1900, however, their postal services had issued a series of postage stamps representing "a magnificent volcano complete with a plume of smoke," while in the foreground were a quay and a station which had been destroyed by an earthquake.

"I had to have official documents," wrote Bunau-Varilla, "to convince the American senators of the natural dangers to which a canal cut through Nicaragua might be liable. I had them under my very eyes . . . the postage stamps of the Republic of Nicaragua. I rushed into every place in Washington where stamps were sold. . . . By going through their stocks I had the good fortune to find ninety stamps, that is to say one per senator. It was the proof of the lie, the proof that volcanoes existed, although the Nicaraguan Government denied the fact.

"I immediately stuck the precious stamps on sheets of paper at the top of which were written these simple words: Postage stamps of the Republic of Nicaragua.

"The smouldering volcano on the stamps had an effect as immediate as the legendary appearance of the Medusa."

The next day, June 26th, 1902, by an almost unanimous vote the House of Representatives, and then the Senate, passed the Spooner Act, which authorised the President of the United States to give preference to the cut through Panama over that through Nicaragua, "provided that they could conclude a satisfactory treaty with Colombia and obtain a secure entitlement from the new Company of Panama for the sale of its concessions."

The Spooner Act involved the United States in negotiations with Great Britain, France (the new Panama Company), and Colombia. If Great Britain felt disposed to forgo the joint ownership established by the Bulwer–Clayton Treaty, she still intended to maintain the neutrality of the canal, whatever form it took, and equality of treatment too. But she was then deeply preoccupied with the South African War, and gave in fairly easily. The negotiations were concluded by the Hay–Pauncefote Treaty, which made the following provisos:

The Bulwer–Clayton Treaty was revoked and the United States were free to assume exclusively the construction and development of the canal. They were to ensure its neutrality, however, allowing the free passage of merchant ships and warships of all nations on a footing of absolute equality. Further, the United States would have the power to maintain along the canal a military police force which they considered necessary to maintain neutrality and public order. They did not fail to make substantial use of it.

Without any difficulty the agreement to make a cut through

Nicaragua was tacitly applied to the Panama Canal. Thus, says André Siegfried, "the United States, sole guarantor of the new sea route, received from the British the equivalent of a mandate, but in fact the canal was to be American, more American than the Suez Canal is British."

There was nothing soft-hearted about the dealings with France. The new company asked for 500 million francs, which they might perhaps have obtained if the talks had proceeded rapidly, as Bunau-Varilla had hoped. Unfortunately the company had procrastinated with President McKinley, who had been fairly well-disposed; after his assassination, however, his successor, Theodore Roosevelt, proved to be much tougher. The offer of 200 million francs for the concession and the equipment had to be accepted under severe pressure, for the foreclosure date was drawing near. This money was naturally used to indemnify the debenture-holders and shareholders of the new company, which meant that anyone who held debentures in the old company received only a few francs, and shareholders received nothing. The French tragedy ended in disaster. The consent of Colombia had to be given before this transaction was valid, and it was obtained on January 4th, 1902.

Once more the indefatigable Bunau-Varilla devoted himself to the work. In spite of a certain amount of friction Colombia ratified the transfer of the French rights to the United States, and then conceded a zone of territory in the isthmus which was to be administered by the States, although it was still in the possession of Colombia. The two countries were to share responsibility for the maintenance of public health and discipline. Colombia would provide for the defence of the canal, but could call on the States for help if necessary. In return the States would pay Colombia the sum of 10 million dollars together with certain additional annual payments.[1]

In this way a strip of land seven miles wide in Colombian territory passed into American control. Later the width of the canal zone was to be increased to ten miles, under the terms of the agreement with the new Republic of Panama, which was created in strange circumstances in November 1904.

[1] After nine years the annual payment was 250,000 dollars, and this has now risen to 430,000 dollars.

VII

A REVOLUTION FOR 100,000 DOLLARS

The Colombian Parliament, when asked to ratify the agreement, found the terms insufficiently generous and refused to accept them. The agreed sum was a windfall for a country which had been brought to the brink of ruin by its continual revolutions. Colombia's apparent greed concealed a plan which if it had succeeded would have been brilliantly clever. The Colombians reasoned that the canal could not be built without their agreement; if it was not completed by the expiration of the concession in 1904 everything would revert to Colombia. The only thing to do therefore was to keep quiet, and after two years the concession and the equipment would come into their hands; then they could sell everything at a high price to the highest bidder. At this point the diabolically astute Bunau-Varilla appeared on the scene again.

For many years Colombia had been subject to revolutions which brought the Government and the rebels into power alternately, although nobody could be exactly sure which party represented order or anarchy. Why, thought the French engineer, could one not organise a nice little revolution which would detach the province of Panama from the Union of Colombian States, and proclaim its independence in the sacred name of democracy? A republic of Panama set up in this way would certainly want to be in agreement with the U.S.A. Panama was in any case dissatisfied with the Colombian Government, which was obviously going to lay its hands on the millions from abroad. As Baron Louis[1] had said: "Give me good politics and I'll give you good finance."

The revolution was carefully planned for November 4th, 1903. Entirely by chance the American gunboat *Nashville* had been moored off Colon for two days.

In spite of everything the secret leaked out at Bogotá and the Government became suspicious. To cope with any trouble they sent a gunboat with a detachment of soldiers under the command of General Tovar, who disembarked at Colon; their leader then repaired alone to Panama, where the authorities organised a great banquet in his honour. The plan was to make General Tovar and his high

---

[1] French financier (1755–1837), Minister of Finance during the Restoration and the time of Louis-Philippe.

command drunk and then take them prisoner. This was achieved quite easily during dessert, after the customary toasts had been drunk.

When they heard of this treacherous act the Colombians swore to rescue their General; the Panamanians would certainly surrender when faced by Government troops. The soldiers therefore went to the station at Colon to take the train to Panama, for there were no cars and no other means of transport.

The American railway company demanded 10,000 francs to transport the soldiers, an enormous sum at the time, especially for Government troops who were rather short of money. The railway company refused to run a train, and there was never a clearer proof that money is the sinew of war. The Government troops wanted to march on Panama, but the rebels opposed them, and the soldiers would have fallen into their hands if the American marines had not disembarked from the *Nashville* and heroically come between them. The Colombian gunboat fired three shells on Colon, which killed an unfortunate Chinese coolie.[1] He was the only victim, apart from Colombia itself, of the revolution. It came to an end the same day at eight o'clock in the evening without a single Panamanian dying for his country. The next morning the Independence of the Republic of Panama was proclaimed, while from the buildings throughout the isthmus flew the new white flag with quartering of *gules* and *azure*, designed the day before by Madame Bunau-Varilla herself. The Government troops came to no harm; a British liner took them back, free of charge, to their barracks in Bogotá.

On November 7th the United States recognised the independence of Panama with enthusiasm, declaring out of disinterested sympathy for this infant Republic that they would not permit any troops, Colombian or other, to land in the isthmus. Out of gratitude the new Panamanian Government decided to negotiate with the States at once for the completion of the canal.

Colombia protested loudly at losing Panama, but President Roosevelt replied, "that he believed himself in duty bound, not only by the clauses of a treaty, but *in the interests of civilisation*, to ensure that world communications by means of the Isthmus of Panama were not disturbed by continuous civil wars which were as ruinous as they were meaningless."

As for the accusation that he had "helped" in the rising, Roosevelt defended himself with ferocious humour:

[1] The fuse of one of these accidentally lethal shells is still preserved in the Cali Museum in Colombia, and André Siegfried states he has seen it.

"Apart from the reports received by our military representatives, our only previous knowledge of the revolution was that apparent to any intelligent person who reads the newspapers and is well informed about public affairs."

On November 18th following, less than a fortnight after "his" revolution (which had only cost him 100,000 dollars all told), Monsieur Philippe Bunau-Varilla, Minister Plenipotentiary of the Republic of Panama, signed with John Hay, Under-Secretary of State, the treaty which gave the Panama Canal to the United States for a mere song.

VIII

"MANU MILITARI"

When the Americans began work on the canal they experienced some of the same difficulties as the French. From the administrative point of view everything was theoretically easy. According to the Spooner Act the President of the United States was legally, and in fact, responsible for the work in Panama. Roosevelt's first move was to appoint a Commission to take charge, but he found Washington acted too slowly in obtaining equipment and credit. The members of the Commission did not agree among themselves, and the civil governor of Panama clashed with the technical director, an engineer named Wallace, who resigned and went into private industry.

Stevens, a famous and popular technician from the railways in the West, took over next, and immediately declared himself in favour of a canal with locks as against a sea-level canal, which still had some supporters in the U.S.A. Roosevelt backed him strongly and his opinion won the day, although there was still friction among the administrators and technicians.

In the end the President became angry and made a speech to silence the bureaucratic croakings. "I will appoint men who will stay on the job until I'm tired of them, or until I tell them to give up. I will call in the army."

And he immediately sent to Panama Lieutenant-Colonel George W. Goethals, of the Army Engineer Corps, who was given dictatorial powers. He was Zone Governor and had absolute authority over the carrying-out of the work. Authority, supervision and technique were centralised in his control, and he was responsible only to the President

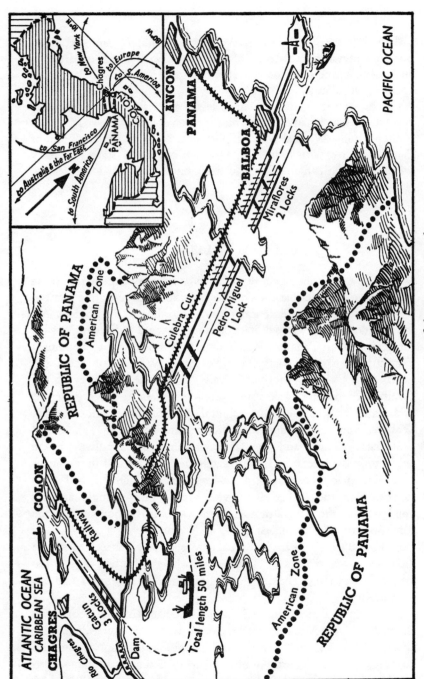

44. Diagrammatic map of the Panama Canal

of the United States. Although America was opposed to autocracy, no other method would work in Panama.

The workshops were opened in May 1904, but no technical work was carried out on the canal before 1907. From that time onwards the great enterprise went forward without a pause until its completion in 1914. During the First World War the canal proved invaluable for the rapid supply of food and explosives.

There was a certain amount of corruption and friction during the building of the canal but it is safe to say that no enterprise was ever carried out with greater regularity, sincerity, energy and scrupulous integrity.

In the first place a route was carefully worked out as follows:

1. In the port of Colon, on the Atlantic coast, a channel thirty-six miles long would lead to the Gatun locks.

2. Three locks would raise ships by twenty-eight feet each to a total height of eighty-five feet and take them into the artificial lake of Gatun, created by a huge dam, which in turn would feed the locks.

3. The Gatun dam, half a mile wide at its base, 107 feet high, was destined to restrain the turbulent Rio Chagres; it consisted of a wall of concrete with a very gradual slope, 2,650 feet wide at its base and 100 feet at its crest, on which a golf-course has been built.

4. The artificial lake of Gatun, with a surface area of 160 square miles.

5. A stretch of thirty-two miles which would take ships to the famous Culebra Cut, which is about eight and a half miles long and ends in

6. The single Pedro Miguel lock (over thirty feet high), which was to lower the ships towards the Pacific by crossing the small Miraflores Lake until they reach

7. The two Miraflores locks (each twenty-seven feet high).

8. Then the ships were to follow the channel dug out in the bed of the Rio Chagres, to the port of Balboa where a final channel took them to the Pacific.

The route is completed by very large-scale harbour services at Panama and Balboa, including quays, oil and coal supplies. All the locks are double, that is to say they consist of two parallel chambers which allow ships sailing in opposite directions to pass through simultaneously. This arrangement also permitted the building of locks in which the water from one chamber could be used to fill the other. These double locks are separated by walls of reinforced concrete over sixty feet wide along which electric trains run. The dimensions of these locks are roughly equal—length 1,000 feet; width, 110 feet; ships with a draught of forty feet and up to 35,000 tons are authorised to pass through.

The locks are closed at each end by a triple series of gates with two metallic leaves, each forty-six to eighty-two feet high and seven feet thick, and each leaf weighs from 300 to 600 tons. The total weight of these forty-two gates is about six times as much as the whole of the Eiffel Tower.

Men were required as badly as materials, healthy intelligent men with team spirit, who would be able to stand the work. They had not to be scared of yellow fever, they needed to live well on plenty of the best food available, and they had to have the maximum amount of comfort after the days of hard work in an equatorial climate. All this was organised methodically and on a large scale.

First of all the fight against yellow fever was begun. When the workshops were deserted it had practically disappeared, although there were sixty-two deaths in 1905. Malaria was still rampant, caused by the anopheles mosquito, which had to be destroyed at all costs. The campaign lasted three years, at the end of which this mosquito, according to J. F. Fraser, was as rare in Panama as the aurora borealis.

Teams of well-trained "oilers" were set up in great numbers, coloured workers who worked all day spraying thousands of tons of kerosene over nests of larvae, surfaces of swamps and stagnant pools. No rubbish of any sort was allowed in the streets of the towns or the canal workshops, for water could collect in any metal container and allow the mosquito to breed there. Whenever the well-known buzzing was heard above the sound of the excavators and the tip-trucks, the "oilers" penetrated resolutely into the jungle fighting the ruthless battle that they intended to win.

The inhabitants were made to protect their houses against the dangerous insects and fix wire mesh over doors and windows. Sewers were built and drinking water was brought to the towns in pipes which replaced the suspect barrels and cisterns. Doctors examined the staff continually and special inspectors kept a check on the domestic sanitation.

By 1910 the mortality rate had been reduced to five per thousand, instead of the six per cent. reached during the period of French control. Hygiene, more than medicine, had overcome the terrible disease, but it is only fair to add that methods were used which had been absolutely unknown twenty years previously during the time of de Lesseps.

Police control was entrusted to Colonel Perry Fyffe, a veteran from the Cuban war, who quickly organised a police force as famous and as respected as the Canadian Mounties. His powers were extremely wide, and when he had caused a few well-known trouble-makers to be hanged in full view of the workshops, or at the gates of the town, his men began to enjoy undisputed prestige.

Colonel Goethals never wore his military uniform in Panama, and every Sunday drove through the towns and workshops holding court, and personally arbitrating on sordid gambling debts or neighbours' quarrels.

On several occasions when strikes broke out for one reason or another, Goethals stopped them by publishing this announcement: "All men who do not come to work because they are discontented will be repatriated free of charge to the United States."

Saloons were strictly limited in number because they had to have an expensive licence and were placed a long way from the workshops. The men who had been used to drinking at any time soon became accustomed to the change, especially when they noticed that in this climate alcohol had an extremely bad effect.

On Sundays Goethals organised sports club meetings and concerts, and attended them in shirt sleeves. The great engineer, with his cheerful nature, was more popular than the French directors of Lesseps' time, who travelled in luxury coaches, wearing top-hats, as though they had been on the Paris boulevards.

"The name of Goethals is one to conjure with in the isthmus," wrote Fraser. "Yet it cannot be said that the man himself is well known. I ran across him in the long open-coached train one day, quietly smoking a cigarette and reading a newspaper, and I doubt if one of the fifty people in the coach knew who he was. Some diverted stream up-country had broken bounds and was interfering with the cutting, and he was on his way to make that stream go the way he wanted. . . .

"Always quiet, calm, autocratic but fair, he has the esteem of all the thousands of men under him."

Someone even composed a song about him, called "Tell the Colonel," and the refrain ran:

"See Colonel Goethals, tell Colonel Goethals,
    It's the only right and proper thing to do;
Just write a letter, or even better,
    Arrange a little Sunday interview."

The only strikes that Goethals had to settle arose from differences between the wages paid to white and coloured workers. In 1910, out of a total of 45,000 men employed, there were 1,200 white men, who formed the major part of the skilled labourers, engineers, foremen and workshop directors. Most of them were Americans who were in charge of Spaniards, Italians and Greeks. Very few Frenchmen were employed.

The unskilled labourers were negroes from Jamaica, Haiti, the Philippines and Martinique, or Japanese and Chinese, but the latter usually stayed in the workshops only for a short time and then worked as shopkeepers.

White and coloured workers were segregated as in the U.S.A. at the time, and there was a great difference between their wages: the unskilled workers were paid in Colombian silver dollars, and were known as "silver employees," while the Whites were paid in American dollars and known as "gold employees." The rates of exchange differed as much as the salaries. On pay-days an armour-plated train arrived, consisting of two cars, one for paying the white workers and the other for paying the coloureds.

All categories of personnel worked a six-day week and on Sundays all the workshops were closed.

The provisions were supplied by the Zone administration and, since Panama produced nothing, everything had to come from New York and San Francisco, thousands of miles away. All the supplies were sold on a non-profit-making basis and distributed by refrigerated trains regularly and generously, often at prices lower than those operating in Europe or the States. The administration also provided all kinds of supplies for the wives and children of the employees, who on their own amounted to 25,000 people.

With this efficient organisation the work went forward rapidly. First-class modern machinery was used—dredgers, excavators, drills, spreaders, pumps, and railway components as well as the equipment which had been abandoned by the French.

"We criticise the French equipment," said Stevens in 1905, "but this is unfair. For the period, it was modern equipment, but nowadays it is like seeing a toy car next to a real car. I do not intend to criticise the French, but I don't understand how they succeeded in doing what they did with the equipment they had."

There had been great technical progress in the intervening twenty-five years and the Americans had unlimited financial means at their disposal, whereas the French had not.

The work on the Panama Canal, including military defence, cost the States nearly 400 million dollars, that is to say twice the amount estimated by Roosevelt when work began, and it was provided entirely from official funds, with no public loan.

The money was allocated as follows:

	Millions of Dollars
To Panama	10
To the new French Panama Canal Co.	40
Cost of work on the Canal.. ..	223
Defence	120
Total ..	393

From 1907 when the isthmus was cleared of disease, until the canal was completed, thousands of workers were occupied in digging, moving excavated earth and building enormous lock-gate sills and lock-chambers. "And yet," wrote one witness, "you never see more than a few men working on one specific job at a time."

The Americans encountered the same problems as the French—landslides and disposal problems—in the famous Culebra Cut, which is now called the Gaillard Cut, after one of the American engineers. During the whole of the work on this Cut there were thirty-two landslides, and during the month of May alone, in 1909, 5¼ million cubic yards had to be cleared, without counting water infiltrations which kept the pumps at work night and day. In August 1912 there was a large-scale landslide near Emperador, which spread over half the trench and buried a large quantity of equipment. Then the Rio Obispo, which had been diverted, burst through into the Culebra Cut and flooded part of it.[1]

"These slides are enough to break the heart of men," wrote Fraser. "But the dogged determination of Colonel Goethals and his fellows, sick to silence when they have to face another break, is one of the finest episodes of the whole business."

But enthusiasm at conquering the mountain made one American foreman, showing Fraser round, say:

"Yes, it is a great ditch. You see those flat cars piled with dirt? Well,

[1] The total amount of earth taken out of the Culebra Cut by the Americans by 1913, when the excavation ended, was 120 million cubic yards. The total amount removed for the whole canal was 360 million cubic yards. The French had removed 80 million, of which 30 million were used by the Americans (A. Siegfried, op. cit.).

by the time the Atlantic joins the Pacific we shall have removed as much dirt as would fill a train of such cars 96,000 miles long, which is getting pretty near four times round the earth. Yes, it is a great ditch."

Considering the extent and danger of the work, in which tons of explosives were used, there were remarkably few fatal accidents. There was only one premature explosion which killed twenty-four men.

Finally, on August 3rd, 1914, the first ship, the *Cristobal*, flying the Panamanian flag, sailed through the fifty-mile-long canal, through the locks, dams and harbour facilities.

In 1915, when the canal was officially opened, the Congress of San Francisco sent a telegram to the family of de Lesseps, and a commemorative plaque was set up in his honour.

Colonel Goethals stated that "the French company pioneered the work of the isthmus. ... Their work deserves only praise and the more one studies their accomplishment the greater is our admiration for those who directed the preliminary work on the canal."

IX

THE KEYS OF THE KINGDOM

No outstanding incident has occurred in the history of the Panama Canal since it was opened. At first it made a financial loss, but this situation soon improved and in 1938 it made a large profit which was devoted mainly to its upkeep and military defence.

"At first," said André Siegfried, "the canal appeared international, in accordance with the Hay–Pauncefote Treaty, but equality of treatment is the only international aspect, and perhaps it could be upheld that according to this Treaty the Government of the United States occupies the isthmus as mandated territory. In fact the Americans are there on their own account, and carry out their own business."

In addition to big business, the Americans, after two world wars, have been more and more preoccupied with the security problem which can only be solved by the use of an increasingly powerful defence system.

At first, when the Panama Canal went through Colombian territory, there was no kind of military or naval protection for it. The Americans realised this at once. When Panama obtained its independence in the absurd conditions described earlier, the new Republic became more or less an integral part of the U.S.A., a kind of 49th State. After buying

Louisiana from France, Alaska from Russia, laying hands on Cuba and the Philippines, the American War Department could not tolerate the thought that Panama might be open to all comers.

In the event of hostilities they had to be in a position to send their two fleets freely and rapidly between the Atlantic and the Pacific, for reasons of naval strategy. If war were to break out the canal would no longer be regarded as "international," and would be more and more vulnerable to attack as the power of armaments continued to increase. Under cover of a surprise bombardment a lock could be destroyed and the canal put out of action for a long time. The States soon realised this weakness and since the canal had been built under military control it was decided that it should remain in military hands.

André Siegfried states that in 1928 Monsieur Georges Bonnet described the entire canal zone as "almost military: everywhere there are forts, fortified islands and powerful batteries. All along the canal are large camps and garrisons. A garrison of 10,000 to 12,000 men, that is one-third of the population, are permanently stationed along the canal. It is for the troops as well as for their staff, that the administration maintains roads, houses, transport, schools, hospitals and clubs. There is intense naval and air activity, and a squadron is based permanently at Balboa, while Cristobal is a base for submarine and military sea-planes. Every year the American fleet assembles off Panama, and it is in this area that it carries out large-scale manoeuvres. . . ."

Shortly before the last war when Germany was beginning to absorb part of Europe, and Japan was threatening, serious precautions were taken against the danger of espionage or any attempt at sabotage. No coloured man was allowed to settle in the military zone.

The United States also realised that the dimensions of the canal were inadequate, particularly the width of the lock-chambers, for the traffic passing through might be doubled in the case of a war, and repair work on one single lock could reduce the capacity of the canal by half, for ships would have to queue in the ports for miles and miles. A large warship passing through the canal could hold up the traffic for an entire day, and certain warships, like the *New Jersey*, made it necessary to take fantastic precautions to prevent her from damaging the locks. During the Second World War, at the time of Pearl Harbour, the two aircraft carriers *Lexington* and *Saratoga* (33,000 tons each), which were later sunk in the Pacific by the Japanese, scraped their sides dangerously as they went through the locks.

The United States therefore are faced with three problems— military, economic and technical—which must all be solved. Money and the devices of politics are not lacking to deal with the first two, but the third is more difficult. The technicians have considered two possible solutions—the first being the building of a second series of locks at some distance from the existing ones. But the slightest vibration from an atomic explosion could destroy both canals and their dams at the same time.

Fortunately, for the time being, nuclear fission is incapable of moving mountains and draining lakes, and serious consideration is being given in Washington to the eventual building of a sea-level canal. A canal of this type could easily be made serviceable after a bombardment, by straightforward clearance, but locks and dams cannot be repaired quickly.

In this way the U.S.A. would return to the first plans of de Lesseps. A sea-level canal of this type would obviously cost an astronomic sum, provisionally estimated at 5,000,000,000 dollars. Yet the United States is not likely to jib at such an amount if it would ensure the inviolability of the canal and guarantee them the command of the two great oceans. Superiority in atomic warfare means the joint mastery of land, air and sea, and it should not be forgotten that the latter covers three-quarters of our planet.

If control of the Mediterranean by means of the Suez Canal may seem of negligible importance in the case of another world war, the same cannot be said of the Panama Canal, which is really the key to the kingdom of earth.

XII

THE SIMPLON TUNNEL

"The Simplon Tunnel has been built under international auspices and the work has been carried out by international collaboration. Our enterprise has had the benefit of mental and physical contributions from Italy, Germany and Switzerland, united in the interests of good will and peace. May the same apply between the peoples of different countries!"

Ed. Sulzer
Speech at the banquet to celebrate
the opening of the Iron Gates,
April 2nd, 1904.

THE DESPOTS OF ancient times lacked mechanical tools and technical experience, but the amount of human labour they had at their disposal may be estimated from a study of the ruins of underground buildings.

Besides the Egyptian tombs, or the underground temples of India, which were vast achievements as well as being artistic masterpieces sacred to the gods, the ancients knew how to construct galleries as conduits for water, and how to connect two neighbouring viaducts.

It is known that there was a colossal tunnel in Babylon dug out under the bed of the River Euphrates, linking two sets of fortifications on the banks of the river, which was already spanned by a wonderful bridge. The Etruscans, and later the Romans, built *emissarii* several miles in length to drain swamps round the lakes of Albano and Fusino.

Few road tunnels were built in ancient times, however, for there was very little need for them, although, as we have already seen, the great Roman roads went into the hillside at Pausillipus and in the Apennines.

At the end of last century the Hagdek tunnel, which is 2,640 feet long, was discovered in Switzerland, going under the valley of the River Aar. This famous underground passage shows that the Romans made it by first sinking vertical shafts through the axis of the route as was done later for the London tube; then the miners worked on the two branches and brought them towards each other until they met. The junction of the Simplon tunnel was effected in the same way.

I

THE TUNNEL WAR

The first Swiss railway tunnel situated at a reasonable height was the Hauenstein tunnel (built at 8,000 feet) linking Lucerne and Basle through the Jura mountains in 1860. Tunnelling methods were still in the experimental stage and this achievement was dearly bought—sixty men were buried beneath a landslide and died of suffocation before they could be rescued.

"The sufferings of these unfortunate men were particularly horrible," wrote J. B. Dumont. "The weaker ones, or those who had been injured in the landslide, died first, and the survivors, who knew that they also were doomed, had the touching courage to bury them, placing the bodies of the masons on one side and those of the miners on the other, arranging a plank and a little straw beneath their heads."

In 1854 Austria opened on the Semmering Pass the first transalpine road which linked Vienna and Venice, consisting of fifteen short tunnels and sixteen viaducts, built at an average height of 3,000 feet.

A few years later, the necessity for a railway route from northern and western France to the Mediterranean led to the consideration of big alpine tunnels. France took the initiative, and between 1857 and 1871 a tunnel seven and a half miles long was made at a height of 4,000 feet beneath the Col de Fréjus between Modane in France and Bardonnecchia in Italy. For ten years this tunnel gave France an effective monopoly over traffic going from Great Britain and north-west Europe to the Mediterranean and the eastern ports.

The building of the Mont-Cenis tunnel was terribly slow—it took nearly fourteen years—and caused many fatal accidents. Forty miners were killed in landslides and the powder factory at Bardonnecchia blew up. But these losses were not in vain, and their causes were not forgotten when the St. Gotthard tunnel was begun under the direction of the engineer Favre.

After starting work at opposite ends of the tunnel, the two teams of men met on February 28th, 1880, when the drill broke through the last obstacle. Favre himself had died during the course of the work but his friends and colleagues now paid him a touching tribute. They had wanted him to be the first to pass through the tunnel and arranged for this to happen symbolically by passing his photograph through the breach which linked the two galleries together.

The approach-ramps for the Mont-Cenis tunnel had led to the building of many large structures, such as auxiliary tunnels, bridges and corniche roads, but they were nothing compared to the work that was necessary on both sides of the St. Gotthard.

The route had to follow hairpin bends and, in order to avoid unnecessarily steep slopes, Favre and his colleagues had to dig seven helicoidal tunnels, three to the north and four to the south of the pass. The line included eighty tunnels of all kinds, forming a total length of about twenty-nine miles, that is 18 per cent. of the entire route, along which there were 324 bridges or viaducts with a span of more than thirty-five feet. The rock was extremely hard and there was a constant danger from sudden water infiltration. This achievement did great honour to the courage of the Swiss and Italian workers on the St. Gotthard tunnel, which was a unique achievement until the Simplon tunnel was built.

The St. Gotthard in fact was the first move in a tunnel war which lasted for twenty-five years. This tunnel supplanted the Mont-Cenis one, and Germany profited from this. She could now control traffic through the Alps, as well as to and from the Rhineland and the Ruhr, Belgium and Holland, Britain, German-speaking Switzerland and even the east of France.

All this took place at the beginning of the twentieth century, which was a period of heavily armed peace, and the economic and strategic situation created by the St. Gotthard tunnel was serious.

The Arlberg tunnel, which was six and a half miles long, and lay at

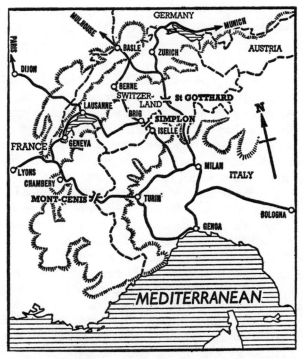

45. Railway lines and principal tunnels of the Alps (1906)

an average height of 4,300 feet, was built between 1880 and 1884 along the Paris–Basle–Vienna line. It was an important Swiss route for a long time, but it was of little value to French traffic bound for the Mediterranean, which now passed through the St. Gotthard.

These three tunnels formed two groups, the western, or Mont-Cenis group and the eastern or St. Gotthard–Arlberg group. This gave a clear preference to the cantons of German-speaking Switzerland, to the detriment of the French-speaking parts and the railway traffic from the south-east of France.

As a result, French-speaking Switzerland and France decided to build another railway line which would follow the valley where the Rhine had its source from Lausanne to Brig, and branch to the south-east towards Northern Italy, going through the Simplon mountains. This long-term decision formed the culminating point in the high strategy of tunnel warfare, which is not yet complete.

II

FROM NAPOLEON TO THE SMALLEST
RAILWAY STATION IN THE WORLD

In ancient times and during the Middle Ages the Simplon Pass was already in general use. A few Roman remains still exist along the route and records show that as far back as the thirteenth century there was a toll-gate and an inn. But until the eighteenth century the route was neither easy nor safe. Napoleon, when he was devising a means of conquering Italy, seems to have been the first to realise the importance of the Simplon Pass as a vital means of communication.

Shortly after the battle of Marengo in 1800 he decided to build an important military road, under the direction of the French engineer Nicolas Céard, with the collaboration of the Valais population. It is thirty-seven miles long, and with its 611 bridges and seven galleries it is one of the finest achievements of last century.

While sledges and the picturesque Fischer coaches with their yellow boxes were crossing the snow-covered Simplon Pass, railways began to go through Switzerland before France thought of finding a shorter means of access to Northern Italy. The Swiss Government and the Swiss Federal Railways were the first to suggest to France and Italy that they should cooperate in a gigantic enterprise on their territory.

But before it entered on its final phase the future railway suffered mishaps in Switzerland comparable to those that led to the final scandal in Panama.

"The cantons of French-speaking Switzerland," wrote Joseph Stockmar in his *Histoire du Chemin de fer du Simplon*, "had considered the possibility of such a tunnel as far back as 1852, before the St. Gotthard led the attack, and they were now reduced to waiting for the financiers who gave their attention to the enterprises from which they expected to draw a profit and neglected the others. The inaccessible districts were sacrificed in advance. . . . The concessions changed hands and many of them were sold before the work began, earning fortunes for their owners. The canton of Le Valais, which was neglected by Swiss high finance, became the prey of speculators."

However, this foul play did not prevent the engineers from drawing up rolls of blue-prints. From 1852 to 1893 no fewer than thirty plans were put forward, from Koller's purely theoretical one to that of a Simplon tunnel through the Jura mountains, which was finally accepted by the Federal authorities. The estimates varied from 20 to 104 million francs, allowing for a tunnel varying from one to twelve miles in length, at altitudes ranging from 2,500 to 7,000 feet.

Negotiations with France were continued, for financial as well as railway engineering assistance seemed indispensable. A company was even formed in 1856, but in 1865, after some work had been carried out in Le Valais, it could not continue for lack of funds, and was declared bankrupt. Then Switzerland decided to approach the French Government directly.

On June 21st, 1870, subsidies were requested, on the lines of the German subsidies given for the St. Gotthard tunnel; but unfortunately the Franco-Prussian war broke out and it was not until 1880 that the question was raised again, this time by Gambetta, who was strongly in favour of the enterprise.

The question remained in abeyance for several years, in spite of the highly favourable report by Emile Loubert, who, strangely enough, saw the project completed when he was over seventy. Some obscure underground parliamentary machinations caused the project to be rejected, and in view of the French default the Swiss Federal Government made no further approaches.

The Swiss negotiated with Italy for no less than twenty-five years, but here they were more successful and obtained considerable financial support. The Swiss still had to bear the expense for the major part of the work and to supply the entire technical organisation. Even today, although half of the tunnel is in Italian territory, the entire maintenance and commercial development of the tunnel are carried out by the Swiss Federal Railways.

In 1897 the 76 million francs necessary had been obtained by means of loans and subsidies; Lausanne and Brig (in Switzerland) were linked together, and Milan was linked to Iselle through Arona. Now the work could be put in hand.

"We're through! Outside! Everyone outside!"

Fifty years later I found myself on the spot where this shout from the miners announced that the greatest enterprise of the early twentieth century was completed. Unfortunately it was also a cry of fear.

The most heroic and spectacular part of the Simplon tunnel was finished. Victory had been achieved over the vast mass of Monte Leone at its base, just as a hundred years earlier Napoleon's road had climbed over it for the first time.

Monte Leone, the Imperial eagle, the white crosses of Savoy and Switzerland united by the first railway line to run underground—all these symbols came into my mind as the truck plunged into the longest tunnel in the world.

At first, as we left Brig, on the Swiss side, it was cold enough for any Bernese bear, but gradually the atmosphere became strangely warmer and then stifling. The engineer Capponi, my escort, and his two colleagues suggested that I should take off my coat as they did. A few miles farther on we shed our jackets with relief, and, though it was mid-winter and we were in the Alps, we reached the deepest subterranean railway station in the world clad only in shirt-sleeves.

This is not the only strange thing about this station, the smallest in the world, at which nobody ever gets on or off a train because no trains stop there. It is placed more or less half-way through the tunnel, at the Swiss-Italian frontier, and there is no customs inspection. There is no station-master either, but only two employees of the Swiss Railways, who do tours of duty of eight hours, changing three times a day, to ensure communication between the stations of Brig and Iselle which are about twelve miles apart. Soon however the points will be electrically operated from Brig and the phantom station will be radio controlled—empty of everything except the blind crickets whose chirping breaks the silence between two trains in this railway catacomb. It is as warm here as in a bakehouse and along with the mice who scuttle between the sleepers they are the only creatures to be found in the tunnel. The mice need not be afraid of cats and they are practically Swiss civil servants. A local inhabitant explained to me with much laughter that the mice act as housekeepers, and thanks to them every scrap of paper or rubbish thrown from the trains disappears.

Monsieur Capponi unrolled before me the immense plans of the tunnel, which is entirely under his supervision. Through these detailed tracings a marvellous, tragic story, already fifty years old, came alive for me.

When the St. Gotthard tunnel was built it had cost the vast sum of 261 million francs, but it had been built at a high altitude (3,770 feet), and Germany had just won the Franco-Prussian war, taking 5,000,000 francs from France and using a substantial proportion of this to finance the work on the tunnel. This was not the case in Switzerland, which was a transit country with industry dependent on imports, or in Italy, which was short of capital and in the midst of internal organisation. The defection of France was extremely noticeable.

The Jura-Simplon Company was constituted in 1890, and given sole right by the two Governments to carry out the tunnel as well as the railway line which was financed by a separate budget and received subsidies from Switzerland and Italy based on mileage. The company granted the enterprise free use of the water-power necessary for building the tunnel and the railway line.

The contract made with the firm of Brandt and Brandau, assisted by the firm of Sulzer, was extremely tough. The firms undertook to complete the work in five years and nine months, a period which was later extended by twelve months, although this period was not exceeded. (The St. Gotthard tunnel, which measured over nine miles, had taken eleven years to build.) Further, the firm was to pay a fine of 5,000 francs per day if there was any delay—reduced later to 2,000 francs. In fact, these fines never had to be paid in spite of the many mishaps, or "acts of God," which, as we shall see, did not fail to occur.

The enterprise was also entirely responsible for health measures and had to provide good housing, without any profit to themselves, for all their workers, and set up a fund to help any men who were ill or injured, as well as an insurance fund for widows and orphans of anyone who lost his life. The preliminary medical inspection was extremely severe, and unheard-of precautions were taken to maintain healthy working conditions and beat the famous "miners' anaemia" which had caused such havoc among the men building the St. Gotthard tunnel.

It should be added too that the relations between the firm and the two Governments were as excellent as those between the two Governments themselves and that the contracts they entered into never led to any serious conflicts.

306

The meagre 76 million francs available made stringent economy essential. It was only possible to lay a single-track line, for a double track would have quadrupled the cost. Also it was necessary to work at the lowest altitude possible so that equipment and materials could be placed on the spot, but the lower the tunnel was placed, the longer it would be. It is for this reason that the Simplon is the lowest of the Alpine tunnels (the average altitude is 2,165 feet) and the longest— about twelve miles in all, of which about five and a half miles are on the Swiss side and six and a half on the Italian.

The engineers Brandt and Brandau then devised a cunning scheme; they planned and carried out two parallel tunnels; the first, Tunnel I, was to be completely finished and take a single-track railway line, while the second, Tunnel II, would be dug out to half the height and half the width, and serve as an auxiliary gallery.

The materials needed and the excavated soil and rock were removed through this second tunnel, while at intervals of 220 yards transverse galleries linked the two tunnels, increasing ventilation and the intake and evacuation of water supplies, together with other services. Later on, when traffic frequency made it necessary, Tunnel II could be completed and a second railway line laid.

But before the work could be started at the two ends essential services had to be established—water supplies; dams to supply water power for electricity and compressed air; turbines for ventilation; workshops for forging the drill-bits and miners' bars; dumps for explosives and administrative buildings, as well as two "villages" which would bring a touch of the American Wild West to these corners of Switzerland and Italy.

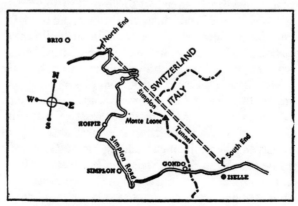

46. The Simplon tunnel and the Simplon road

The preliminary survey work, carried out in 1878 to determine where the initial excavations should begin, was done with masterly precision and was a mountaineering exploit in itself. The topographers had to take their valuable heavy instruments to the summit of Monte Leone, and there, at a height of 10,000 feet, establish a small observatory where they could carry out their very dangerous surveying. Yet in February, 1905, when the two headings met, there was only a difference of 8 inches in direction and $3\frac{1}{2}$ inches in height. The length of the tunnel was shortened by 2 feet $7\frac{1}{2}$ inches, all of which proved that the surveying work had been brilliantly carried out, for the corresponding differences in the St. Gotthard tunnel had been of the order of yards rather than inches.

The contractors kept a careful eye on the men's morale. The workers were "tunnel-minded" it is true, for bonuses were given and paid the day they were earned, to make the best effect. Engineers, foremen and labourers (who were mainly Italian) worked together in perfect cooperation until the tunnel was finished, and this atmosphere was an additional factor from the security point of view.

After a banquet given later to celebrate the opening of the famous "iron gates," the engineer Sulzer spoke as follows:

"Our main principle has been to show the greatest possible regard for the human element and to achieve in this respect genuine progress over the system previously adopted in carrying out work of this kind; we wanted to remove the fear that is inspired by large-scale tunnel building, to restore the reputation of this kind of work, which had previously been under a cloud, and to do our utmost for the future. . . . Our earnest wish is that in years to come there will be no going back from what we have done, and that those who follow us should go further, with greater success, than we have done. . . ."

III

HUMAN MOLES

In the miniature station the temperature rose to 86° F., my forehead was covered with perspiration and my head swam in an atmosphere full of fine dust. In the distance I heard a muffled roar, and then the telephone rang. "A train from Paris has just entered the tunnel," a plate-layer told me, inviting me to go into a side-gallery so that I could estimate the amount of air that was displaced. There seemed to be a hurricane blowing through the tunnel. The train pushes a huge plug of compressed air in front of it, at the rate of fifty-five miles per hour, and if I had not been in shelter it would have swept me off into space like a straw before the locomotive accomplished my disintegration. As soon as the train came into sight another squall of fresh air reached us and was then swallowed up by the tunnel. The crickets' chirping was heard again, while I listened to some fascinating explanations.

Work on the tunnel began at both ends in August 1898, and on December 4th, the day sacred to Saint Barbe, patron saint of miners, a moving ceremony was held at the two sites. The Bishops of Sion in Switzerland and Novare in Italy gave their blessing to the enterprise.

Blessing was necessary, for the mountain that was being attacked was extremely complicated from the geological point of view; it contained rock which had to be dealt with by the mechanical drill worked by compressed air (the Brandt system), micaceous schist which exploded in the headings like shells after being dug out with pick-axes, and limestone, giving off dust and gases which were equally dangerous when combined with heat and water. The Simplon tunnel was begun in the same way as the St. Gotthard was finished, making use of technical improvements which were installed as the work went on.

The drill with toothed removable cogs first mined the holes in which ten or twelve sticks of dynamite were placed at a time. The order was given and the whole gang withdrew to a distance of 550 yards; a few seconds later the muffled explosion was heard. Then the men came to remove the tons of fallen rock as quickly as possible so that the machines could go on. The tunnel progressed rapidly, about thirty-five feet a day on the average, which meant that 150 to 200 tons of excavated material had to be removed by trucks drawn by horses, for the first stage, because smoke from steam-trains was out of the question in this suffocating atmosphere. Then electric motors driven by compressed air finally took the soil and rock out into the open.

The dynamite was not brought by rail, for the slightest jerk might have led to disaster. The nitro-glycerine was carried by the men on their backs, and great precautions were taken, naturally, including the use of a violet lantern to indicate their arrival. This was the signal for everyone to stand out of the way.

As the tunnelling proceeded the heat became unbearable, and ventilation was a constant problem, solved by setting up two enormous turbines at each end of the tunnel. The air rushed towards Tunnel I, taken by pipes as far as the last transverse gallery, for all the others were sealed off when not in use. Atomised water brought by pipes trickled on to the burning rocks and turned into steam, which cooled the air.

There was one drawback to this ventilation system, however. Miners working at the head of Tunnels I and II beyond the last transverse gallery had no fresh air and could only get it every 250 yards when they made another of these galleries. The air was then forced through pipes by hydraulic pressure. This was no small problem, for it entailed making the temperature of the water contained in twenty tank-waggons with a capacity of thirteen cubic feet fall by 54° F. in one hour. This was achieved however by allowing the fresh air to accumulate behind linen mesh curtains which were moved as the tunnel progressed.

In order to proceed more quickly Tunnel I was dug out in two

47. Double gallery excavation: longitudinal-section

galleries, a lower gallery and an upper gallery, as shown in the sketch. As each section was completed the intermediary floor was demolished. This method also made it possible to increase the points of attack in the upper galleries and carry out tunnelling and clearance operations close behind the drills.

A thousand men, divided into two gangs, worked in this Swiss-Italian tunnel. Each team worked eight hours at a stretch and three times a day a convoy of trucks took the men backwards and forwards. Sunday was their only free day, and even then security teams kept watch at the farthermost end of the tunnel.

On Sundays all types of Italian accents could be heard in the mushroom villages which had been built at the two ends of the tunnel (near Naters in Switzerland and Balmalunesca in Italy), for they each sheltered about five thousand souls—engineers, contractors, masons, builders, labourers and their wives and children.

310

Families lived in houses and the single men where they chose—in barracks or lodgings, and inns with multicoloured façades advertising in every dialect all the specialities of Italy: *Cantina canavese, Sartoria lombarda, Calzoleria veneta, Fiaschetteria toscana, Cantinone delle Puglie,* etc. It was like a microcosm of Italy where accordions and guitars could be heard whenever there was a moment's respite.

But from six o'clock on Monday morning the village was silent while the Piedmontese and Neapolitans went to take their dry working clothes down from the ceiling, where they were fastened by a string marked with a number to show to whom they belonged.

Some of the difficulties encountered in the operation held up the work considerably but did not affect the final completion. These difficulties were of varying types but all formidable in their own way: high temperatures, lack of ventilation, hot or cold streams, density and pressure of the rocks as well as avalanches. These were nature's attempts to fight against her violation.

It should not be forgotten that the tunnel was just like a mine gallery

48. Double gallery excavation: cross-section

dug out at a depth of 8,200 feet, and subject to the progressive rise in temperature that is usual under the crust of the earth. This problem had been foreseen, but it had not been expected to be greater than that encountered in the St. Gotthard tunnel, where the temperature varied between 91° and 93° F. In the Simplon tunnel it rose to 104° and even 129° F. The situation was remedied to some extent by saturating the atmosphere with cold water, but this never reduced the temperature by more than a few degrees. The water was diverted from the River Rhône on one side and the Diveria on the other, and was brought in the open air along canals between rows of piles, then in pipes under pressure. Before the water was forced into the galleries it was used to operate the turbines which worked the drainage-pumps, manufactured compressed air and generated electric power.

Avalanches were not likely to occur inside the tunnel but they caused serious hold-ups when they blocked the watercourses. Power was cut and ventilation and refrigeration were interrupted. The temperature rose suddenly, and the alarm had to be given so that the miners could leave at once, for the atmosphere soon became unbearable and dangerous.

Inside the tunnel water was destructive, not helpful. During the course of the work many cold springs broke out here and there and they were only brought under control with great difficulty, for the slight incline of the route gave the water no chance to escape quickly. On May 13th, 1901, a cataract poured through the roof at the rate of 330 gallons a second and swamped the tunnel, while the men ran away in a panic. This was the source of the River Nembro which flowed from within the mountain 2,300 feet above the tunnel and had found this outlet by the laws of gravity. Work was stopped for several days until the water could be dammed by sandbags which directed it towards the entrance. But on June 11th there was another inundation of the same kind which caused the temporary disappearance of a little lake on the mountain side. Sometimes, when the quantities of water were not too great, these springs were skilfully used to cool the galleries and the engineers considered them more of a nuisance than a problem. But worse catastrophes were to come: the threat of flooding had been averted but the explosions of misplaced mines caused hot springs to burst out of the rock and in contact with the burning rock they grew even hotter. During the whole duration of the work there were no less than 228 cases of water infiltration, ranging from mere trickles to boiling torrents.

On November 22nd, 1903, as the men came to carry out clearance work at a distance roughly half-way along the route, they found that the gallery was full of steaming water giving off a vapour which made their lungs smart. Fortunately they were able to escape, but this 560-feet-long stretch of water, with a temperature of 128·8° F., made it impossible for anyone to stay in the tunnel. Skilful pumping operations, which entailed heroic expeditions to put the strainers in place, reduced the heat, but early in 1904, in the Brig tunnel, another torrent boiled up 650 feet farther on. This time it could not be brought under control, and ten months before the completion of the work this had to be the extreme point of the tunnel in a northerly direction; it was impossible to stop the flow of water because the workshops were too far away and it was impossible to guarantee the necessary refrigeration. It was found that the tunnel could not be taken any farther.

Strong iron gates had to be built, and set in solid brickwork, to close off this gallery and keep the dangerous 820-feet-long stretch of steaming water out. As soon as this northerly point was fixed work could begin on the widening of the tunnel and the brickwork lining.

It has never been possible to stop this spring, which still runs at a temperature of 77° F., but it has since been diverted into a channel. A little door opens on to one of the miniature red-walled grottoes it forms, and through it I was able to dip my hands in the water. I was told that it has miraculous properties for curing rheumatism, and tunnel staff with a tendency to arthritis do not hesitate to make use of it.

The density of the rock, in particular the famous Antigorio gneiss on the Italian side, necessitated superhuman work at all stages. The drill-bits wore out against these emery-coated walls or became blunt with the effect of the heat, although they were injected with cold water. The pick-axe strokes made the jumper-bars bend, and in one single day it was necessary to reforge hundreds of drill-bits and thousands of bars.

The rocks exerted heavy pressure in certain areas of the galleries, crushing the props until they bent and snapped like matchsticks. Iron and concrete frames had to be used to prevent the mountain from collapsing into the tunnel. Superhuman efforts were necessary to fix them in place, for vaults 17 feet wide and 125 feet long had to be made first.

The human element provided few additional problems, but there were occasional strikes in sympathy with the labour agitations which occurred over most of Europe at this period. The strikes were usually called to stop the system of fines and obtain higher wages, although they were 30 per cent. higher than those paid in this part of Italy. In

June 1901 the men at the north end of the tunnel threw in their lot with those at the south end; work was suspended for a fortnight and the army had to be brought in to restore order. The strikers obtained some improvements, of which the most important was the creation of a workers' committee which could represent the men in negotiations with the management.

IV

THE MEETING POINT

The noisy truck set us down at the exact spot where, on February 24th, 1905, the famous junction took place, transforming the Italian and Swiss mole-runs into a great international tunnel.

As we have seen, work stopped completely on the Brig side on May 18th, 1904, when the iron gates locked out the steaming sub-terranean flood.

There were no hold-ups on the Italian side and work went on regularly. In Switzerland the sound of picks on jumper-bars could already be heard. The junction would soon take place... still a few yards to go. Betassa, the Italian works manager who handled his pen with a degree of lyricism only equal to his care in using dynamite, wrote in his daily report of February 20th:

"In three or four days' time, the proud Monte Leone, which tried to kill us with hot springs, will fall into my hands, just as Port Arthur fell into the hands of the Japanese." Betassa had struck the first pick-axe blow on the south side at Iselle, on August 13th, 1898. Understandably, he wanted to have the honour of giving the last.

The Swiss journalist E. David gave an eye-witness account in his book on the Simplon Tunnel published in Lausanne in 1906, describing how excitement and enthusiasm had possessed all the men during the days before the great event:

"Yesterday evening the dinner given for the engineers and men was extremely lively. The probable developments were discussed and everyone described his own theories about the amount and pressure of the water, the type of rock and the incline of the different strata. The engineers made twenty sketches on the table of the cross-section of the two headings. One or other of them rose from the table every moment and counted out three, four or five steps from the wall to the middle of the room: 'That's all that's left,' he would say, 'no more'; then he would sit down again, stand up and talk excitedly.... An Italian newspaper had anticipated the completion and the telegrams of congratulation were already arriving. . . ."

But in spite of the general optimism things did not turn out as in the St. Gotthard tunnel, and the Italian workmen did not meet colleagues with cheerful faces and outstretched hands. On February 24th, at half-past six in the morning, the men working at the head of the tunnel ignited the dynamite which was to free the enormous mass of water and divert it towards the channels prepared to receive it in Tunnel II. But the derailment of a train removing rubbish held up the relieving team. The other team were warned by telephone and all declared that they would go on working. Betassa, who was on the job with his gang as on the first day, withdrew to the regulation distance of 550 yards. Then ten thunderclaps were heard, and almost at once a river of steam rushed into the series of dams that had been built to hold it and the temperature rose at once to 107° F. Betassa telephoned.

A train-load of engineers left Iselle immediately to examine the state of the tunnel. A cloud of steam and carbon dioxide made the atmosphere more and more suffocating. The lack of oxygen snuffed out the miners' lamps one by one. Men collapsed, and their colleagues could hardly hold them up by their shoulders; some could not walk and sat down on the rails. They had to be forced into the trucks which were hastily brought up. The lethal expanse of water spread out wider and became deeper, and the engineer Sulzer ordered everyone to leave. The Italian foremen translated his command and it sounded like some curse from Dante: "Traforo! Fuori, tutti Fuori!"

The trucks arrived with difficulty and in a state of confusion at the Iselle end of the tunnel, where men overcome by the poisonous gas were being taken away to hospital on stretchers. At the end of the day there were two deaths to record, the engineers Bianco and Grassi, who had waited until the last moment to make sure that all the men had left the tunnel. These were the only victims on that day of the enterprise that had lasted for forty-two months.

Two months later a small monument was built at Iselle as an immediate and moving tribute to the sixty men who had lost their lives during the course of the work. In spite of all the precautions that had been taken these unfortunate men did not have the pleasure of seeing the famous iron gates open a fortnight later, when the danger from the gases seemed to be over.

The loss of life was great, on the same scale as the tunnel; the President of the Swiss Confederation and King Victor Emmanuel of Italy also paid a touching tribute to the victims when they inaugurated the tunnel and the first train went through, decked with the flags of the two countries.

On June 1st, 1906, the work on the railway line was completed and the line electrified, so that the Simplon tunnel was at last open for commercial development. In future it was the Swiss Railways who had to decide on the completion of Tunnel II, and work began in December 1912, after the serious disadvantages of the single-track line had become plain.

When Italy took part in the 1914 war the work was held up until 1917 for lack of man-power, since there was mobilisation on both sides of the tunnel.

The history of the second tunnel was uneventful; it was finished in 1921 and opened on October 16th, 1922.

France finally realised that this new route to Italy via Switzerland was worthwhile, and built the Frasne–Vallorbe short cut in 1915 by making the Mont d'Or tunnel through the Jura. It was about three and a half miles long and similar difficulties arose to those encountered in the Simplon. A large watercourse also broke into the tunnel, escaping from the River Doubs, and began to flow towards Switzerland. It was intelligently dealt with, however, and the stream was kept in French territory.

The opening of the Simplon restored to France and French-speaking Switzerland the balance which had been disturbed by the building of the St. Gotthard, but it left the canton of Berne somewhat isolated. In 1906 the inhabitants of Berne financed the building of the Lötschberg tunnel on the Berne–Simplon route. It was nine miles long, and built at a height of 4,000 feet.

The Alpine tunnel war seemed to be over; but now tourist needs have expanded, and there is great competition over road-tunnels. It looks as though a new "war" has just begun.

XIII

THE RECLAIMING OF THE ZUYDER ZEE

I

THE COUNTRY OF LAND AND SEA

B Y A.D. 2000 the Zuyder Zee will have become geographical history and will have disappeared from maps, just as the isthmuses of Suez and Panama have been transformed by man's resolute hand. This will be the last act but one in the continual drama of the war between the Netherlands and the sea. "God made the world, but we made our own country," say the Dutch with pride. To which can only be added: God made the world in seven days, but the descendants of the Bataves (the original inhabitants of the Netherlands) built theirs in seven centuries.

Originally the Batavian archipelago was nothing but an expanse of black polder clay cracked and dried under the summer sun. It was looked on by the Greeks as a phantom country to which the Argonauts sailed, and Homer placed the gates of Hades there. Among the earliest explorers of these distant countries was the naturalist Pliny, who counted twenty-three major islands which were visible twice daily on the ebb-tide.

The Bataves were fearless navigators who spent their time fishing from long dug-out boats. A good example of one of these was found on the bed of the Rhine and is now preserved in the Museum at Utrecht. These strange boats should not be confused with the Viking *drakkars*, since their unwarlike construction seems to show that they were designed solely for coastal navigation and not for voyages of conquest.

In the first centuries after Christ, the Bataves, like the Gauls, Helvetians and Iberians, were subjected to Roman rule and were subsequently converted to Christianity. This constituted the first period of Western Civilisation.

The second period began when Charlemagne settled the diocese of Utrecht, the Batavian *magna civitas*, and ended with the Viking invasions.

The third epoch in her history is characterised by huge floods, the formation of the Zuyder Zee and, finally, the reclamation of the inundated lands, which will have brought immense benefit to the Netherlands before the end of the twentieth century.

Since the thirteenth century one-fifth of the Netherlands has been submerged by the sea, by its rivers or by soil subsidence, opening the way to the tides; by the erosion of the sandy coastline, by the breaking up of ice-floes and melting snows swelling the waters of the Rhine and the Meuse; finally by the violence of the equinoctial tides.

Here, in brief, is an account of seventeen centuries of disaster. During the third century part of the coast of Zeeland and Holland was engulfed by the sea and in Zeeland, near Domburg, the ruins of a Roman temple can still be seen at low tide. In 832, in Friesland, 2,500 dwellings were destroyed by a storm. On December 14th, 1287, 50,000 people were drowned between Stavoren (on the Zuyder Zee) and the mouth of the River Ems. On November 19th, 1421, the North Sea carved out the gulf of Biesboch (the land of rushes), creating an archipelago in Zeeland, at the same time claiming 100,000 victims in seventy-two villages. The lake of Haarlem was formed in 1530, but this was not caused by the action of the sea alone, as will be shown. Between 1597 and 1716 the area around Amsterdam was inundated eleven times by terrible floods. In 1809 the provinces of North Holland and Gelderland were flooded, the former by the sea and the latter by the waters of the Rhine. In 1826 North Holland was severely inundated, causing an appalling epidemic brought about by rotting cattle carcasses.

But the greatest, the real catastrophe, was in the thirteenth century: the formation of the Zuyder Zee.

Conquered and successively occupied by Spain, France and Germany, largely reclaimed and defended unceasingly against constant attacks from the sea, the Dutch soil is the proud possession of its inhabitants. The motto of the House of Orange, "Je maintiendrai," remains the symbol of a thousand years of brave endurance and of individual as much as collective struggle.

Northern Europe starts on the banks of the Rhine, but Holland still retains something Latin in the behaviour of her people, in her flowers, in certain Spanish details of the architecture of her towns, in the colouring and furnishing of her homes, in the enthusiasm of her crowds and the noise of her fairs. But this impression disappears as soon as you travel north into Friesland, and cross the black polders patterned with a glistening network of canals and inhale the salt winds blowing through the grass where black and white cows chew the cud under their sacking coats in the rain, and from afar the dull glint of the North Sea threatens like a symbolic sword.

Here all the place names recall the conflict between land and sea. The Netherlands means the low countries, situated below sea level; Holland means the hollowed land; Zeeland, that of the sea, since it is an archipelago; Friesland is the farthermost part and Gelderland, the rich land, since it is high-lying.

In the thirteenth century a vast inland sea was formed between these three provinces. Sailors called it the Zuyder Zee (the Southern Sea) in contrast to the North Sea. By this time the Netherlands had lost to the sea and rivers more than one-fifth of her land. To avoid disappearing from the face of the earth her inhabitants had to engage in battle and reconquest on a vast scale, and the campaign is still going on. But the country had already qualified for the famous saying which was rightly or wrongly attributed to one of her great rulers, William the Silent, "There is no need to have hope in order to undertake something, nor to achieve success—in order to persevere."

The Dutch made this their faith. They fought before they conquered. They encircled their islands and islets with huge dykes which gradually became works of art and the object of a cult known as "the golden ring," after that metal which has been prized from time immemorial. They then took an oath on their heroically defended lands:

"We swear to defend our country with three weapons: the spade, the fork and the cart. And we shall defend the land and her people against invasion with spear and shield, inch by inch, and with the help of God."

Sea water is a deadly foe that poisons the earth. Fresh water from the rivers is another enemy for it penetrates the subsoil, bringing down sand to sterilise the humus. Yet another catastrophe was created by the Zeeland peasant himself who destroyed the soil in searching for peat and marsh gas for his warmth and livelihood. He dug holes which, in time, became craters and then lakes, made yet larger by erosion. Each town or village with its peat-bog harboured a serpent in its breast. The lake of Haarlem, formally the site of ancient peat-bogs, enlarged by flooding, in this way became a real inland sea, which had to be removed. The Zeelanders, in burning their soil, had opened the flood-gates to the tide. Opinions varied as to how to deal with this element which was swamping the Netherlands from all sides. "Build higher dykes," said some; "Make reservoirs," said others. But there was nowhere to dig in a country already short of land for her own sustenance.

The sand not only engulfed the Netherlands and silted up her canals, but in obstructing the ports, it created an even worse problem in bringing her world-wide shipping trade to a standstill. In the eighteenth century the great ports of Rotterdam and Amsterdam, now silted up, could only harbour ships of low tonnage. Such shipping could not plough the seas and bring back spices and gold from the East. Trade was gradually strangled and the merchant navy lost its superiority to the English who now took the lead. Such were the perils created by the sea and rivers over centuries, and which put the very existence of the Netherlands into jeopardy. Added to this— and it was no minor disaster—the mudworm appeared in 1730 and seriously undermined the dykes. There was only one weapon with which to fight this destructive opponent and that was stone, which had to be brought by waggon and barge from Germany, Belgium and even northern France.

In this land, rotted with sea water and sand, and which seemed to have been abandoned by God, the Dutch embarked on a ruthless war of defence and attack. They fought the sea with dyke and dam and the land with dredger and drain.

But an authority was required to consolidate and coordinate all efforts. This was an important ministry of State, the *Waterstaat* (Ministry of Water), whose functions were unique.

The department is, in fact, of fairly recent origin (1798). It was advocated in 1726 by the Dutch hydraulic-engineer Kruik, but it was the formation in 1750 by Louis XV in France of the Department of Roads and Bridges that inspired the Netherlands in 1754 to create an inspectorate for inland waters, from which the *Waterstaat* developed.

The Ministry of Water is today a large administrative organisation whose diverse functions include water transport and the agricultural administration of reclaimed land. It also has its own well-equipped laboratories and training schemes which have produced world-renowned engineers.

The *Watershap*, or senior dyker, who works with and under the supervision of the engineers, is an old-established post, an almost hereditary job, since its members are largely the descendants of the *dijkmeisters* (the dyke masters) who have been elected by the polder dwellers since the Middle Ages, and whose authority extends well beyond the protection of the dykes.

The ancient corporation of dyke workers is one of the curiosities of Holland. A man is a dyker by inheritance and tradition, and no outsiders are admitted "to the honour of working on the dykes."

The dykers of each polder are divided into three gangs or crews of ten men. The first consists of the *timmerlieders* (carpenters) who saw up the breakwater piles and put them in position; the second is that of the *dijkwerkers* (dyke workers) who bundle up the willow faggots and make fascine mats; lastly is the gang, without any specific jobs, who help the first two groups. Each group has its own *baas* (boss) and book-keeper responsible for the administration of the dykes, the payment of wages and coordination between various branches. Each also has its own tavern where the gin flows freely when they admit an apprentice dyker (often at the age of twelve) to the honour of becoming an associate. These apprentices are now trained in special technical schools situated in the reedy marshes of Friesland.

The dykers in former times were also farmers, but they were the first to make for the dykes when danger threatened and the alarm bell was sounded and the crier ran through the streets of the village, beating on a drum and crying, "Help! Help! Old and young. Rich and poor—every man to the dyke!"

Everyone went, for the dyke was a communal defence against an enemy which attacked not with sword but with the tide. They still tell the tale in Nijmegen of the people whose men-folk in time of flood propped up the dyke with their shoulders, while the women fed these descendants of Atlas. They stayed in this position, backs arched, for a week until the waters subsided.

The construction of a dyke was a painstaking task: the main operation was the formation of a breakwater consisting of huge wooden piles driven five feet down into the ground, joined by struts and a network of matting. Sometimes the dyke was built with a gently sloping bed of stones sunk into the seabed and topped by a bank of earth reinforced with straw matting upon which a layer of grass was sown to bind the earth. These short dykes round the islands and polders sometimes reach a width of 300 feet.

Rush, straw, clay and stone—these were the crude materials used for centuries by the dykers, but their weakness was often exposed by the great tidal-waves. The most recent of these (February 1953), it will be remembered, caused world-wide sympathy.

Defence against the sea alone was not enough. It was also necessary to combat the fresh water from canals which insidiously filled up the peat-bogs, undermining the arable land and transforming the country into a sponge-like area in the Rhine and Meuse deltas, where river floods followed on tidal waves.

This water had continuously to be pumped out and returned to the canals where locks controlled its flow along with the shipping, since these waterways were the only means of communication between the polders.

It was for this purpose that the famous windmills came into existence. These picturesque structures, although known to the Egyptians in 4000 B.C., did not appear in the Netherlands until 1408, and were not used on a large scale until the seventeenth century under the direction of Jan Adrienz Leeghwater (1575–1650). He was a great pioneer of the Dutch waterways; his name meant "low water," but he was known familiarly to his companions by the nickname "John the wind." He drew up the first plan for the drainage of the sea of Haarlem by means of 160 windmills, but the project was not realised until 225 years later, in 1852, when steam-driven mills were used.

These mills pumped off the water, but did nothing to prevent the silting-up of canals and ports and the blocking of sluice-gates and locks. For this service dredging-machines were provided. They were originally very rudimentary. The *krabellaar* (scratcher), which was first constructed in 1435, was a sailing boat which dragged a harrow beneath its hull. It literally scraped the canals or dug navigable channels in the mud and sand of the ports. This odd vessel, known familiarly to the Dutch as a *Taupe*, was used until the beginning of the nineteenth century.

There was also the camel-boat (*scheepkamel*), another curious craft which acted as a caisson and thus assisted the merchant vessels entering a silted-up port by lightening their draught. Finally mud-mills were used; these were very heavy barges fitted with a system of endless chains with buckets that picked up the sand and mud and tipped it on to the lighters. These showed considerable progress over the *Taupes*, which actually did nothing to remove the mud. The chain and bucket system was worked by man-power; huge double wooden wheels were linked by cross-bars, similar to those used in water-mills, on which some poor fellow had to stand all day long. This equipment, smaller in scale but heavier than that used in quarries in seventeenth-century France, was rather like the treadmills in English prisons. The wheels were later placed horizontally and turned by carthorses, like the early threshing machines.

The shovel, wheelbarrow, windmill and later mud-mill were successively the tools of seven centuries' struggle against water and sand. We see them depicted in the works of Dutch painters like Mostaert and Porbus the elder, who placed them in the background of their paintings.

Between 1200 and 1900 Holland thus reclaimed 1,305,000 acres of the 1,425,000 she had lost to her lakes and to the sea. In this struggle she proved herself worthy of the stirring motto "Luctor et emergo" inscribed on the coat of arms of the province of Zeeland, of which one of her poets has said, "This is where the land is the sea and the sea is the land."

II

THE SOUTHERN SEA

In early times a fresh-water lake into which emptied a number of rivers occupied the existing site of the Zuyder Zee. This was the Flevo, which in its turn emptied into the sea by means of the River Flevus (Vlie). It was protected from the ocean by a semi-circular broken line of sandbanks joining Holland to Friesland. Traces of these can still be seen near the islands of Texel, Vlieland, Terschelling and Ameland. The Flevus flowed into the sea by way of a delta, the mouth of which stretched from the island of Vlieland to that of Terschelling.

The area of the lake gradually increased as erosion and storms wore down the so-called dyke which eventually broke in 1177, and the fresh water of the Flevo slowly merged with brine. The link in this chain was finally broken in 1232 and the islands of Friesland were formed in this most recent of European inland waters.

This vast gulf is itself divided into two parts: to the north, the Wadden Sea (sea of sandbanks) and to the south, the Zuyder Zee, now enclosed by its famous dam.

The Zuyder Zee is quite shallow, with a maximum depth of twenty-five feet, and the sea enters by the Maasdiep lying between North Holland and the island of Texel, with two channels to the east and west of the island of Vlieland. Of a total area of 3,125 square miles, this inland sea measures eighty-six and fifty-five miles at its two widest points across. Navigation is dangerous, due to the shallows and the mud-banks where seals from Greenland once came to disport themselves. It harbours four inhabited islands: Wieringen, Marken, Schoekland and Urk, where the inhabitants (especially those of Marken) still retain their picturesque costumes and ancient customs. They are for the greater part fishermen who fish in the Zuyder Zee mainly for plaice and dab; but the local anchovies compete with those from Norway.

The Zuyder Zee is also the outlet for several coastal rivers, the most important being the Amstel which flows through Amsterdam. This splendid city of commerce and art where the old canals recall Bruges and the new tall buildings New York, was at one time the major port of the Zuyder Zee, to which it was linked by the Y (or Ij) canal, a waterway of nearly 15,000 acres. The North Sea canal (fifteen miles long) which now joins Amsterdam to Ijmuiden on the coast, was started on March 8th, 1862, and came into service on November 1st, 1876. It has since undergone large-scale developments, the most remarkable being the construction of the huge Northern Lock (1919–1930).

The Zuyder Zee and Amsterdam were an important focal point for world maritime traffic in the fifteenth and sixteenth centuries, and through the Maasdiep and Vlieland channels huge ships brought riches from the Dutch East Indies to Amsterdam, the Venice of the North. When the ports silted up the traffic gradually diminished until the Zuyder Zee became a lake for poor eel and anchovy fishermen, who nostalgically called it the "Sea of Dreams," in memory of its glorious past.

The tragedy of salt water was then added to that of sand. In the early days of its formation the Zuyder Zee was a fresh-water lake whose salt content increased only gradually through its contact with the North Sea and which never reached more than a third of the degree of salinity of the sea.

The waters of the Rhine became salted, not because of the Zuyder Zee, which could not contaminate them, but as a result of prospecting for iron in the Ruhr and potassium in Alsace, producing polluted water from the excavated salt. The salt content of the Rhine was thus doubled between 1850 and 1900 and an international agreement was necessary to stop the pollution.

Sea water also seeped into the Zuyder Zee through the North Sea–Amsterdam Canal which brought in heavy loads of salt through each lock-gate to the already saturated lake.

It was the horticulturists who first gave the alarm which was then taken up by the farmers who, in digging deeper and deeper wells, eventually drew only brackish water unfit either for drinking or for use in their famous dairies where the cows began to produce salt butter.

The only way to rid the Zuyder Zee of salt was to close it to the sea and to build at its narrowest point a dyke that would isolate it from the invader. The separation from the sea would have an important consequence. When the Zuyder Zee was isolated it could at the same time be drained and a large part of the land lost in the thirteenth century could be brought back under cultivation. This splendid dual undertaking was bound to be thought of sooner or later in a country which had always possessed the world's finest hydraulic engineers. But at the beginning of the last century there was no known means of constructing such a dyke.

The only known method was to maintain as little contact as possible between the land and her adversary, the sea, by decreasing the length of the shoreline of the Zuyder Zee. This was so broken up into bays and creeks that the total shoreline was nearly 250 miles, one-fifth of the coast line of the whole Netherlands.

A plan to isolate the Zuyder Zee had been sketched out in 1667 by Hendrik Stevin, son of the famous mathematician and engineer who conceived the idea of floating docks. But Stevin's dream of building dykes round the Zuyder Zee had only one purpose—the prevention of excess salt content—and took no account of the technical means necessary for its execution.

In 1840 work was begun on the draining of the lake of Haarlem (fifteen miles long, seven miles wide with a maximum depth of fifteen feet). It took just over three years to complete and it encouraged the hope that the 45,000 acres brought back under cultivation would only be the beginnings of land reclamation. It was of the greatest economic benefit to the Netherlands as it formed the basis of future development of the polders.

Work of this kind went on unceasingly from this period onwards. Between 1825 and 1865 the Netherlands successfully reclaimed 517,000 acres. From the creation of the polders in the sixteenth century until 1900, a total of 850,000 acres was reclaimed from the sea and lakes. In draining the Zuyder Zee a further 550,000 acres will eventually be brought back under cultivation, that is one-twelfth of the total area of the Netherlands. Any country would be dazzled by the idea of such a bloodless conquest.

Stevin's plan was not discussed again, however, until the middle of the nineteenth century when, in 1865, the Netherlands Mortgage Society became interested in the idea. J. A. Beyerinck, the engineer who was made responsible for drawing up the details of the plan, proposed the construction of a dyke running from Enkhuysen to the island of Urk, with the draining of the southern part of the Zuyder Zee, consisting of about 480,000 acres. The project was submitted for the sanction of the *Waterstaat* who stated that it was possible but of little economic value to the nation.

The Netherlands Mortgage Society withdrew its request for a concession in 1870 and a Commission was set up in 1876. It declared that the plan was beneficial but scarcely remunerative. It must be made profitable, not merely constructive.

The Zuyder Zee Association was formed during Government reshufflings in 1886. It was a private organisation for the study and execution, with the help of private capital, of the best drainage scheme placed before it. At this point Cornelius Lely appeared on the scene.

In 1886 Cornelius Lely (1854–1929), graduate of Delft University, was only a humble thirty-two-year-old *Waterstaat* engineering assistant, whose life could well have been spent among the civil servants of The Hague, if he had not had the good fortune to be dismissed for administrative reasons.

Owing to his precarious financial situation, he and his eleven children sought refuge under his father's roof and were maintained by this admirable man in their straitened circumstances. Both father and son enthusiastic supporters of the Zuyder Zee Association and devoured its publications to such an extent that it is said its library had to close down as they monopolised the entire contents. Eventually Cornelius applied and was accepted for the very minor post of secretary to the Secretary General of the Association.

In 1886, the Zuyder Zee plan was still regarded as a wild risk which neither official circles nor the powerful Dutch financial concerns took seriously. In the same year the Secretary General had to resign owing to the financial embarrassment of the Association after the Government had refused them a subsidy. The impoverished Lely now became Secretary General and at the same time continued to work on his plan.

For the next three years, supported by his father who advised him to continue with his work in spite of everything, Lely finished outlining his project, which was later to be adopted almost down to the last detail. A copy was made and sent to the *Waterstaat* officials. But in the meantime, on the verge of starvation, and worried by the continued dependence on his father, he got ready to emigrate to Brazil.

One day in 1890, while preparing for his departure, he received an eventful telegram and putting it in his pocket went to see his father, as was his daily custom. In a street of The Hague he met one of his friends who politely enquired as to the date of his departure. "Out of the question now," replied Cornelius, "I've found a good job here in Holland." And he added modestly, "I've just been appointed Minister of the *Waterstaat*." It was quite true; young Queen Wilhelmina had just sanctioned the appointment on the advice of her Prime Minister, Poovliet.

Lely's plan was to be carried out under his personal supervision. For the remainder of his life he perfected his work and became according to Van Veen "not just master of the waves, but master of the masters of the waves."[1]

Lely's project was at first confined to draining the southern part of the Zuyder Zee by means of a dyke, one and a half miles long, lying between North Holland and the island of Wieringen; from the far end of Wieringen a twenty-mile dyke would run to Piaam on the Friesian shore enclosing the Zuyder Zee at its narrowest point. The Zuyder Zee was thus to be divided into two parts; the Wadden Sea to the north and Lake Ijssel to the south.

About half the area of Lake Ijssel, into which the coastal rivers would still run, would be reclaimed to make polders. It would be necessary to leave a lake in the middle to allow the passage of any marine traffic and to irrigate the polders in case of drought. Finally Lake Ijssel would be linked to the sea at Wieringen by a canal operated by five groups of locks.

The towns on the shores of Lake Ijssel would be connected by canal with those on the Wadden Sea. There old silted-up harbours would be replaced by deep navigable channels. Grouped round Lake Ijssel four polders—two on the Holland and two on the Friesland side—would be enclosed by dykes. These polders with their network of canals, roads and ditches for drainage would be, like all the other polders in the country, placed under the authority of the *Waterstaat*. To prevent any possible enemy invasion on the shores of North Holland, a circular fort would be built on the island of Wieringen, and the canal locks made in such a way that they could for strategic reasons inundate the approaches to Amsterdam. Strangely enough it was on the site of the proposed fort on April 17th, 1945, Liberation Day, that the Nazis blew up the Wieringen dykes to prevent the landing of Canadian troops.

According to Lely's plan the work would take thirty-three years and cost 318 million florins; the construction of the big dyke alone was to take nine years at a cost of 30 million florins.

The turn of events which placed Lely in an undreamed-of position did not however give him dictatorial powers, and although his plans for the conquest of the Zuyder Zee had been accepted, he still had to combat the characteristic apathy of the Netherlands administration.

[1] I. R. Van Veen, *Dredge, Drain and Reclaim*. The Hague, 1948.

Lely, who had been trained as an engineer, learned from his Council of Ministers that democratic government provides a good lesson in patience. He conscientiously submitted his report for consideration to a State Commission. Now this was at the end of the last century when the Zuyder Zee plan had not yet gained a foothold; although favourably received, his plans were again put on one side and meanwhile he was made Governor of Surinam, Dutch Guinea.

Public interest grew stronger, however, as the salt content of the Zuyder Zee rose. In 1916, heavy floods burst the dykes and ravished the coasts, and the world war made the neutral Netherlands aware of food shortages. The whole nation, driven by necessity, finally recognised the worth of Lely's project, which was economically and psychologically calculated to bring out the best in a race famous for its energy and tenacity. Lely, now sixty-three and in his third term of office, from 1913 to 1918, at last had his plan approved by the General Assembly of the Netherlands on June 14th, 1918.

These were the main points of the plan:

(1) Increase in agricultural produce through a new method of large-scale farming, the Netherlands having previously been divided into smallholdings due to continued division of land through the system of inheritance.

(2) Creation of industry and growth of industrial employment for agricultural labour made redundant by the new method of farming.

(3) Gradual abolition (five years) of the salt content of the arable land bordering on the Zuyder Zee.

(4) Decrease in number and eventual removal of small dykes.

(5) Development of the vital land area.

The Netherlands is in fact one of the most thickly populated countries in the world, with 833 inhabitants per square mile, compared with 210 in France and fifty-seven in the U.S.A. If the U.S.A. were populated in the same proportion as the Netherlands it would have 2,000 million inhabitants, that is two-thirds of the world's total population.

These statistics illustrate the need of the Netherlands for more land. From 2,600,000 inhabitants in 1830, the population rose to exceed 5 million in 1900 and 10 million in 1950, and Dutch experts calculate with alarm that this population will be doubled again within the next fifty years.

By 1918 the population problem had been recognised and with it the urgent necessity of Lely's master-plan. He was to have the great joy, after waiting thirty years, of seeing work begin on the first Wieringen dam, on June 29th, 1920.

III

THE END OF THE ZUYDER ZEE

The construction of the dam, a twenty-seven-mile-long barrier, took much less time than Lely had calculated, technical skill and mechanisation having progressed since the drawing up of his plans. As soon as the country knew that the work was under way everyone from the top-ranking engineers down to the humblest labourer was inspired by enthusiasm. In four completely separate areas the following operations were started and completed almost simultaneously:

1. The *Amsteldiepdijk* (Amstel deep dyke) which joined North Holland to the west coast of the island of Wieringen. This was 8,000 feet long and was constructed in the same way as the big dam.

2. *Den Oever* (Pine beach), the name of a village on Wieringen where the western part of the dyke begins. This area consists of:

(a) An important harbour for fishing vessels, with internal and external pools and a lock basin for the passage of ships (maximum 2,000 tons) from the Wadden Sea to Lake Ijssel.

(b) The *Stevin* group of three series of five sluices regulating the level of Lake Ijssel.

(c) The *Leemans* pumping station for the draining of the water from the future Wieringen polder.

3. *Kornewerzand* on the Friesland coast is at the eastern end of the dam and is almost identical in construction with Den Oever, but only allows for the passage of vessels of up to 600 tons into Lake Ijssel, through the Lorentz[1] group of two sets of five regulating locks.

4. *Breezand*, an artificial island, or rather temporary polder, half way between North Holland and Friesland on the site of the *Afsluitdijk* (the enclosing dyke). This island has two ports, one on the Wadden Sea, the other on Lake Ijssel, which supply provisions to a fleet of some 500 ships of all types that ply on either side of the dyke. In this vast "marine service station" a pontoon of boats was anchored where the

---

[1] Named after Professor Lorentz of Leyden University, whose studies of tidal movements were invaluable in the Zuyder Zee undertaking.

workmen and engineers of the dyke lived, totalling a force of 10,000. Work on the Amsteldiepdijk site was started on June 29th, 1920, and was completed in July 1924. But the big dyke was not really started until 1927 when its big workshops had been set up.

The materials used were very varied and the dyke was, so to speak, a meticulous counterbalance of the laws of hydraulics and the resistance of matter. The outline of the dam was more or less trapezoid with an embankment on the Wadden Sea side.

Firstly, a thick layer of clay blocks was placed on the sea floor. A heavy black, strong clay, whose geological formation dates from the Morainian period of the Diluvian era, was found in plenty on the bed of Lake Ijssel. It was very economical and perfectly suited for this work, since it was impervious. This wonderful soil was an unexpected find and was excavated by the bucket load from an inexhaustible mine.

The journalist Eli Lotar, who visited the site in 1929, put down his impressions in an article published in *Jazz*, November 15th, 1929:

"Here on the gulf of the Zuyder Zee we are in a unique and distant place, without name. It will not become a real land until one can walk across its waters in clogs. The work of draining the sea is a hard task. It may take fifty years, but at the end the fishermen will work on the land, reaping the harvest of a tideless sea of corn.

"At present it resembles a convict settlement. Life is all hard labour. There are over 200 workmen in this area who work like slaves with a slave-like resignation. Although they know that the work will not be finished in two, five or even ten years, but more like fifty, they yet dream of its completion. A life-time sentence of hard labour. . . .

"There are two types of workmen. Those on the dykes and those on the sluices. I've seen them both. They form two completely different worlds with different ways of life.

"A row of hutments, looking like an abandoned train, stands on the dyke. At six in the morning the workmen leave their miserable dwellings, with wellington boots slung over their shoulders. They will not be back until ten at night, worn out and dropping with fatigue.

"Each goes his own way on the dyke, taking up the job he left off the night before. They level the grey mud, placing it on straw mattresses, or make a vast jig-saw puzzle out of the granite blocks for building the causeway. They work silently. Occasionally the foreman says something, but only if it is absolutely necessary. There is not a sound except the noise of winding cranes, transporter bridges and suction pumps. An enormous crane stands at the end of the dyke. It is this piece of machinery which actually extends the dyke out into the sea. The crane tips huge bargeloads of clay into the water; these are almost as quickly swept away. The operation continues without apparent result over a long period. But one day the battle is won and a mound of clay rises above the surface, lapped by the tide. To stop this tiny island disappearing, the crane tips on double loads until the dyke has risen several feet. This struggle and gesture of defiance against nature is such a magnificent and moving spectacle that one could watch it indefinitely.

"The workmen on the sluices are another type. They work on solid dry land, unaware of the perils of the sea. They can drink their tea and sleep through the dawn. They are thinner and less robust than their counterparts on the dyke, who look like cowboys with their big hats, boots, whips and large cigars always jammed between their teeth.

"Nothing counts here except work. At night time the men just wearily go home to bed. . . . I swear that the incredible monotony and simplicity of this life is one of the most heart-breaking things imaginable . . . and one of the most beautiful."

The stirring up of so much mud and the removal of so much clay was contrary to the laws of nature, and nature retaliated with a plague, known even to the ancient Egyptians: mosquitoes. Fortunately, they were the non-stinging variety, but nevertheless they spread into the houses and along the coast roads to such an extent that it was impossible to open any windows. Children rolled them up like snowballs and threw them at each other.

Yet, as La Fontaine said: "What nature does, she does well," even when she is crossed. About the same time millions of young eels, obeying their mysterious laws, returned from the Saragossa Sea to the almost fresh water of the Zuyder Zee. It is not known how these young sea eels became aware of the extraordinary provender (i.e. the mosquitoes) to be found in the hunting grounds of their forefathers. They massed together in front of the sluices, sleeping during the day and searching for food at night.

To let the eels through, the temporary gates of Lake Ijssel were opened, demonstrating their utility before they really came into service. The eels threw themselves on the manna, bringing an end to the mosquitoes. This extraordinary event overpopulated Lake Ijssel with eels, to the joy of its fishermen.

But to go back to the clay. It had to be excavated at low tide and in fine weather. It was then loaded on to big barges with moveable bottoms pulled by tugs along the line of the dyke. There the earth was dropped in two parallel lines forming giant furrows which, at low tide, were flush with sea level.

Powerful dredgers then levelled off these furrows into two ridges between which heaps of sand were pressed down by force-pumps. Finally fascine mats of reed and willow were placed on this base and held down by blocks of basalt, on to which were placed still more blocks of clay.

On the Wadden Sea side, the "furrow" of clay was still further protected from the waves by fascine mats placed at a gently sloping angle as in the old days. This bank was then covered in wicker-work; and still more ballast of stone, basalt, bricks and even cement was used.

The top of the causeway was then covered in earth and sown with grass to bind it. Then the engineers handed it over to the department of roads and bridges who built a modern roadway.

The layout and building of the dyke were comparatively easy as the sea bottom was fairly level. But underwater channels, cutting across it, presented the engineers with a great problem. There were two of these: Vlieter (to the west) and Middelgronden (to the east), 5,000 and 1,650 feet across respectively, through which the current raced at a fantastic speed, particularly at ebb-tide.

At first these were left untouched. But as the building of the dyke progressed, further currents appeared, due to the narrowing of the outlet to the sea. These currents, like an advancing army, tried to break down the barrier, as Bennouilli, a well-known hydraulic engineer, had predicted. They grew in strength, as if nature were increasing the vigour of her attack with each round.

Tunnels and eventually pockets were hollowed out under the dyke, devouring the building materials. Where there were breaches in the dyke these materials were carried away into Lake Ijssel and irretrievably lost. It is calculated that 50 per cent. of the materials already in place were thus scattered.

As a result, underground dykes, known as "dam brakes," had to be built. Fascine mats were dropped on to the bottom of the channels and weighted down with blocks of clay to fill in the gaps. The lower currents now joined forces with the upper currents, making powerful underwater allies.

The fight now became a race. At top speed mountains of clay were piled on to the reed and willow matting. Gradually the currents divided up into smaller streams and their force eventually dispersed.

There was a time, however, when it seemed as though the current would win. This was the most breath-taking moment in the history of the construction of the dyke, when the last breach was about to be closed. The Vlieter channel had reached a depth of eighty-five feet during a south-westerly gale. It was no longer possible to obstruct this head-strong current which could so easily sweep the dyke southwards, tearing it like a fishing-net pulled down by the sea. There was no time to lose. A temporary dyke had to be built fifty feet in front of the Lake Ijssel side to help the weakened barrier. The whole of the dyke's fleet and anything that could sail the Wadden Sea and Lake Ijssel and carry a load of earth or stone, however small, was mobilised. At full speed, by steam and sail, even oar and scull, large ships and skiffs carried their cargoes to the threatened area. After hours of frantic work in the teeth of a gale the Vlieter channel was closed. Everyone in the neighbouring countryside and indeed the whole of the Netherlands was alarmed, realising the results of what could have been yet another national disaster, and it made an indelible impression on the minds of all who lived through the crisis. Finally, on May 28th, 1932, at 1.30 in the afternoon, the last breach was sealed and the dam united Friesland and North Holland. At this instant, Lake Ijssel became tideless and the waves subsided for the first time in exactly six and a half centuries (1282).

The calming of the waters was followed by a deafening noise from the ship's sirens of the entire Zuyder Zee fleet, now no longer to be of service.

On the site of the last breach a simple concrete monument was erected, a square tower inscribed on one side:

Here the dyke was closed on May 28th, 1932

On the reverse, facing the Wadden Sea, was engraved the proud and defiant inscription:

A living nation works for the future.

The sluices, then the pumping stations, were finished soon after the dyke.

Before studying the actual draining of the Zuyder Zee, and the construction of the polders, let us take another look at the dyke itself. It looks like a narrow strip of land stretching beyond the horizon and emerging twenty feet above sea level. Starting at Den Oever and going towards Friesland, the dyke begins with an embankment. A few hundred yards from here, where the buses from Alkman stop, is an excellent inn. On the right there is a small wooden building which houses a map of Lake Ijssel and a splendid model of the dyke showing its machinery in miniature. There is an engineer who gladly answers any questions.

A petrol station stands opposite with a signpost, like those on the edge of the Sahara, warning us that the next petrol pump is twenty miles away.

Continuing towards Friesland one encounters the group of sluices placed in juxtaposition between cement columns into which slide forty-ton iron hatches, each sealing off conduits of forty feet in diameter and placed fifteen feet below sea level. Through these double gates on either side of the dyke flows the surplus from Lake Ijssel or sea water from the Wadden Sea when drought lowers the level of the lake.

The dyke is about 300 feet wide and carries a cement motorway, a cycle track and a pavement for pedestrians, still leaving enough space to build another motorway or a railway.

From a distance the dyke looks like a long thin needle but it is in fact a mountain of building materials: 3 million cubic feet of stone, 40 million cubic feet of clay blocks, 70 million cubic feet of sand. Placed together they would make a cube with sides 1,000 feet long.

On a spring afternoon the scene is striking. Drenched by fine rain, driven along by an icy wind, a works engineer and I walked a little way along the dyke. The landscape became intelligible as my companion explained its history. The jovial pump operator waved to us. Beneath us workmen laboured in the depth of the sluices. A windmill stood silhouetted in the distance and beyond that lay bright fields of daffodils and tulips. A Vermeer painting on one side and a pile of scrap-iron and hutments on the other. To the right and to the left lay two expanses of water, equally rough and facing each other like caged animals. Amongst these poetic contrasts, the engineer talked figures.

The financing of the work on the Zuyder Zee was a Government undertaking. It became apparent that the cost of draining would be beyond the bounds of private finance, in that the price of the work would be greater than the land to be reclaimed. It could not therefore be carried out by private investment as it would theoretically result in bankruptcy. On the other hand, the economic value, considered from a national point of view, was sufficient argument for the Dutch Government to finance the work on its own from available revenue.

The construction of the main as well as the auxiliary dykes needed such quantities of material that four big Dutch firms pooled their resources. The large enclosing dam cost 120 million florins and the subsidiary work 80 million. This figure did not seem excessive to me but I was reminded that most of the material was found on the spot. This comparative cheapness was in line with the ideas of Andries Vierlingh, a well-known hydraulic engineer and dyke-master in the eighteenth century, who said:

"It is not sufficient to build dams and dykes, they must also be built as cheaply as possible in the interest of the community."

And he added:

"God has provided us with the building materials; wattles, stones, clay, straw and reeds. We do not need anything else, but we must use them with dexterity and intelligence. . . ."

IV

HARVEST IN A.D. 2000

Once the Zuyder Zee was enclosed and became the fresh-water lake known as Lake Ijssel, the *Waterstaat* turned its attention to the establishment of the polders.

In 1926 an experimental 100-acre polder was made at Andijk in North Holland. Dyked, drained, purified of salt, generously fertilised, sown and reaped, it produced, by August 1927, unhoped-for results. Similar work could then be carried out on a larger scale.

The Wieringen polder was started in 1927 while the dyke was still under construction. It was first isolated from the sea by a dam, then pumping commenced at Lely and Leemans, to the north and south of the island. This drainage took eight months. The resulting soil was actually no better than a damp, muddy clay and incapable of bearing the weight of a man, much less that of a tractor.

Further drainage made the ground more solid and additional ditches were then dug by ploughs with shaped ploughshares to collect any remaining salt water, which was then evacuated into the sea. Forty-seven fixed and thirteen moving bridges were built and ninety-five miles of roads to carry supplies and people to all parts of the polder so that the remaining work could be undertaken simultaneously.

Poor fodder crops were grown in the still soft and polluted earth to keep it in place and rid it of weeds. Trees were also planted, as much to break up the monotony of the landscape as to bind the soil still further.

The workers' temporary buildings were eventually replaced by 500 permanent farmhouses grouped round villages including administrative buildings, churches and schools. In 1940 the Wieringen polder was completed—an already rich area of abundant harvests.[1]

Apart from the Wieringen polder, the remaining land area of Lake Ijssel was divided into three:

1. The north-east polder (120,000 acres) with the villages of Urk, Lemmer, Emmeloord and Schokkerhaven, started in 1929 and finished in 1942, totalling 50,000 inhabitants by 1950.

2. The south-west polder (Markerwaard) (140,000 acres) not yet under construction.

3. The south polder (Flevoland), the largest: 240,000 acres, started in 1949, and divided for easy administration into two sections (east and west).

The last two polders will include about fifty villages of between 1,000 and 5,000 inhabitants housing a total population of 150,000. They will form the twelfth province of the Netherlands, with the

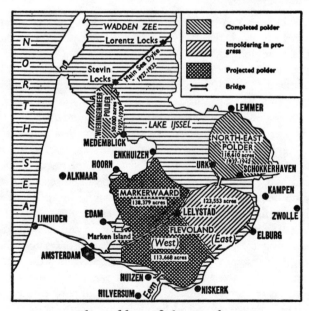

49. The polders of the Zuyder Zee

---

[1] The Wieringen polder was an experiment. Consequently its cost was often higher—in particular on the canal network—than would have been the case if there had been previous experience of any of the difficulties encountered. The north-eastern polder was able to profit from this initial experience.

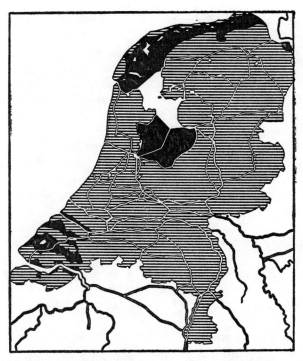

50. Map of the Netherlands showing the probable shape of the
Zuyder Zee about the year 2000 (after Elzevier, October 11th, 1952)

capital of Lelystad, named after the great polder pioneer. The overall
price of the work will amount to 375 million florins (1953) and the last
two polders should be completed by 1980.

The Dutch reckon that by that date the total land thus reclaimed from
the sea should feed 350,000 people. The land is not open to speculation
as it belongs to the Government and people of the Netherlands, and
not an acre is for sale.

The setting up of villages and the farming come under two separate
organisations; the civil engineering authority for buildings, roads and
bridges and the agricultural authority, which has complete control,
without political interference, over the new collective farming.

"The head of the agricultural organisation is therefore given complete authority and although he does come under the Ministry, is
nevertheless chief administrator, head of police, manager, etc. This
important post has the ancient title *bailli*. He is advised by a council,

of which he chooses the members, who have the right to advise but not to vote."[1]

The Government lets the reclaimed land at 120 florins per acre per year, with leases renewable every twelve years. These are automatically cancelled if a farmer neglects his land or infringes the "recommendations" of the agricultural authority. The average farm consists of about 120 acres and is managed as a family business, with the aid of the most modern equipment and machinery.

The rent may seem somewhat high, but these newly reclaimed lands are extremely productive. The major crops are cereals, sugar beet, potatoes, beans and peas.

It is predicted that the fight against the sea in the Netherlands will not stop at the Zuyder Zee. Thoughts are already turned towards the year 2000 when, after a gigantic battle with the Wadden Sea, it is hoped to reclaim some million acres, double that of the Zuyder Zee scheme.

The Netherlands would by this time have reclaimed 4,187 square miles, that is, one-fifth of its territory. The polder peasant could then forget the gloomy saying which resulted from the huge tidal wave in the eighteenth century:

"The first farmer will work himself to death, the second will be destitute and the third will just manage to scrape a living."

[1] *Nouvelles de Hollande*, December 15th, 1942.

XIV

THE VOLGA AND TENNESSEE
HYDRO-ELECTRIC DAMS

THE USE OF steam-power, which was so highly developed during the nineteenth century, was followed by the use of water-power, and soon maybe nuclear power will rule the world; after that some other type of power will take over, something which is still beyond our conception . . . space, perhaps.

In the meantime every nation in the world is attempting to increase both its potential and its output. France undoubtedly had the honour of first making water-power available for electricity. The first pressurised water main was built in France in 1869 in the Dauphiné mountains by the paper-manufacturer Aristide Bergès, inventor of water-power. The two French engineers Fourneyron and Fontaine invented the turbine, but the names of their two American colleagues, Francis and Pelton, should be linked with theirs.

Today the harnessing of water-power produces easily 40 per cent. of world energy, and this is only a beginning. In countries where there is a shortage of coal, such as Scandinavia, Switzerland and Italy, water produces 90 per cent. of the power for industrial and domestic consumption.

There are large-scale hydro-electric installations in Algeria and the Aswan dam built on the Nile between the Sudan and Numidia, near the quarries which supplied the stone for the pyramids, was until recently one of the largest in the world.

The building of a dam not only supplies power; it is also a factor in agriculture, general economy, and geo-politics, for it can ensure a regular flow of water and the irrigation of valleys which would otherwise be dry or infertile; it can bring new life to unproductive areas; it can retain inhabitants who would otherwise have left poor soil and it can permit a nation, a régime or a political party to prove the strength and stability of their institutions.

A comparison between the work that has been carried out along the Volga and in the Tennessee Valley proves that the most powerful régimes in the largest countries in the world have not failed either in the field of engineering or of propaganda. The spiritual difference between the two régimes as shown in their slogans—the T.V.A.'s "built for the people," and Volga-Don's "the triumphant march of Communism"—is too obvious to call for analysis. But a comparison between the enterprises carried out in the U.S.S.R. and the U.S.A. shows that there is no notable difference either in technique or in the expression of enthusiasm and pride in having brought these vast enterprises to a successful conclusion.

I

"COME BACK IN TEN YEARS' TIME"

The Russian hydro-electric schemes were more revolutionary than the American ones, for after the collapse of the Tsarist régime the Soviets were unable to find the slightest spark of economic life which they could revive. About 1920 the Volga-Don basin was untouched just as the Tennessee Valley was sterile. The leaders of the Russian Revolution realised that economic recovery was as important as the political reorganisation of the country, and Lenin was preoccupied by it until the day he died.

In 1920 H. G. Wells had a famous interview with the Communist dictator and reported their conversation on electric power in Russia in his book *Russia in the Shadows*.

Lenin told Wells that he had just set up a State Commission to study the electrification project and that the Congress of Soviets had ratified the plan for it. Paradoxically Wells had remained a "typical liberal" and could not share Lenin's enthusiasm.

"For Lenin," wrote Wells, "who like a good orthodox Marxist denounces all 'Utopians,' has succumbed at last to a Utopia, the Utopia of the electricians. He is throwing all his weight into a scheme for the development of great power stations in Russia to serve whole provinces with light, with transport, and industrial power. Two experimental districts, he said, had already been electrified. Can one imagine a more courageous project in a vast flat land of forests and illiterate peasants, with no water-power, with no technical skill available, and with trade and industry at the last gasp? Projects for such an electrification are in process of development in Holland and they have been discussed in England, and in those densely populated and industrially highly developed centres one can imagine them as successful, economical, and altogether beneficial. But their application to Russia is an altogether greater strain upon the constructive imagination. I cannot see anything of this sort happening in this dark crystal of Russia, but this little man at the Kremlin can; he sees the decaying railways replaced by a new electric transport, sees new roadways spreading throughout the land, sees a new and happier Communist industrialism arising again.While I talked to him he almost persuaded me to share his vision. . . .

"'But these are only sketches and beginnings,' I said.

"'Come back and see what we have done in Russia in ten years' time,' he answered."

Ten years later—Lenin had died in the meantime—the hydraulic equipment was far from being completed, but the Russians were already using the dam and power station on the Volkhov river in the north to operate electrically driven ploughs and heat artificial incubators.

In spite of the propaganda that they addressed unceasingly to the capitalist world the Russians had the courage to admit that they would not succeed without difficulty and that the worst problems were caused not by their lack of experience but by the distrust that the vast conception of their plan inspired in the workers. They did not deny sabotage, waste or even misuse of the money of which they were so short.

"On many occasions," wrote A. Zoritch and D. Zasvalski in Dnieprostroi, "when the work was going ahead, the Volkhovstroi was questioned and there were demands that the work should stop. On many occasions the work was threatened by total and disastrous destruction.

"Everyone should realise how much effort and sacrifice was necessary before this power station could be built, and in what circumstances the country found itself. There was no iron, no bricks, no excavators, no tools, there was literally nothing, when it was decided to undertake this historic enterprise. At least half of the Volkhovstroi was created with materials which were assembled gradually, thanks to the efforts of a revolutionary nation, over a period of years, from all over the devastated country. Iron was brought from Baikal, a long way away, on the backs of camels; somewhere in the Ukraine submerged caissons were discovered which were refloated down the Desna and the Seym with incredible difficulties; abandoned, forgotten factories were searched for fly-wheels and scrap iron was melted down.

"Men specially appointed for the task went all over the country to find raw material, wood, steel, cement, wire, engines, and wheat for the workers; all this was collected in dozens of towns, in hundreds of districts, travelling in broken-down waggons harnessed to trains which took weeks to go from Tchoudov to Leningrad; everything that went into the building of this fine, astonishing, European dam on the Volkhov river was got together nail by nail, pound by pound. It was not yet possible to buy abroad, organise supplies and stable exchange; this came much later.

"Everything which could be collected and made at this period within the country was assembled, manufactured and dispatched to Zvanka, the railway centre with a branch line going over a bridge to Volkhovstroi. It was a terribly difficult task; when the comrades who took part in the work remember this period they smile in embarrassment and do not know how to explain their success. They do not understand it themselves. It all seems to be a miracle."[1]

Yet in 1927 the Volkhovstroi dam was finished and although it produced only 78,000 kilowatts—as much as an average-size dam in the Tennessee Valley—its success had an immense repercussion on the prestige of the Soviet economy.

It took five years to build, and it was an experiment, a training ground. Manual labour and hand tools, especially spades and wheelbarrows, had built most of it, but gradually they were replaced by modern machines bought abroad or manufactured on the spot as best as they could be.

In 1928 the Dnieper dam was begun, strangely enough on the site of the former lands that Queen Catherine II had given to her lover, Count Orlov—described by a French wit as the "Monsieur Pompadour of Russia."

The Dnieprostroi dam was nearly four and a half miles wide, and nearly 200 feet high, with a lake ten miles wide; it also included a lock 400 feet long by sixty feet wide. A new town, Zaporozhe, was built near the dam with several factories round it.

The Volkhovstroi dam had been a piece of improvisation. In contrast, eleven plans were carefully worked out for the Dnieprostroi before one was adopted. Labourers were replaced by machines and horses by the railway. For the first time in Russia mechanisation measured up to the task, and 20,000 workers, sent from all corners of the U.S.S.R., worked on the vast dam for nearly ten years. They were mainly young people under the age of thirty who had absorbed Marxist propaganda for twelve years, and no longer elderly moujiks still longing nostalgically for the days of the Tsar. And engineers with new loyalties took over the direction of the work, replacing the

---

[1] A. Zoritch and D. Zasvalski, *Dnieprostroi*. Paris, 1932.

"capitalist" technicians who had been kept on or attracted to Russia after the October Revolution, and then sent back to their own countries, or sometimes even liquidated, once their services were no longer needed. If the new workers lacked experience they proved their initiative and revolutionary enthusiasm.

In 1932 the Dnieprostroi embankment was in place and the power station was in operation from 1936 onwards; the whole undertaking had cost 200 million roubles, a sum which is difficult to evaluate in terms of non-Russian money; the dam produced 560,000 kilowatts, that is 75 per cent. of Russian hydro-electric power. It was not only an immense technical success but also a fine political achievement. Although it was destroyed in 1942 during the German advance, it is at present being reconstructed and will include some major improvements.

II

THE NEW VOLGA BOATMEN

Any mention of the Volga inevitably brings into one's head the famous *Song of the Volga Boatmen*, punctuated by a musical syncopation reminiscent of Honegger's symphonic poem "Pacific 231." Today in the riverside workshops, behind the railway lines, the sounds are those of loudspeakers blaring out orders to the workers on the cranes and trucks, mingled with slogans praising the Great Work.

The Soviet Russians are incomparable political psychologists and know how to encourage human effort with the minimum of cost; they do not offer high wages or great comfort, as in the United States, but they appeal to personal pride and the community spirit. In this way they have raised the Stakhanovite worker to the status of a deity, paying him homage in graphs showing the rise in output.

The workers' minds must not be left in peace during their free time and they are made into fanatics by "shock literature" in praise of large undertakings, such as a reportage-novel by Galaktionov and Agranovski called *The Birth of Great Buildings*. This book glorifies the new Soviet pioneers working on the hydro-electric project at Stalingrad; at the same time it expresses hatred of the capitalist builders whose dams collapse like ant-heaps beneath the foot of the passer-by while Russian concrete is rock-like and indestructible.

"We could," say the authors, "draw up a long list of similar cases

concerning the work of the Americans, British, French, Italians and Germans. A large volume has been written by Professor A. Guelfer entitled *Causes and Types of Destruction in Hydro-Electric Undertakings.* The index alone shows that such disasters occur frequently abroad."
And in particular in the United States. Why?

"Dollars, dollars, and dollars again. Money plays its part in every plan, determines the type and site of every undertaking, and dictates at the same time the duration and quality of the work. When American hydro-technicians build their dams they do not think of electric power but of dollars. . . . And that is why in the U.S.A. human progress can be identified according to the expression of Karl Marx with 'that hideous pagan idol which would only drink nectar from the skull of a sacrificial victim.'

"In our country no dam rising to a height of 175 feet has ever collapsed into the mountains. The rivers on the plains have never carried away either the left or the right side of a dam. And our water-courses are kept so well under control that none of them has ever flowed to the side of the dams and gone down cracks among the rocks. Our towns extend and prosper near the hydro-electric projects and the collective farms cultivate their crops quietly beside the rivers which have been dammed, using the electric power so generated.

"There are no disasters in our country; since the Soviet régime came to power there has never been a single breakdown, in spite of the vast, unprecedented scale of our hydro-electric enterprises. We find this natural; it does not give us any particular pleasure, just as one feels no deep satisfaction in possessing one's own head complete with chin, nose and ears in the right places. This is how it should be. Yet it appears that we are justified in being proud of the quality of our dams, generating stations and canals. It appears that heads are not always complete in other countries."[1]

Let us see the Russian worker at work on the Volga–Don Canal in a documentary film.[2]

"The evocative power of art, adhering strictly to fact, places the spectator in the atmosphere of the vast building project and helps him to share the feelings of the builders. Here you see the Prorokov family who handle huge excavators like easily controlled high precision instruments. Here are Zoïa Poliakova and Maroussia Boldy-Rèva, experts in electric arc-welding, the Stakhanovite mechanics V. Téretchkine, E. Simak, A. Ouskov, V. Mikhailov, etc. How different they are

---

[1] *Etudes soviétiques*, No. 63, pp. 77 and 79 (1954).
[2] *Volga-Don* (1954). Produced by Fédor Kisséliev.

from each other and yet how easily their image remains engraved in the memory of the spectator!

"The Cossacks gather on the quay to watch sailing ships in the newly created Sea of Tsymliansk. The plains, which were previously arid and devastated by dust storms, are now green. Rice and cotton grow not far from vines and orchards.

"Then on July 27th, 1954, cheering breaks out, for this is the magnificent opening day. The ship *Joseph Stalin* enters the canal, greeted by sirens. The people celebrate their victory by singing and dancing and the Cossack horsemen gallop to the rhythm of life. Water flows over the steppes of Stalingrad and the Don, the turbines work faster and faster and machines sow happiness in the fields of the collective farms. And soon the song of all creatures and all things breaks into a hymn of praise to the genius of man."

This is unfortunately all we know about the idyllic life of the Soviet worker, but thanks to many technical studies which have filtered through to the capitalist world we can at last discover a little more about the fantastic extent of the Russian achievement and the enterprises which are now in progress.

After 1945 the Russians, whose war effort matched their heroism, found themselves faced with ruins on a gigantic scale which had to be rebuilt. They realised how essential Anglo-American aid had been in the winning of the war and that ideology and courage could achieve nothing without machine tools and munitions. They seemed to be deeply aware of their inferiority in the industrial field and as a result they decided to make huge strides in their own field, that is to say electrical power. They made use of their rivers, which are the greatest in the world, flowing slowly yet steadily and forming an inexhaustible source of kilowatts.

"No country," says X. Velathcourt, "possesses such resources of hydro-electric power as the Soviet Union. It possesses 108,000 water-courses, flowing at the rate of 5,230 cubic yards of water per year, which are a potential source of energy for the production of more than 2,500 million kilowatt hours per year, four times more than the rivers of the U.S.A. can supply and fifty times more than the hydro-electric power possible in a country like France, where water supplies are nevertheless good."

The plan set before the Council of Soviet Ministers in 1950 certainly represents the most complete and detailed project ever drawn up in the U.S.S.R. since October 1917. This is the fifth five-year plan, and certain aspects of it deal more particularly with the building of dams in

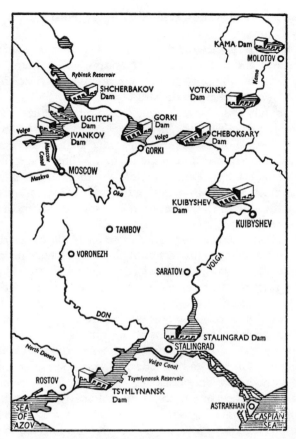

51. The hydraulic system of the Great Volga (from *Molodoï Kommounist*, May 1954)

the Volga Basin and the linking of this river to the Don by the Stalin Canal.

It is quite plain from the various reports published since 1950 on the execution of the entire project that the plan was reshaped several times whenever internal political events affected it in any way. From year to year plans and execution were modified for mysterious reasons; for instance one dam disappeared for reasons which were never explained, and we may diffidently suppose that these were due to difficulties encountered equally often by engineers in capitalist countries.

The Russian plan is less closely integrated from the economic point of view than the American, for, apart from the production of electric power, the water that is harnessed has to supply the irrigation zones of the Volga and near the Ural Mountains. The Russians have made immense efforts to develop large-scale general agriculture and sylviculture by planting thousands of trees to keep in place the soil which is worn away by the wind from the steppes, and also re-afforestation carried out on a scale and in accordance with revolutionary methods which are unique in the world.

Hydro-electric resources do exist today west of the Ural Mountains but this energy only represents a quarter of the total production; the remainder is supplied by thermo-electric power stations using coal, fuel oil, lignite and even wood, raw materials which exist in great quantities in Russia.

The development of the rivers, and the canals which link them together, remains, in fact, one of the questions which preoccupies the Russians most. Power and transport are inseparable and one day, if peace is maintained, Russia will certainly possess the most highly developed canal network in the world.

The Stalin Canal is no more than the fulfilment of a grandiose dream by Peter the Great, whom the Soviet Russians now consider to have been as revolutionary as themselves. The astonishing master-builder Tsar had already built a navigable canal between the Illovlia and Kamychynka rivers and the tributaries of the Volga and the Don. Thirty-five thousand soldiers and thousands of serfs laboured on the groundwork for three years, but feudal traditions and religious taboos conspired to prevent the completion of this project, which was in advance of its time, and only a few miles remain.

As soon as Lenin came to power he resurrected the Tsar's idea, but it was Stalin who carried it out. The canal is sixty-two miles long and the total height of the reaches is about 300 feet, greater than the corresponding height on the Panama Canal. The Russian canal links together by means of locks the Azov Sea and the Caspian Sea and, in fact, means that the Straits of Gibraltar are linked through the Mediterranean to the foot of the Ural Mountains.

Among other canals envisaged on this scale and now at various stages of construction mention should be made of the Turkmenistan Canal, the canals between the Caspian Sea and the Aral Sea, the Dvina and the Dnieper, the Dvina and the Kama; the two latter practically link the Baltic Sea to the Caspian Sea and the Azov Sea.

These canals are not merely means of communication, they are used in the intensified programmes of irrigation, drainage and sylviculture. Russians have always liked woodwork, and it should be remembered that the use of the saw was not introduced into Russia until the eighteenth century, while the Empress Elizabeth forbade the use of the axe under the threat of fines, for she believed that it caused excessive waste.

Huge factories are also planned near to the canals. They will be employed in iron smelting and the manufacture of chemical products, both equally important for the atomic plants which are apparently now being built near the Ural Mountains, between Asia and Europe, no doubt to provide means either of defence or attack.[1]

III

MOUJIKS IN ALABAMA: GUNTERSVILLE, 1930

When the Russians laid out their canals for the . purposes of navigation or irrigation they worked on virgin land which only needed the hand of man to make it fertile. The Americans, on the other hand, had to work on soil which had been made sterile by uncontrolled and thoughtless exploitation.

The Tennessee river in the south-east of America is a tributary of the Mississippi. Two centuries ago the land was inhabited by the Cherokee Indians, who lived comfortably from their fishing and hunting. Then white emigration drove them away and, in their place, brought wholesale destruction—destruction which was by no means limited to the Tennessee Valley. The Civil War followed, from 1861 to 1865, and left behind nothing but ruin, poverty, depopulation and waste land.

"All that remained of Tennessee was a desert with devastated soil and weary people. Both land and men had lost everything. . . . Fortun-

---

[1] The five large hydro-electric power stations built on the Russian rivers flowing into the Mediterranean basin have the following capacity:

	kilowatt hours per year
Lower Dnieper (Kakkovska)..	250,000
Upper Dnieper	650,000
Volga (Kuibyshev–Stalingrad)	3,700,000
Volga–Don (Tsymlyamski)	160,000
Turkmenistan Canal	100,000

The total production of electric power in Russia in 1953 was 130,000 mill. kilowatt hours, and reached 182,000 mill. in 1956, compared with 344,000 mill. in the U.S.A. in 1950.

Finally, the Davydov plan, which is to link the rivers of the Ienisséi and the Ob, is a gigantic undertaking already being studied and envisages an increase in production of 80,000 mill. kilowatt hours.

ately wild game had increased to such an extent that the inhabitants could live on it until the first harvests, pigs and poultry appeared."[1]

After the Civil War came the disastrous floods of February to April, 1867, when streams poured down from the Tennessee Mountains, swollen by fourteen inches of rainfall, for the trees had been used for railway sleepers or pit props or made into pulp for paper. Finally the sides of the valleys slid down in a river of humus displaced by the torrential streams.

This disaster followed half a century of intensive cultivation which had impoverished the soil; no attempt had been made to restore its fertility by a judicious change of crop or the use of fertilisers. In 1933, out of 9,000,000 acres of arable land, 1,000,000 were irreparably lost and 7,000,000 were due to go the same way unless something were done.

"The exploitation of the mining resources in the valley offered an even more striking example of thoughtless destruction: copper ore was discovered at Ducktown, a mountain in Tennessee; a mine was opened and a foundry set up. Wood was taken for fuel from the surrounding forest, which was soon devastated for over nine miles round about. Worse still, the fumes from the foundry proved to be toxic and killed all the vegetation. When the soil was stripped of its protective covering it was soon attacked by erosion which caused cracks twenty to twenty-five feet deep. As a result the surroundings of the mine have today a kind of lunar aspect."[2]

The local squabbles which followed the Civil War, the clandestine struggle against the negroes who had been freed from slavery, the violent manoeuvres of the Ku-Klux-Klan, the rise to power of the unscrupulous adventurers known as "carpet-baggers," plunged the valley into a state of anarchy which caused repercussions as far afield as Washington.

For nearly a century there had been a small but steady flow of commercial traffic along the rivers that run into the Tennessee, but it was gradually brought to an end by competition from the railways; all that remained in 1930 were the "chicken boats," which brought the weekly farm produce to the small local markets.

The farms had less comfort than those in the poorest countries of Europe or the homes of the moujiks in the time of Pushkin. They consisted as a rule of about forty acres, and the farm houses, which were built of wood and discoloured by the rain, usually had only three or four rooms. Two-thirds of these farms drew their water from wells;

[1] Donald Davidson, *Tennessee*. New York, 1946.
[2] Foch (R.), *La Haute Autorité de la Vallée du Tennessee*. Paris, 1952.

354

out of 1,200 families living round Guntersville, only thirteen possessed baths; no more than twelve had indoor lavatories and 60 per cent. had none at all; twenty-seven families had the telephone and thirty-four had electricity.

One family out of five possessed a car, and half of these were more than seven years old, which meant that, by American standards, even in Alabama, they were old crocks. Only one-third of the country people owned farms, and the average yearly income of these farms was 367 dollars.

The majority of the Guntersville inhabitants received only a primitive form of education, 10 per cent. of the women had never been to school at all and many of the children followed their bad example. The health of the community was equally poor; a third of the population was subject to malaria.

It was understandable in these circumstances that the young people left their parents to stew in their own juice and emigrated in large numbers. The State of Tennessee lost 120,000 inhabitants in this way and Alabama 154,000; some went to the agricultural areas in the West, others to the industrial towns in the East.

Such was the state of Guntersville, Alabama, thirty years ago.[1]

After the Wall Street crash in 1929[2] the rest of the United States found itself in a similar situation to that of Alabama, although the overall picture was not quite as black. Fourteen million people were unemployed and production fell to as low as 14 per cent. of the normal figure; 3,300 coalmines were closed owing to the absence of demand. In 1932 the national income fell by 50 per cent. and the drop in the price index caused civil servants' salaries to be cut by 30 per cent. Different rates of exchange came into existence in different districts. Rioting broke out more or less everywhere and there were deaths in Iowa in 1933.

From the agricultural point of view the catastrophe followed the same pattern: half the farms had to be mortgaged and there was a notable decline in the land under cultivation, especially wheat and cotton. Enforced sales took place in distressing circumstances and tax collectors were molested.

It was at this point that F. D. Roosevelt introduced his New Deal, and by a series of severe measures succeeded in bringing about the recovery of the American economy. These salutary reforms, and in

[1] Henry Billings, *All Down the Valley*. New York, 1952.
[2] Statistics published b , the New York Stock Exchange estimate the total losses for the single day of Oc⊤⌐ʋer 28th, 1929, at 15,320,379,515 dollars.

particular the creation of the Civilian Conservation Corps and the National Recovery Act, led to the creation of the Tennessee Valley Authority, an independent project for building dams, regulating the flow of rivers in the Tennessee Valley and making them navigable, with the right to supply electric power at rates competing with those offered by ordinary power stations.

IV

THE AUTHORITY IS SET UP

Before Federal legislation was passed various plans had been put forward locally for improvement in the Tennessee Valley, but the approach was usually based on short-term considerations rather than on the setting up of a rational overall policy.

An attempt to create a navigation channel in a section of the river had been made in 1830, but it was soon abandoned after heavy floods. In 1875, Colonel Goethals, who later took charge of the Panama Canal, made another attempt, lasting fifteen years, but he was equally unsuccessful. In 1906 a private company suggested building a dam at Muscle Shoals in Alabama, where the Tennessee river describes a loop, but this plan attracted little interest in Washington. In 1916, however, when intensive German submarine warfare made it impossible to import Chilean nitrate, which was essential for the manufacture of explosives, there was no alternative but to build the great Wilson dam and two factories, which were closed down when the war came to an end.

In 1921 Henry Ford, who already felt suffocated in his automobile factories at Detroit, suggested that he should buy the whole area and build a gigantic factory which would draw its power supply from the Wilson dam. He made fabulous offers but politics intervened and prevented him from being successful. Nobody knew what to do with the wartime factories which had also become a heavy liability since production had stopped; then about 1930 heavy floods drew public attention to the soil erosion in Tennessee and the State seemed to be on the point of drifting down the Mississippi and sinking like some scuttled ship in the Gulf of Mexico.

Between 1931 and 1933, 138 plans were put forward, until Roosevelt formulated the T.V.A., imposing his will on the politicians and the valley itself. Here are the main points from the President's message on

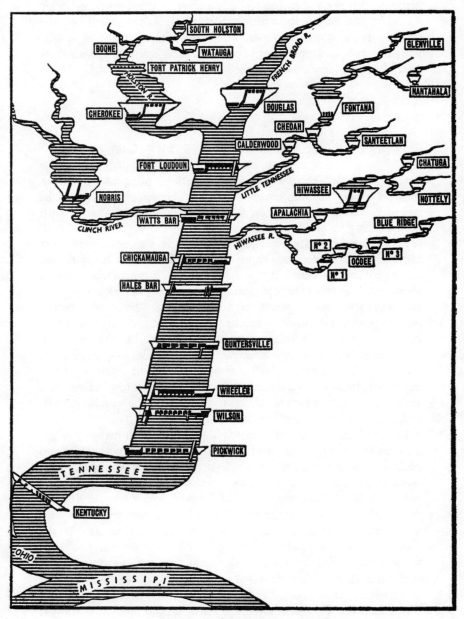

52. The dams of the Tennessee Basin

April 10th, 1933, which was to become the charter of one of the most gigantic enterprises of all time:

"It is clear," he wrote, "that the Muscle Shoals development is but a small part of the potential public usefulness of the entire Tennessee river. Such use, if envisioned in its entirety, transcends mere power development: it enters the wide fields of flood control, soil erosion, afforestation, elimination from agricultural use of marginal lands, and distribution and diversification of industry. In short, this power development of war days leads logically to national planning for a complete river watershed involving many States and the future lives and welfare of millions. It touches and gives life to all forms of human concerns."

In order to implement this plan, the President recommended "legislation to create a Tennessee Valley Authority—a corporation clothed with the power of government but possessed of the flexibility and initiative of private enterprise. It should be charged with the broadest duty of planning for the proper use, conservation and development of the natural resources of the Tennessee river drainage basin and its adjoining territory for the general social and economic welfare of the nation.

"Severe lessons," said the President, "had taught us the human wastage that resulted from lack of planning. It was now time to apply planning on a larger scale and link together, in one great enterprise, the many States which had a direct interest in the basin of one of the greatest American rivers.

"This is really a return to the bold spirit of the pioneers. If we succeed in this we can go forward step by step, developing the other great natural resources in other States of our country."

The T.V.A. project was approved by Congress and legislation was passed granting it an autonomy "in which," wrote Foch, "no element could be changed without causing repercussions on the others." The T.V.A. was to bring recovery to the Tennessee Valley by integrating in one plan the land, the natural resources and the welfare of the inhabitants, the whole enterprise being governed by the six fundamental points set out in Roosevelt's message:

1. Maximum flood control.
2. Full development of navigable waterways.
3. "Enforced" production of electric power as far as this was compatible with flood control and improved navigability.
4. Perfection of new agricultural techniques.
5. Intensive afforestation.
6. Social and economic welfare of the inhabitants.

In a country of private enterprise like the U.S.A. this revolutionary attempt at controlled economy was far from meeting with the necessary unanimous approval. The electricity companies in particular, led by one of their tycoons, Wendell Willkie,[1] took their objections to the Federal courts. Willkie lost his case but meanwhile David Lilienthal,[2] after a series of friendly high-level talks, led him to share his point of view on the social aspect of the enterprise. The fact that Lilienthal was able to pay him 78,600,000 dollars by way of compensation helped to appease his wrath.

Not all the adversaries of the T.V.A. were disarmed so easily, but in the end they had to give way grudgingly when faced with the results. In 1946 Robert Taft, the Republican candidate, who was a passionate opponent of the T.V.A., was asked what he would do with it if he were elected. "I've been against it," he replied, "but since it's there, I shan't destroy it."[3]

Lilienthal brought the same qualities to the direction of the T.V.A. that Goethals had brought to the final work on the Panama Canal. He possessed faith and a strong sense of realism. In spite of his youth he already held, he said, "that men should no longer consider poverty as an inevitable misfortune and think that exhausting work, dirt, famine and floods are either the machinations of the devil or the punishment of heaven."

The organisation of the T.V.A., based on that of the Panama Canal, was in fact just as revolutionary for the United States as were the events of 1917 in Russia when the Tsarist régime was overthrown. The T.V.A. gave rise in America to a vast swing of public opinion and a considerable literature, a kind of "economic Bible," including principles of behaviour, prophecies and even a social doctrine which as it gradually emerged came surprisingly close to a kind of apocalyptic communism. It should be added, however, that the strained relations between the U.S. and the U.S.S.R. after the war had a dampening effect on this way of thinking.

The T.V.A. was absolutely independent from the administrative

---

[1] Unsuccessful opponent of Roosevelt in the 1940 Presidential Election.

[2] David E. Lilienthal was born in Illinois in 1899, and, after studying at Harvard, set up a business attorney's office in Chicago. As a member of the Public Service Commission of Wisconsin, he became interested in the organisation of electricity supply companies. He was a strong advocate of nationalisation in this field. He was only thirty-four when Roosevelt appointed him to the three-man board of directors of the T.V.A., and he later became president; in 1946, at the request of President Truman, he left the T.V.A. to become president of the Atomic Energy Commission when the factories at Oak Ridge were converted to peace-time use.

[3] Raymond Cartier, Les 48 Amériques, Paris, 1953.

point of view, outside the scope of Federal jurisdiction and unaffected by the boundaries of the six States in which it was to operate. It was financed by annual Government grants (its initial budget in 1933 was 750,000,000 dollars)[1] and dealt directly with large-scale enterprises and industrial concerns.

The first three-man board of directors, consisting of Lilienthal, Norris and Harcourt Morgan, were precluded from any personal financial interest in the undertaking, but they had the power to appoint or dismiss any of their subordinates irrespective of the regulations governing public administration. One of the directors said that he hated "paper-work and bureaucracy, and was ready to accept a certain amount of disorganisation if he could have loyalty, initiative and enthusiasm instead."

Political and racial discrimination were to have no place whatsoever in the recruitment of staff. Certain rules of segregation were not to be broken, however, and the proportion of coloured workers on the building sites was to be the same as in the surrounding areas. The coloured men would work in separate gangs and live in their own camps, but they would have exactly the same wages as the whites. The rights of the trade unions over the T.V.A. employees were also limited in 1935 and a distinction was made between the treatment of workers in private enterprise and those employed in Government-controlled organisations such as the T.V.A.

Between 1933 and 1940, 200,000 workers were recruited, and all, whatever their level of skill, were screened by "security experts," and were paid wages in accordance with the average rates in Tennessee. The senior staff, the engineers and administrators, came from all over the U.S.A., but the subordinate staff were recruited as far as possible on the spot, without any interference from the unions, despite their great power. The skilled workers were selected by examination and interview, but had to follow advanced courses in the latest methods for this kind of work.

Most of the staff lived in prefabricated houses at a rent of twenty-seven dollars per month; these were taken down and re-erected[2] along with the workshops as work progressed. Some men preferred to live in caravans towed by their own cars.

These houses were all exactly alike, apart from the colour of their

---

[1] Up to June 1955 total investment amounted to 3,250,000,000 dollars. (World Almanac 1957.)
[2] These houses are now used as rented accommodation for the many tourists who visit the Tennessee Valley to see the new buildings.

paint, and each one consisted of a living room, a bedroom, a bathroom and naturally a w.c. Most of the furniture, including the bed, was built in. This type of comfort played no small part in "selling" T.V.A., especially to the older members of the farming community who were used to open-hearth fires and outside conveniences.

Young trees were planted in the best sites which had escaped erosion and when the dams were completed their reflections could be seen in the artificial lakes.

The natural unity of the Tennessee Valley was now restored and the provisional capital of this rehabilitated territory was set in Chattanooga, which stood at Moccasin Bend on the Tennessee river. Small towns, forming administrative centres, grew up close to the dams.

v

THE TENNESSEE TRINITY: CONCRETE, STEEL AND WATER

"The plans for the future of the valley should result from the collaboration between numerous organisations and individuals, and their final success depends equally on the initiative and cooperation of everyone." This was Lilienthal's basic doctrine.

The T.V.A. began by purchasing the land and buildings which were to be under its control—a quarter of the area of the valley, 20,000 farms, four small towns; then it was necessary to fill in the cracks in the earth, demolish churches, re-site cemeteries and finally rehouse 75–100,000 people who would be turned out of their homes by the work to be undertaken.

In spite of the rights it possessed the T.V.A. rarely resorted to intimidation; it bought the land in an entirely above-board way at rates 15 per cent. higher than the current prices. The low density of the population and the absence of speculators made this task easier, however, and there were no distasteful incidents.

The next move was the setting up of the workshops, and after laboratory tests had been carried out vast quantities of materials and equipment were placed in position and brought carefully into use. Only a few private firms took part in the work, although all types of hydro-electric equipment, including turbines, alternators, transformers, sub-stations, cables, etc., were ordered from every manufacturer in the U.S.

Space does not allow a full account of all the hydro-electric projects undertaken throughout the valley, nor a description of each of the dams. Most of these had a three-fold purpose: firstly, to store water for electric power, secondly, to achieve flood-control, and thirdly, to work the locks on the navigable rivers. Like white mushrooms they began to rise almost everywhere at the places which had been selected in advance by means of aerial photography in collaboration with the resources of geology and the art of hydraulic engineering.

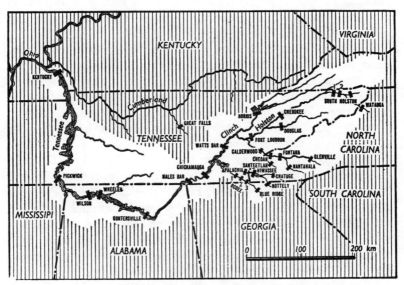

53. Map of the Tennessee river showing its tributaries and their dams

The map shows the fan-like outline of the five tributaries flowing into the Tennessee river, over a length of 373 miles, while a dozen smaller streams run down into them from the Appalachian Mountains. The Tennessee flows into Alabama at full strength, going through Chattanooga and then bending at Guntersville and Muscle Shoals. From there it flows due north and at its broadest point crosses the State of Tennessee, pouring 60 million tons of water annually into the Ohio river, which forms the boundary between the states of Missouri and Kentucky.

The Tennessee river is 620 miles long. It is an easy-going river, running through open valleys or across plains, and its bed varies greatly in width while ridges of soil protrude here and there. Its drainage basin extends over six of the southern States, covering a total area of 40,000 square miles. In 1933 the population of the area was 1,500,000; by 1945, after the work had been completed, it had increased to 4,500,000.

There are thirty dams in the drainage basin: nine on the Tennessee river itself, five on the Holston and one on the Clinch—the Norris dam, which now supplies power to the "atomic city," Oak Ridge National Laboratory; there is one dam on the French Broad, six on the Little Tennessee and eight on the Hiwassee. The lakes lie at heights of between 330 and 1,640 feet above sea-level.

The dams vary in width from 500 (Ocoee 3) to 9,500 feet (Kentucky dam), but they are all much smaller than the Grand Coulée[1] and the vast dams in the U.S.S.R. They are not particularly high, the lowest (Ocoee 2) measuring thirty feet and the highest (Hiwassee) 330 feet. The most powerful is the Wilson dam, with an output of 444,000 kilowatt hours per year, and the least powerful Ocoee 1, with an output of 18,000 kilowatt hours per year.

Only the Great Tennessee river is navigable, from Fort Loudoun until its junction with the Ohio, by means of nine locks over a distance of 625 miles, that is, the width of France from Calais to the Pyrenees. The total area of all the lakes amounts to 1,000 square miles, which is four times the size of the Lake of Geneva, and their total shoreline is as long as those of the Pacific and Atlantic coasts of the U.S. combined.

The Tennessee basin has unexpectedly become the greatest centre in the United States for freshwater yachting. Every summer thousands of small sailing boats or motor boats take advantage of the water as it rushes towards the dams on its way to produce kilowatts.

In 1945 the total annual production of all the dams owned by the T.V.A. was 3,100,000 kilowatt hours. By 1952 new installations increased this figure to 6,000,000. The volume and quantity of materials used represent an equally spectacular aspect of the total achievement. One hundred and seventy-three thousand acres of land had to be cleared to make room for the lakes; 1,864 miles of roads had to be built or rebuilt and 140 miles of railway line laid out; 40,000,000 cubic yards of rock had to be blown up in order to site the dams and finally 113,000,000 tons of cement, stone or earth had to be used, that is to

[1] The largest dam in the U.S., on the boundary of the State of Washington and the Canadian frontier, near the Pacific coast. It is built on the Columbia river, standing 460 feet high and measuring 10,000 feet across. The lake it creates holds nearly 216,000,000,000 cubic feet of water, measuring 150 miles in length.

say, twelve times the total mass of the seven greatest pyramids of Egypt. These figures are given by David Lilienthal in his book *T.V.A.: Democracy on the March.*

This colossal clearance and irrigation programme only took eight years, although it must be remembered that five of the dams were already in existence and only had to be modernised.

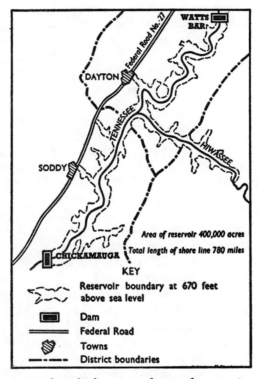

54. The Chickamauga dam and reservoir

In 1942 torrents of rain fell over the valleys of the Ohio, the Mississippi and the Tennessee. Only the last of the three States was spared, thanks to push-button control, as David Lilienthal described it:

"But in 1942 . . . orders went out from the T.V.A. office of central control to every tributary dam. The message came flashing to the operator in the control room at Hiwassee dam, deep in the mountains of North Carolina: 'Hold back all the water of the Hiwassee river. Keep it out of the Tennessee.' The operator pressed a button. Steel gates closed. The water of that tributary was held. To Cherokee dam on the Holston went the message: 'Keep back the flow of the Holston.' To Chickamagua dam just above the industrial danger spot at Chattanooga: 'Release water to make room for the waters from above . . .'

"The rate of water release from every tributary river was precisely controlled. The Tennessee was kept in hand. There was no destruction, no panic, no interruption of work. Most of the water, instead of wrecking the valley, actually produced a benefit in power, when later it was released through the turbines."

VI

NEW LIFE IN THE VALLEY

David Lilienthal was fortunate enough to see the completion of the work that he had undertaken, and he published an extremely realistic, unprejudiced account of the project. Yet, he writes: "I recognise that in writing about the Tennessee Valley Authority I cannot be wholly objective. No one can be so absorbed in this work as for a decade I have been and remain thus passionless about a task so altogether heartening. The reader, then, is warned at the outset that he will find no tone of Olympian neutrality in this book . . . there are convictions stated and conclusions pressed."

Democracy on the March was written in 1943 when work on the T.V.A. projects was barely finished, and the book provided a basic document for those who wanted to boost or decry the scheme by an analysis of its history and results. Lilienthal glorifies the American economy, quoting figures and statistics proving that as a result of T.V.A. all American citizens and the inhabitants of Tennessee in particular are better off.

The Tennessee Valley has become a 1,500-feet-high stairway of water fertilising the tiered fields on the slopes of the hills: "Water falls upon a mountain slope six thousand feet above the level of the river's mouth. It percolates through the roots and the sub-surface channels, flows in a thousand tiny veins, until it comes together in one stream, then in another, and at last reaches a T.V.A. lake where it is stored behind a dam. Down a huge steel tube it falls, turning a water wheel. Here the water's energy is transformed into electricity, and then, moving onward towards the sea, it continues on its course, through ten such lakes, over ten such water wheels. Each time, electric energy is created. That electricity, carried perhaps two hundred miles in a flash of time, heats to incredible temperatures a furnace that transforms inert phosphate ore into a chemical of great possibilities. That phosphatic chemical, put upon his land by a farmer, stirs new life in the land, induces the growth of pastures that capture the inexhaustible power of the sun. Those pastures, born of the energy of phosphate and electricity, feed the energies of animals and men, hold the soil, free the streams of silt, store up water in the soil. Slowly the water returns into the great man-made reservoirs, from which more electricity is generated as more water from the restored land flows on its endless course.

"Such a cycle is restorative, not exhausting. It gives life as it sustains life. The principle of unity has been obeyed, the circle has been closed. The yield is not the old sad tale of spoliation and poverty, but that of nature and science and man in the bounty of harmony."

The Tennessee land has been enriched with vast quantities of superphosphates which were given free of charge, and now the soil provides its full yield. In 1943 4,520 square miles had already been reclaimed on the hillsides by means of powerful bulldozers driven either by petrol or electricity.

In the district of Limestone alone the area of pasture land increased in ten years from 350 to 50,000 acres and the tiered fields from 11,500 to 138,550 acres. In order to retain the fertility of the soil and produce food for the farmers and their animals, the system of general farming was adopted, for unlike the collective farming method practised in the U.S.S.R. the social and economic unit in Tennessee was still the family; the Mormons in fact had praised its age-old virtues seventy-five years previously.

Fifteen thousand experimental farms were established, along with buying and selling centres which stored cereals and supplied well-selected seeds in return. The time when the farmers watched in dismay as tropical rainstorms washed their land away is over. Every spring life returns to the soil, which is unharmed, moist and ready to supply sap for the summer crops.

Guntersville, which was a ruined town, has now become a splendid port and small destroyers call there on their way from the Gulf of Mexico, sailing along the Mississippi as far as the Appalachian Mountains.

Malaria has now disappeared, thanks to a highly ingenious practice. Whenever the anopheles larvae appear in excessive numbers on the banks of their favourite lakes the water-level is suddenly lowered by a special device. The insects then settle on the dry banks and die.

The farms now resemble electrically operated factories for, in addition to the agricultural machinery, they are equipped with electric heating and pumping systems, as well as a machine for dehydrating vegetables and fruit and a deep-freeze which can keep strawberries fresh all the year round.

At Muscle Shoals the American Government has also set up one of the most powerful fertiliser-producing plants in the world, which supplies the whole area. During the war this plant provided 60 per cent. of the 90,000 tons of phosphorus required for incendiary bombs, many of which were dropped over Germany.

It is customary to think of the States as full of huge factories pouring out smoke and seething with workers. Light industry, however, has always been a speciality of the Tennessee Valley, and today includes the manufacture of cheese, mattresses, bottle-washing machinery, hats, footwear, pencils, plastics, hammer-handles and harness for horses, which abound in the neighbouring states.

The State of Tennessee produces as many kilowatts as bushels of wheat or sweet corn and supplies electricity to a large section of the southern states. The T.V.A. sells this power to the towns, which then pass it on to the consumer at prices well below those current in Europe.

But the T.V.A. is more than a producer of electricity and a philanthropic institution. It is also a vast potential source of war production, for it contains the largest aluminium factory in the U.S.A. The town of Alcoa for example is abbreviated from the name "Aluminium Company of America," which supplied most of the metal for aircraft between 1942 and 1945. Lilienthal states that "it takes as much electricity to construct a heavy bomber as an average family would consume in four centuries." During the war the Norris dam supplied most of the electricity for the production of atomic bombs at Oak Ridge.

The Americans realise that, if it came to another war, the T.V.A. alone could not supply enough power for a new war effort, which would probably be on an incomparably larger scale than the last one. But they also believe that economic planning is not always an evil and that a collaboration between State ownership, private finance and free people can give positive results. Their thoughts are turning therefore towards other rivers, such as the Mississippi and the Colorado, which one day will certainly be taken over and developed by a body such as the T.V.A.

APPENDIX

NOTE OF THE KING'S EXPENSES ON THE BUILDINGS
OF VERSAILLES BETWEEN THE YEARS 1664 AND 1690
Manuscript document by Marinier, Colbert's clerk
(In thousands of livres)

Masonry	21,186	
Carpentry and timber ..	2,553	
Roofing	718	
Leadwork and purchase of lead..	4,558	
Cabinet-making and marquetry	2,666	
Locks and chiselling.. ..	2,289	
Windows	300	
Mirrors	221	
Painting and gilding not including purchases of pictures	1,676	
Sculpture, not including purchases of classical work	2,696	
Marble-work and purchase of marble	5,043	
Bronze, iron and copper ..	1,876	
Iron and wrought iron pipes, including those for the pump at Marly	2,265	
Pavements, flooring-tiles and cement	1,267	
Gardens, fountains and rockwork	2,338	
Château de Clagny et Glatigny, without purchase of land	2,074	

Pump at Marly (without the pipes and purchase of land)		3,674
Work on the Eure and Maintenon rivers (without purchase of land)		8,612
Compensation for the lands and inheritances taken for the Château and outbuildings of Versailles		5,912
Old pictures and statues ..		509
Gold and silver fabrics purchased out of the building funds		1,075
Silverwork, apart from that supplied by the royal silver[1]		3,245
Coins, crystals, agates and other rare collections ..		566
Workmen's wages		1,381
Excavation work and transport		6,038
Various and extraordinary expenses		1,799
Salaries of the inspectors and officials in charge of the said buildings and works at Versailles and its outbuildings, with supervisors and others, paid		1,000

Total: 87,537,989, 4 sols 4 deniers

[1] *Note* (in Marinier's handwriting): All these large pieces of silverware were taken to the Mint by the silverware treasurer.

Translator's Note: It has been estimated that a French *livre* of this period is roughly equivalent to five shillings or seventy U.S. cents at the present day.

"With the other payments made for furniture, large collections, large pieces of silverware and others, not purchased from the building fund, it will be found that Versailles and its dependent buildings have cost the King more than 100 million livres, without maintenance expenses, of which those paid amount to 200,000 livres and those which are not to 300,000 livres."

SELECT BIBLIOGRAPHY

1. THE TOWER OF BABEL
   Childe, V. Gordon .. New Light on the Most Ancient East. 4th Edition, London, 1952.
   Parrot, André .. *Ziggurats et Tour de Babel*. Paris, 1949.
   Parrot, André .. *La Tour de Babel*. Paris, 1953.
2. THE PYRAMIDS
   Baedeker, Carl .. Guide to Egypt and the Sudan, 8th rev. ed. 1929.
   Edwards, I. E. S. .. The Pyramids of Egypt. London, 1947.
   Breasted, J. H. .. Ancient Records of Egypt. Vols. I-V. Chicago, 1906–7.
   Lauer, J. P. .. *Le Problème des Pyramides d'Egypte*. Paris, 1952.
   Maspero, Gaston .. Egyptian Archeology. London, 1902.
3. THE GREAT WALL OF CHINA
   Geil, W. E. .. .. The Great Wall of China. London, 1909.
   Grousset, René .. *Histoire de la Chine*. Paris, 1942.
   Macartney, Earl .. Journal of the Embassy to China, Ed. by Sir George Staunton. London, 1797.
   Lum, Peter .. The Purple Barrier. London, 1960.
4. THE ROMAN ROADS
   Charlesworth, M. P. Trade Routes and Commerce of the Roman Empire. London, 1924.
   Forbes, R.-J. .. Notes on the history of ancient roads and their construction. Amsterdam, 1934.
5. VERSAILLES
   Bloomfield, Sir R. .. History of French Architecture, 1661–1774. London, 1921.
   Funck-Brentano, F. *La Cour du Roi Soleil*. Paris, 1937.
   Lenotre, G. .. .. *Versailles au Temps des Rois*. Paris, 1934.
   Narbonne, P. .. *Journal de la vie à Versailles pendant les règnes de Louis XIV et Louis XV*. Paris, 1886.
   Nolhac, Pierre de .. Versailles and the Trianons. London, 1906.
   Nolhac, Pierre de .. *La Création de Versailles*. Paris, 1925.
6. THE ATLANTIC CABLE
   Bright, Charles .. History of the Atlantic Cable. New York, 1903.
   Martyn, Henry .. The Atlantic Telegraph. New York, 1892.
   Russell, W. H. .. The Atlantic Telegraph. London, 1868.
   Appleyard, R. .. Pioneers of Electric Communication. London, 1930.
   Clarke, Arthur .. Voices Across the Sea. London, 1958.

7. THE TRANSCONTINENTAL RAILWAY
Flint, H. S ..   .. The railroads of the U.S.A., their history and statistics. Philadelphia, 1868.
Galloway, J. D.   .. The First Transcontinental Railroad. New York, 1950.
Gunther, John   .. Inside U.S.A. London, 1947.
Holbrook, S. H.   .. The Story of American Railroads. New York, 1947.
Marshall, J. ..   .. Santa Fe, the Railroad that Built an Empire. New York, 1947.
Reck, F. M.   .. The Romance of American Transportation. New York, 1938.

8. THE LONDON UNDERGROUND
Baker, C.   ..   .. The Metropolitan Railway. London, 1951.
Howson, H. F.   .. London's Underground. London, 1951.
Passingham, W. J. .. The Romance of London's Underground. London, 1935.

9. THE FORTH BRIDGE
Phillips, Philip   .. The Forth Bridge. Edinburgh, 1889.
Smith, H. Shirley .. The World's Great Bridges. London, 1953.

10. THE EIFFEL TOWER
Eiffel, G.   ..   .. *La Tour de 300 mètres.* Paris, 1890.
Poncetton, F.   .. *Eiffel, le Magicien du Fer.* Paris, 1939.

11. THE PANAMA CANAL
Beatty, Charles   .. Ferdinand de Lesseps. London, 1956.
Bonaparte-Wyse, L. *Le Canal de Panama.* Paris, 1886.
Bunau-Varilla, P. .. *Le Canal de Panama.* Paris, 1906.
Courau, R. ..   .. *Ferdinand de Lesseps.* Paris, 1942.
Fraser, J. F. ..   .. Panama, and What it Means. London, 1913.
Padelford, N. J.   .. The Panama Canal in Peace and War. New York, 1943.
Siegfried, A.   .. *Suez et Panama et les routes maritimes mondiales.* Paris, 1948.

12. THE SIMPLON TUNNEL
David, J. El.   .. *Le Tunnel du Simplon.* Lausanne, 1905.
Simms, F. W.   .. Practical Tunnelling. 4th Edition, rev. and enlarged by D. K. Clark. London, 1896.

13. THE RECLAIMING OF THE ZUYDER ZEE
Veen, J. van ..   .. Dredge, Drain and Reclaim: The Art of a Nation. The Hague, 1955.
X.   ..   ..   .. Fights against Floods. The Hague, 1953.

14. THE VOLGA AND TENNESSEE HYDRO-ELECTRIC DAMS
Galatkionov, V. D.   The Canal Volga-Don. Moscow, 1953.
Zoritch, A. and
Zasvalski, D.   .. *Dnieprostroi.* Paris, 1932.

Billings, H. .. .. All Down the Valley. New York, 1952.

Davidson, D. .. Tennessee. New York, 1946.

Lilienthal, David. .. T.V.A.: Democracy on the March. London, 1944.

Rouse, H. and Ince, S. A History of Hydraulics. Iowa Institute of Hydraulic Research. Iowa, 1957.